THE ULTIMATE GENERAL KNOWLEDGE QUIZ BOOK

THE ULTIMATE GENERAL KNOWLEDGE QUIZ BOOK

OVER 7,000 GENERAL KNOWLEDGE QUESTIONS

COMPILED BY
KEN RUSSELL & PHILIP CARTER

ARCTURUS

Published by Arcturus Publishing Limited
for Indigo Books
468 King St W,
Suite 500,
Toronto,
Ontario M5V 1L8

This edition published 2004

Illustrations by Peter Coupe
Cover by Communique
Design by Zeta Fitzpatrick @ Moo Design

26/27 Bickels Yard, 151-153 Bermondsey Street
London SE1 3HA

ISBN 1-84193-016-4

Printed and bound in India

Contents

SECTION 1

20th Century

20th Century — 1900

1 The first flight of the airship 'Zeppelin' flew over this lake?

2 Where did the 'relief' in South Africa take place?

3 Where was an amnesty granted to the Filipono rebels?

4 Which country won the first international trophy for lawn tennis?

5 Who was leader of the Tory government?

6 Who was President of the USA on 6 November?

7 'Who composed 'Nocturns'?

8 Which controversial Irish writer died?

9 Which plague in India abated?

10 Britain and Germany sign a pact over which country?

11 The Allies end the siege of where?

12 Which country did Russia annex?

13 In which city is the underground train system opened?

14 The British annex the Boer Republic of?

15 Which King is shot dead?

Answers **1** Lake Constance **2** Mafeking **3** The Philippines **4** USA **5** Lord Salisbury **6** William McKinley **7** Claude Debussy **8** Oscar Wilde **9** Bubonic **10** China **11** Beijing **12** Manchuria **13** Paris **14** Transvaal **15** King Umberto

1901 — 20th Century

1 Who died at Osborne House on the Isle of Wight on 22 January?

2 What in 1901 was first classified by the Austrian pathologist Karl Landsteiner?

3 Whose play 'Three Sisters' was first performed in Russia on 31 January?

4 Which US President was assassinated?

5 What awards were first presented on 10 December?

6 Which painter, famous for his scenes of the Moulin Rouge in Paris died?

7 Which actress was born Magdalena von Losch on 27 December?

8 Which uprising in China ended on 7 September?

9 What caused the death of 400 people in New York on 2 July?

10 Who in 1901 became President of the Cody Military College and International Academy of Rough Riders?

11 Which city became the temporary seat of Australia's government?

12 Which 19-year old artist from Barcelona set up his studio in Montmartre, Paris and became known as 'Le Petit Goya'?

13 Which future Emperor of Japan was born?

14 Who was the future 'King of Hollywood' born on 1 February?

15 Which writer published his novel 'The First Men on the Moon'?

Answers **1** Queen Victoria **2** Blood types **3** Anton Chekov **4** William McKinley **5** Nobel Prizes **6** Henri de Toulouse-Lautrec **7** Marlene Dietrich **8** The Boxer uprising **9** A heat wave (110°F in the shade) **10** Buffalo Bill **11** Melbourne **12** Pablo Picasso **13** Hirohito **14** Clark Gable **15** HG Wells

20th Century 1902

1 Which British colonial statesman died?

2 The eruption of Mount Pele wipes out a whole town in which country?

3 Which satirist died?

4 Which two countries agreed on joint supervision of Macedonia?

5 Where was the Nile dam built?

6 What link between Bulawayo and Salisbury was completed?

7 Which book did Beatrix Potter publish?

8 In which town in the British Isles was a state of emergency declared on 1st September?

9 Who succeeded Lord Salisbury as Tory Prime Minister?

10 The anarchist Gennaro Rubino made an attempt on the life of whom?

11 Which car maker wins the first Paris-Vienna motor race?

12 In which city did the underground railway open?

13 In which Spanish town did 500 people die in strike clashes?

14 The head of secret police is killed in which country?

15 Great Britain, Germany and Italy blockade the coastline of which country?

Answers **1** Cecil Rhodes **2** Martinique **3** Samuel Butler **4** Austria and Russia **5** Aswan **6** Railway **7** The Tale of Peter Rabbit **8** Dublin **9** Arthur Balfour **10** King Leopold II **11** Marcel Renault **12** Berlin **13** Barcelona **14** Russia **15** Venezuela

1903 — 20th Century

1 Whose story ‘The Call of the Wild’ was first published?

2 Who was born Eric Arthur Blair on 25 June?

3 How was Martha Jane Canary, who dressed in male attire and claimed she was the equal of any man, and who died in 1903, better known?

4 What was the name of the new bicycle race announced in Paris on 19 January?

5 Who was the inventor of the rapid-fire gun who died on 26 February?

6 Which singer made his debut at the Metropolitan Opera House in New York in 1903?

7 Formed on 10 October, who was leader of a new movement to obtain votes for women with their motto ‘Deeds not words’?

8 Who on 10 December became the first woman to win a Nobel Prize?

9 On 22 January the USA and Colombia signed a treaty to allow the construction of what, to take place?

10 Who published his work ‘Man and Superman’ in 1903?

11 Who was the young Italian teacher put under special investigation by police in Berne, Switzerland, in June 1903?

12 In which American city did a fire in a theatre kill 578 people on 31 December?

13 Bix Beiderbecke, who was born on 10 March, 1903, became a jazz virtuoso on which instrument?

14 Which French impressionist painter who had lived in the South Seas since 1891, died on 8 May?

15 Which inventor introduced the safety razor in 1903?

Answers **1** Jack London **2** George Orwell **3** Calamity Jane **4** Tour de France **5** Richard Gatling **6** Enrico Caruso **7** Emmeline Pankhurst **8** Marie Curie **9** The Panama Canal **10** George Bernard Shaw **11** Benito Mussolini **12** Chicago **13** Cornet **14** Paul Gauguin **15** King Camp Gillette

20th Century 1904

1 Where in India dis an earthquake kill more than 10,000?

2 In which city did the 1904 Summer Olympic Games take place?

3 Which fleet did Japan annihilate?

4 Which underground system opened?

5 Japan lays siege to a large town, where?

6 Who invented the scientific novel?

7 What was the name of the Russian General assassinated in June?

8 France severs diplomatic links with whom?

9 Which famous French painter died in August?

10 Which two American states were admitted to the union on 7 February 1904?

11 The Prime Minister Delyannis is assassinated, where?

12 A famous pair agreed to make motor cars, who?

13 Which famous Czech composer died on the 1 May in Bohemia?

14 The author of 'The Seagull' and 'The Cherry Orchard' who died in Russia on 15 July 1904?

15 Where in China did Japan beat Russia?

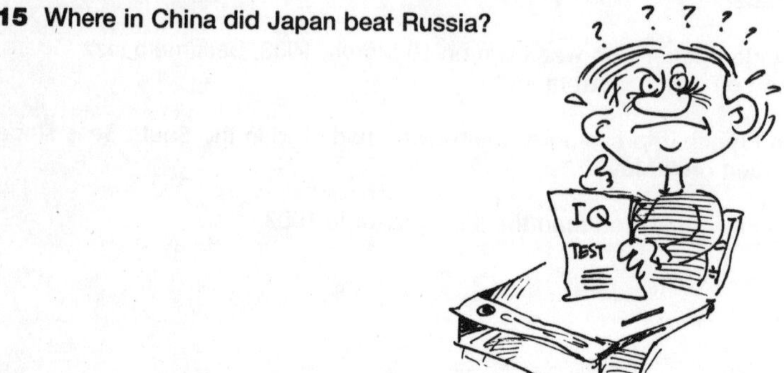

Answers **1** Lahore **2** Saint Louis, Missouri **3** In May, the Russian fleet in the Straits of Tsushima **4** New York **5** Vladivostok **6** Jules Verne **7** Bobrikov **8** The Vatican **9** Henri-Fantin-Latour **10** Oklahoma and New Mexico **11** Athens **12** Charles Rolls and Henry Royce **13** Antonin Dvorak **14** Anton Chekov **15** Mukden

1905

20th Century

1 What type of tests were invented by Alfred Binet in April 1905?

2 Who was the doctor who created homes for homeless children who died on 19 September?

3 Which type of public punishment was finally abolished, in the state of Delaware, in 1905?

4 What drug for the relief of pain, first went on sale in Britain on 30 October?

5 Who proposed his 'Theory of Relativity' on 1 July 1905?

6 As a result of a plebiscite of 1905, Norway separated from which country?

7 Who, in 1905 in Vienna, produced his most successful operetta 'The Merry Widow'?

8 Born in 1828, who is the author of 'Twenty Thousand Leagues Under the Sea', who died on 24 March?

9 After appearing to have died going over the precipice of the Reichenbach Falls, who was brought back to life by public demand in March 1905?

10 Which city was founded in 1905 by European settlers and named after a local African leader, replacing Livingstone as the capital of Northern Rhodesia, later Zambia, in 1935?

11 Born in 1905, who was destined to become the UN Secretary-General for eight years until his death in a plane crash in 1961?

12 Which US President took the oath of office on 4 March?

13 For what did an American astronomer Percival Lowell, first inaugurate a search in 1905, that was to last until 1930?

14 Who was the French philosopher and leading exponent of existentialism who was born on 21 June?

15 What is the name of the world's largest diamond discovered in South Africa in 1905?

Answers **1** Intelligence **2** Thomas John Barnado **3** The pillory, or stocks **4** Aspirin **5** Albert Einstein **6** Sweden **7** Franz Lehar **8** Jules Verne **9** Sherlock Holmes **10** Lusaka **11** Dag Hammarskjold **12** Theodore Roosevelt **13** Pluto **14** Jean Paul Sartre **15** Cullinan

20th Century 1906

1 Which Nobel Prize-winning physicist died?

2 Where were 10,000 people killed by a typhoon?

3 Who were killed in Natal by British troops?

4 Who was exiled to Siberia for life?

5 What was the name of the world's biggest battleship?

6 Which city was destroyed by an earthquake?

7 Who was declared successor to Leopold as King of the Congo?

8 Which air-powered race took place in London for the first time?

9 In which country were one million people starving?

10 What is the name of the most powerful warship to be launched?

11 When Mount Vesuvius erupted, which town was destroyed?

12 Who is crowned as the Shah of Persia?

13 The impressionist artist, who painted 'The 'Card Players' and Montagne Sainte-Victoire', who died at Aix-en-Provence on 22 October, several days after catching a cold whilst sitting before a model?

14 What did the Labour party call for?

15 Who won the rugby international between England and France?

Answers **1** Pierre Curie **2** Tahiti **3** 60 Zulus **4** Leon Trotsky **5** Satsuma **6** San Francisco **7** Prince Albert **8** Hot-air balloon **9** China **10** The Dreadnought **11** Ottaiano **12** Mohammed Ali Mirza **13** Paul CÉzanne **14** Femme Suffrage (Women's rights) **15** England

1907 — 20th Century

1. The Choctaw Indian nation was instrumental in developing which new American state, founded in 1907?
2. Which ill-fated Cunard liner broke all records for crossing the Atlantic Ocean in October?
3. Who was the creator of 'Tintin', born 22 May?
4. Which ballet dancer made his first public appearance with the Saint Petersburg Imperial Ballet?
5. Who on 22 March declared a campaign of 'Satyagraha' or civil disobedience?
6. Born Gladys Marie Smith, who was America's sweetheart who began her film career in 1907?
7. On 25 July a group of twenty boys from widely differing backgrounds in England were ferried across Poole Harbour to Brownsea Island, for what purpose?
8. Born in 1843, who was the composer of the Peer Gynt suite who died on 4 September?
9. Which Oscar-winning Knight and later Baron was born in Dorking, Surrey on 22 May?
10. Who was the singing cowboy, born 29 September 1907, who was in the movies accompanied by his trusty horse, Champion?
11. Who was the German Kaiser awarded an honorary degree at Oxford on 15 November?
12. Who was the Olympic swimming champion born on 17 February 1907?
13. The author of 'Jungle Book' who won the Nobel Prize for literature?
14. Who was the actress born on 9 November 1907 who had a successful pairing with Spencer Tracy in several movies?
15. Which Italian educator introduced her method of teaching young children in 1907?

Answers **1** Oklahoma **2** Lusitania **3** Georges Remi, alias Hergé **4** Vaslav Nijinsky **5** Gandhi **6** Mary Pickford **7** To go camping, they were the first Boy Scouts **8** Edvard Grieg **9** Laurence Olivier **10** Gene Autry **11** Kaiser Wilhelm II **12** Buster Crabbe **13** Rudyard Kipling **14** Katharine Hepburn **15** Maria Montessori

20th Century 1908

1 'Room with a view' was published. Who wrote it?

2 Where is there riot between Hindus and Moslems?

3 Fords first famous car is produced, what is it called?

4 Where is the famine where 4,000 died?

5 Which boxer wins the heavyweight championship?

6 Which town in Italy is devastated by an earthquake?

7 Austria sends troops to, where?

8 Who is the new Australian labour Prime Minister?

9 Who succeeds to the throne in China?

10 Crete declares its independence from whom?

11 Who were the two females jailed as suffragettes?

12 Austria buys Bosnia Herzegovina from the Ottoman Empire for how much?

13 A flying machine is built by whom?

14 Britain's new Liberal Prime Minister named?

15 Which celebrated Russian composer of operas, such as 'Snow Maiden' and orchestral works, including 'Little Russian Fantasia' died on 11th June 1908, aged 64?

Answers **1** E.M. Forster **2** Calcutta **3** Model 'T' **4** Uganda **5** Jack Johnson **6** Messina **7** Serbia **8** Andrew Fisher **9** Emperor Puyi **10** The Ottomans **11** Emmeline Pankhurst and her daughter Christabel **12** 2.5 million Turkish pounds **13** The Wright Brothers **14** Herbert Asquith **15** Nikolai Rimsky-Korsakov

1909

20th Century

1 What instrument was played by Benny Goodman, born 30 May 1909?

2 US President William Taft decided to create a US naval base at which site in the Hawaiian Islands?

3 Who first reached the North Pole in 1909?

4 Who was George Meredith, who died in 1909?

5 Who, on 25 July, became the first aviator to fly across the English Channel in a heavier-than-air machine?

6 Who was the Apache Indian chief who died peacefully at Fort Sill on 17 February?

7 Who, on 14 January, called England "the best country in the world for rich men"?

8 "All your shopping under one roof" was the slogan of which store that opened in London on 15 March?

9 Under the Boundary Waters Treaty of 1909 what was put under the joint control of the US and Canada?

10 Which British king watched his horse win the Derby in 1909?

11 In which country in 1909 did Albert I accede the throne on the death of Leopold II?

12 Of what did Henry Ford say "You can have any colour you like, as long as it's black"?

13 Who wrote "Anne of Green Gables" published in 1909?

14 Who was the first Prime Minister of Ghana, born 21 September 1909?

15 Which new country created by a proclamation of 7 December, brought together the four UK colonies of Cape of Good Hope, Natal, Transvaal and Orange River?

Answers **1** Clarinet **2** Pearl Harbour **3** Robert E. Peary **4** An English novelist and poet **5** Louis Bleriot **6** Geronimo **7** Winston Churchill **8** Selfridge's **9** The Great Lakes **10** Edward VII **11** Belgium **12** Ford Model T **13** Lucy M. Montgomery **14** Kwame Nkrumah **15** Union of South Africa

20th Century 1910

1 Where did Leo Tolstoy die?

2 Which port did France take in Morocco?

3 Which famous nurse died in London?

4 Who became the British Labour Party's new Chairman?

5 Which comet passed within 13 million miles of the earth?

6 In which country was slavery abolished?

7 Which famous criminal is hanged for the murder of his wife?

8 The largest vessel afloat is launched?

9 Known as 'le Douanier', who was the French painter who died?

10 Which mountain erupted in Italy?

11 Japan annexes which country?

12 Italian army seizes Tripoli from whom?

13 Who, in 1910, wrote the novel 'Prester John'?

14 Turkish troops battle with rebels, from where?

15 Vaughan Williams first symphony is performed. What is it called?

Answers **1** Astopovo **2** Agadir **3** Florence Nightingale **4** Ramsay MacDonald **5** Halley's Comet **6** China **7** Dr. Crippin **8** Olympic **9** Henri Rousseau **10** Mount Etna **11** Korea **12** The Turks **13** John Buchan **14** Albania **15** 'A Sea Symphony'

1911

20th Century

1 The name of Sir Arthur Sullivan's librettist who drowned in his swimming pool at his home on 30 May?

2 Who was crowned King of England on 22 June?

3 Who first reached the South Pole on 14 December?

4 What was stolen from the Louvre on 22 August?

5 Who wrote his first hit, 'Alexander's Ragtime Band', in 1911?

6 For what category did Count Maurice Maeterlinck win the Nobel Prize in 1911?

7 Whose opera 'Der Rosenkavalier' was launched to a rapturous reception in 1911?

8 Who was the entertainer, born Asa Yoelson in Saint Petersburg, Russia, who made his musical comedy debut in La Belle Paree in 1911?

9 In which London street (off the Mile End Road) did a famous siege take place on 3 January?

10 For what was the 'Spirit of Ecstasy' statuette commissioned in February 1911?

11 Which American journalist, who instigated a prize for literature and journalism died in 1911?

12 Who was the golfer who won the fifth of his six British Open Championship titles in 1911?

13 Who was the French President from 1969-1974, who was born on 5 July 1911?

14 What place in Nevada, whose name in Spanish means 'the meadows' was first incorporated as a city in 1911?

15 Which famous annual motor race in America was first held in 1911?

Answers **1** Sir W.S. Gilbert **2** George V **3** Roald Amundsen **4** The Mona Lisa **5** Irving Berlin **6** Literature **7** Richard Strauss **8** Al Jolson **9** Sidney Street **10** Rolls-Royce cars **11** Joseph Pulitzer **12** Harry Vardon **13** Georges Pompidou **14** Las Vegas **15** The Indianapolis 500

20th Century **1912**

1 'Unsinkable' liner sinks in the Atlantic?

2 In the Balkans, which country did the Ottoman's invade on 14th October?

3 Who formed a new cabinet in South Africa?

4 A new air mail service starts from London to where?

5 Abdication of boy Emperor Puyi in which country?

6 Ottomans grant autonomy to which country?

7 Greeks occupy Samothrace in which region?

8 Balkan armies invade which country?

9 Which unit of defence is set up in England?

10 Albert Berry performed which aerial feat for the first time?

11 Who was the new President of France?

12 The House of Lords rejected Home rule for which country?

13 Carl Laemmie founded which entertainment centre in Los Angeles?

14 Name the British composer who died? He shared the same name as an early English poet

15 Who published his 'Theory of Psychoanalysis' in Switzerland?

Answers **1** Titanic **2** Serbia **3** Louis Botha **4** Paris **5** China **6** Albania **7** The Balkans **8** Turkey **9** Royal Flying Corp **10** Parachute jump **11** Raymond Poincare **12** Ireland **13** Universal Studios **14** Samuel Coleridge-Taylor **15** Carl Jung

1913 — 20th Century

1 Who was the suffragette martyr who threw herself under the King's horse in the 1913 English Derby?

2 George I, who was assassinated in Salonika in 1913, was the King of which country?

3 Who was the German engineer who gave his name to the engine he invented, who drowned in the English Channel in 1913 while on a voyage to England?

4 Which Russian composer shocked the public when his 'The Rite of Spring' was premiered in 1913?

5 The author of 'Sons and Lovers', published in 1913?

6 Who in 1913 said "Conscience is the internal perception of a particular wish operating within us"?

7 Which building, when completed in New York in 1913, became the world's tallest building?

8 Which actress who went on to play Scarlett O'Hara was born on 5 November 1913?

9 Which US President opened the Panama Canal on 10 October?

10 The summit of which peak in Alaska was first reached in 1913, by explorer Hudson Stuck?

11 What was the name of the world's biggest airship which exploded on 17 October with the loss of all 28 lives aboard?

12 Who was the Archbishop and first president of Cyprus, born 13 August 1913?

13 What invention by Englishman Arthur Wynne, first appeared in the Sunday Supplement to the New York World in December 1913?

14 Which British film actor was born James La Planche Stewart on 6 May 1913?

15 Who in 1913, produced 'The Squaw Man', the first film made in Hollywood?

Answers **1** Emily Davison **2** Greece **3** Rudolf Diesel **4** Igor Stravinsky **5** D.H. Lawrence **6** Sigmund Freud **7** The Woolworth Building **8** Vivien Leigh **9** Woodrow Wilson **10** Mount McKinley **11** Zeppelin L2 **12** Makarios **13** The crossword puzzle **14** Stewart Granger Cecil B. De Mille

20th Century 1914

1 In which country was it reported that nine million people were starving?

2 Of what was James Bryce speaking when he said: "It is the greatest liberty ever taken with nature"?

3 Which Belgian town falls to the Germans?

4 Which pier in England was destroyed by a suffragette's bomb on 17 April?

5 Who was assassinated by a Serbian in Sarajevo, Bosnia?

6 A rally was held in Hyde Park, London against the decision to allow British troops to fight whom?

7 Where in England were 300 Germans detained under 'The Defence of the Realm Act'?

8 Which Church leader died in Rome?

9 A British expeditionary force lands where in Europe?

10 Who demonstrated the 'automatic pilot' by flying over Paris with his hands over his head?

11 Who did William II declare war on in Berlin on 1 August?

12 Shaw's 'Pygmalion' caused a sensation by including a swear word in the text. What was the word?

13 In which country was the first electric traffic light erected?

14 On 4 October at Sheerness, Kent, which ship blew up causinig 700 deaths?

15 In Mexico, civil war broke out between which two great leaders?

Answers **1** Japan **2** Building the Panama Canal **3** Liege **4** Yarmouth **5** His cousin Archduke Franz Ferdinand **6** Ulster Loyalists **7** Olympia, London **8** Pope Pius X **9** France **10** Lawrence Sperry **11** Czar Nicholas II **12** 'Bloody' **13** USA **14** HMS Bulwark **15** Pancho Villa & Venustiano Carranza

1915

20th Century

1 Who was the British nurse executed by the Germans on 12 October 1915?

2 Who was the American educator who urged black people to uplift themselves by educational attainments, who died in 1915?

3 Which romantic poet died on active service on route to the Dardanelles in 1915?

4 Who published his autobiographical novel 'Of Human Bondage' in 1915?

5 Who was the French singer, known as 'The Little Sparrow' who was born 19 December 1915?

6 Who defeated Jack Johnson to win the World Heavyweight boxing crown in 1915?

7 What, in London, was made illegal in an attempt to cut down excessive drinking on 13 October 1915?

8 Whose novel 'The Thirty Nine Steps' was published in 1913?

9 Which American inventor was made President of the US Naval Consulting Board on 7 October?

10 Which playwright, who married Marilyn Monroe was born in 1915?

11 The Crimean Monument in Waterloo Place, London was erected in 1915 in whose honour?

12 Who made his film 'Birth of a Nation' in 1915?

13 Victor Emmanuel III was king of which country that entered World War I in 1915?

14 What was the name of Charlie Chaplin's 1915 movies about a hapless vagabond?

15 George Joseph Smith, sentenced to death on 1 July for murdering three wives within a few months of bigamously marrying them, became known by what nickname?

Answers **1** Edith Cavell **2** Booker T. Washington **3** Rupert Brooke **4** Somerset Maugham **5** Edith Piaf **6** Jess Willard **7** Buying a round of drinks **8** John Buchan **9** Thomas Edison **10** Arthur Miller **11** Florence Nightingale **12** D.W. Griffith **13** Italy **14** The Tramp **15** The Brides in the Bath murderer

20th Century — 1916

1 The name of the President of China who died in 1916?

2 Who became Regent of Ethiopia?

3 In England, King George calls for a restriction on the use of which commodity?

4 Which US President was elected?

5 What was the name of the diplomat sentenced to death in Dublin for his part in the Easter uprising?

6 What new method of communication was invented in Chicago?

7 Who was on board HMS Hampshire when it was sunk by a mine off the Orkney Islands?

8 Which Irish poet was killed at Ypres on the 31st July?

9 What was the name of the islands purchased from Denmark by the USA?

10 Name of the American novelist, author of 'The Portrait of a Lady' and 'Washington Square', who died in 1916?

11 Britain and Germany exchanged internees over a certain age. What age?

12 Who was the new Prime Minister of Greece?

13 In England, women were allowed to drive what kind of vehicle for the first time?

14 What weapon wes used for the first time in the Battle of the Somme?

15 Clarence Saunders opened the first shop of its kind in Memphis, Tennessee. What kind of shop?

Answers 1 Yuan Shikai **2** Haile Selassie **3** Bread **4** Woodrow Wilson **5** Roger Casement **6** The tele-typewriter **7** Kitchener **8** Francis Ledwidge **9** The Virgin Islands **10** Henry James **11** 45 **12** Spiridion Lambros **13** Taxis **14** Tanks **15** Self-service store

1917

20th Century

1 What name was adopted by the British royal family in 1917?

2 What was the professional name of Gertrude Margarette Zelle, executed by the French for spying in October 1917?

3 What term, since 1917, has denoted those who regard the Russian revolution as a model that all Marxists should follow?

4 Who was the French painter of ballet scenes who died on 26 September 1917?

5 What was the name of the dynasty that ruled Russia for three centuries, prior to the 1917 revolution?

6 How was William Cody, who died in 1917, better known?

7 Born in 1868, who was the US ragtime composer and pianist who died on 1 April 1917?

8 Who was the 35th President of the United States born on 29 May 1917?

9 Which sculptor whose works include 'The Kiss' and 'The Thinker' died near Paris on 17 November 1917?

10 Around which Belgian town did a third battle, also known as the Passchendale campaign, take place from 31 July - 10 November 1917?

11 Which famous American composer joined the French Foreign Legion in 1917?

12 The subject of two motion pictures, in 1938 and 1941, what is the name of the village community founded in Omaha in 1917 by Monsignor Edward Joseph Flanagan for homeless boys between 10 and 18 years of age?

13 What was invented by Dr. Ludwik L. Zamenhof who died in 1917?

14 What type of machine gun was tested and adopted as a standard for the US army in 1917?

15 Which city was the winter home of the Czars of Russia prior to the Revolution of 1917?

Answers **1** Windsor **2** Mata Hari **3** Communist **4** Degas **5** Romanov **6** Buffalo Bill **7** Scott Joplin **8** John F. Kennedy **9** August Rodin **10** Ypres **11** Cole Porter **12** Boy's Town **13** Esperanto **14** Browning **15** St. Petersburg

20th Century 1918

1 Who was the future Irish leader who was among 500 Sinn Fein members jailed in 1918?

2 Where did the Germans launch a great offensive on the Western Front on 21 May?

3 With which Empire did Germany sever diplomatic relations on 29 July 1918?

4 Who was massacred in a cellar at Ekaterenburg in Russia on 16 July?

5 In Britain, some women won the vote. How old did they have to be?

6 Which country formed an alliance with Germany and Austria on 7 May?

7 The capital of Russia moved from Petrograd to where?

8 Russia signed a peace treaty with Germany, where?

9 On the Western front British forces raid which Belgian port?

10 What was the name of the artificial soap in Germany?

11 The German forces retreat from which famous line?

12 What was the name of the first aircraft carrier launched?

13 The name of France's new Commander-In-Chief?

14 Damascus was freed from whose rule?

15 What was the name of the Republic established in Germany?

Answers 1 Eamon de Valera **2** The Somme **3** The Ottoman Empire **4** Czar Nicholas II and his family **5** Over 30 **6** Rumania **7** Moscow **8** Brest-Litovsk **9** Zeebrugge **10** Nekal **11** Siegfried Line **12** HMS Argus **13** Ferdinand Foch **14** Turkey **15** Weimar

1919

20th Century

1 Who was the Manassa Mauler who became World Heavyweight boxing champion on 4 July 1919?

2 Who met Richard Rogers in 1919 and began a songwriting partnership that lasted more than 20 years?

3 What was the name of the peace treaty to end World War I signed in 1919 between Germany and the Allies?

4 Ratified in America in January 1919, what was the 18th Amendment?

5 Who was the composer of 'I Pagliacci', who died in 1919?

6 Which movie company did Mary Pickford, Douglas Fairbanks, Charlie Chaplin and D.W. Griffith found on 17 April 1919?

7 What was Adelina Patti, who died in 1919 famous for?

8 Which team of aviators became the first to fly the Atlantic non-stop on 15 June 1919?

9 Who was the stylishly dressed French lady tennis player who won Wimbledon on 5 July 1919?

10 Unveiled on 18 July 1919, who designed the Cenotaph in London's Whitehall?

11 Who composed 'The Planets' suite, first performed in 1919?

12 What first was achieved in Britain by American-born Nancy Aster on 28 November 1919?

13 In which country did General Ian Smuts succeed Louis Botha as Prime Minister on 31 August?

14 Who first 'split the atom' on 3 January 1919?

15 What event in March 1919 was said to confirm Einstein's 1915 Theory of General Relativity?

Answers 1 Jack Dempsey **2** Lorenz Hart **3** Treaty of Versailles **4** Prohibition ("of the manufacture, sale or transportation of intoxicating liquors") **5** Ruggero Leoncavallo **6** United Artists **7** She was an opera singer **8** Alcock and Brown **9** Suzanne Lenglen **10** Sir Edwin Lutyens **11** Gustav Holst **12** She became Britain's first woman MP **13** South Africa **14** Ernest Rutherford **15** An eclipse of the sun

20th Century 1920

1 Which Somali guerilla, known as the 'Mad Mullah' was killed by a chance bomb in Somaliland in December 1918?

2 War is declared between Russia and which neighbouring country on 28t May?

3 The treaty of Versailles cut which country to a quarter of its former size?

4 Which game of ancient Chinese origin, and played with tiles shaped like small dominoes was first introduced into the United Stastes in 1920?

5 Which new political party was formed in London on 31 July 1920?

6 The Red Army defeated whom in Moscow?

7 The voice of which famous singer was heard all over Europe during a wireless broadcast by Marconi?

8 Which ex-President of USA was awarded Nobel Peace Prize?

9 Where did the League of Nations Permanent Court open on 16 June?

10 Who was the leader of the guerillas in Mexico, who surrendered to the government on 8 July?

11 Who is the new regent of Hungary?

12 Who was the leader of the Red Army who defeated the last of the white generals, Baron Wrangle, in the Crimea on 10 November?

13 The first 100 women are admitted to which University to study for full degrees?

14 China and which other country were admitted to the league of nations?

15 In Geneva, Britain and France reach agreement on the frontiers of which two countries?

Answers **1** Mohammid bin Abdulla **2** Poland **3** Hungary **4** Mah Jongg **5** The Communist Party of Great Britain **6** The white army **7** Dame Nellie Melba **8** Woodrow Wilson **9** The Hague **10** Pancho Villa **11** Miklos Horthy **12** Leon Trotsky **13** Oxford **14** Austria Syria and Palestine

1921 — 20th Century

1 Who declared himself 'Il Duce" on 7 November 1921?

2 Which former professional ballroom dancer achieved fame in a 1921 film 'The Four Horsemen of the Apolcalypse'?

3 Who first introduced the world to Hercule Poirot in 1921?

4 Which German composer, best known for his opera 'Hansel and Gretel' died in 1921?

5 Which Nobel Prize was won by Albert Einstein in 1921?

6 Where in America was The Unknown Soldier buried on 9 November?

7 What Czech word, meaning 'compulsory labour' was first used in a 1921 play R.U.R.?

8 Who was the law enforcement officer who assisted Wyatt Earp in bringing law and order to Tombstone, Arizona, who died in 1921?

9 What did John Boyd Dunlop, who died 25 October 1921, invent?

10 Who is the son of Prince Andrew of Greece and great-great-grandson of Queen Victoria who was born on 10 June 1921?

11 What in August 1921 replaced orchestras in Broadway New York's biggest cinemas?

12 Who in Germany, on 29 July 1921, was elected president of the National Socialist German Workers Party?

13 Which was Charlie Chaplin's first full length film, starring Jackie Coogan in the title role which premiered on 3 February?

14 Which city became the capital of Iraq in 1921?

15 Who was the famous son of the American heiress Jennie Jerome, who died in 1921?

Answers **1** Benito Mussolini **2** Rudolph Valentino **3** Agatha Christie **4** Englebert Humperdinck 9ck) **5** Physics **6** Arlington Cemetery **7** Robot **8** Bat Masterson **9** The pneumatic tyre **10** Prince Philip, the Duke of Edinburgh **11** Organs **12** Adolf Hitler **13** The Kid **14** Baghdad **15** Winston Churchill

20th Century 1922

1 Britain signs a treaty of alliance in London, with whom?

2 Who resigned as Chancellor in Berlin?

3 Who is the new leader of the British Labour party?

4 Who is the new ruler in Beijing?

5 What is the new federation of peasant unions called in China?

6 Where in Germany did the Nazi party hold their first rally?

7 Who is the new Chancellor of Germany?

8 What did the Ottoman empire abolish?

9 Famous x-ray pioneer dies?

10 Which Irish leader is killed in ambush?

11 Who became the new Caliph of the Ottoman Empire?

12 A book, which is to become one of the most famous novels in the world, is published by Irish author James Joyce. What is it called?

13 Which region in Turkey did the Greeks evacuate after they signed the Macedonia treaty?

14 Who was the Chief of the Imperial Staff, shot dead in London on 22nd June?

15 Who became Italy's new dictator?

Answers **1** Iraq **2** Joseph Wirth **3** Ramsay MacDonald **4** Wa Peifu **5** Haifeng **6** Munich **7** Wilhelm Cuno **8** The Sultanate **9** Roentgen **10** Michael Collins **11** Abdul Majid II **12** Ulysses **13** Thraco **14** Sir Henry Wilson **15** Benito Mussolini

1923

20th Century

1 Where in France did the first 24-hour motor race take place in May 1923?

2 Born on 2 December 1923, by what name was the Greek-born US soprano Cecilia Kalogeropoulos better known?

3 Which horror-film actor played the title role in the 1923 movie 'The Hunchback of Notre Dame'?

4 The national capital of Turkey was moved to Ankara on 12 October 1923, from which city?

5 Which American President died in office in 1923?

6 King Faisal became constitutional monarch of which country in 1923?

7 Which American inventor was the first person, in 1923, to demonstrate sound on moving film?

8 What was the name of the city, now called Harare, which became the capital of Southern Rhodesia in 1923?

9 Who was the "Catch 22" author born 1 May?

10 Which Russian leader stepped down after suffering a massive stroke on 9 March?

11 Which future movie actress won the Norwegian figure skating championship for the first time in 1923?

12 Which Earl died as a result of an insect bite on 4 April, two months after opening the tomb of Tutankhamun?

13 Which French fashion queen decreed on 16 February that even sweaters can be chic?

14 Who was the American Secretary of State under Presidents Nixon and Ford who was born on 23 May 1923?

15 Of who did Lenin write on 4 January: "His rudeness is becoming unbearable in the office of General Secretary"?

Answers **1** Le Mans **2** Maria Callas **3** Lon Chaney **4** Istanbul **5** Warren Harding **6** Iraq **7** Lee De Forest **8** Salisbury **9** Joseph Heller **10** Lenin **11** Sonja Henie **12** The Earl of Carnarvon **13** Coco Chanel **14** Henry Kissinger **15** Joseph Stalin

20th Century 1924

1 Who, in 1924, wrote 'The Vortex' and produced it in London with himself in the leading role?

2 Who, whilst serving six years imprisonment for sedition in Allahabad, fasted for 21 days?

3 USA limited immigration and barred Japanese, but gave citizenship to whom?

4 Who was the middle class lawyer who made a revolution on behalf of workers and peasants, who died in Russia aged 54/?

5 Russia's capital, St Petersburg, was renamed as?

6 Who became the new President of France?

7 Which British author wrote 'A passage to India'?

8 Which Geek patriarch was expelled?

9 Founded in Paris in 1924, for what is FIDE the world governing body?

10 Which new film corporation was formed in the USA on 16 April?

11 Which German dictator was freed on parole after being jailed for treason?

12 Who was the British Governor of Sudan who was shot dead by the Egyptians?

13 Who lost his seat in South Africa's general election?

14 Who won 5 track event gold medals at the Paris Olympics?

15 What was the name of the first 'hardboard' material?

Answers **1** Noel Coward **2** Mohandas Ghandi **3** Native Americans **4** Lenin **5** Leningrad **6** Gaston Doumergue **7** E.M Forster **8** Constantine II **9** Chess, the Federation Internationale des Echecs **10** Metro-Goldwyn Mayer **11** Adolf Hitler **12** Sir Lee Stack **13** Smuts **14** Paavo Nurmi **15** Masonite

1925 — 20th Century

1 Who wrote 'The Great Gatsby' published in 1925?

2 Which German physicist, who gave his name to a unit of frequency won the Nobel Prize for physics in 1925?

3 Which 19 year old dancer was the talk of Paris when she opened at 'Le Revue Negro'?

4 Who in 1925 wrote the novel 'Mrs Dalloway'?

5 Who is the patron saint of foreign missionaries and aviators and - with Joan of Arc - the patron saint of France, who was canonized in 1925?

6 Which book, written by Adolf Hitler whilst in prison was published on 18 July 1925?

7 What name was first applied to the sleek, streamlined art form synonymous with elegance and sophistication?

8 Who wrote 'The Vortex' which made its West End debut in 1925?

9 Who was the author of 'King Solomon's Mines' who died in 1925?

10 Who was inaugurated as US President on 4 March?

11 Which musical show featuring the song 'Tea for Two' was premiered in March 1925?

12 Who is the blues singer who plays a guitar which he calls Lucille, born in 1925?

13 What did Norway rename Christiana as in 1925?

14 Which city was renamed Stalingrad in 1925?

15 Who was elected President of the German Republic in 1925?

Answers **1** F. Scott Fitzgerald **2** Gustav Hertz **3** Josephene Baker **4** Virginia Woolf **5** Saint Theresa of Liseaux **6** Mein Kampf (My Struggle) **7** Art Deco **8** Noel Coward **9** H. Rider Haggard **10** Calvin Coolidge **11** No No Nanette **12** B.B. King **13** Oslo **14** Volgograd **15** Paul Von Hindenburg

20th Century 1926

1 Who became the new Emperor of Japan?

2 First schedule London flight to India lands where?

3 Who demonstrated the first mechanical television system to members of the Royal Institution?

4 Cobham made a 16,000 mile return flight from London to where?

5 Which country leaves the League of Nations?

6 A world famous chemical industry was formed. What was its name?

7 Famous book for children 'Winnie the Pooh' was written by whom?

8 Nazi party rally was held at?

9 Italian-born star of silent movies, such as 'The Sheik' dies in USA?

10 Josef Pilsudski takes control of which country?

11 Who set up a world land speed record of 174.224 mph?

12 Which singer gave her farewell performance at Covent Garden?

13 World famous escape artist dies?

14 Which American became the first amateur since 1897 to win the Open Golf Championship?

15 Who completed a record 28,000 mile trip to Australia by air?

Answers **1** Hirohito **2** Delhi **3** John Logie Baird **4** Cape Town **5** Brazil **6** ICI **7** A.A. Milne **8** Nuremberg **9** Rudolf Valentino **10** Poland **11** Malcolm Campbell **12** Nellie Melba **13** Harry Houdini **14** Bobby Jones **15** Alan Cobham

1927

20th Century

1 Who was the US amateur golfer who won the British Open on 15 July 1927?

2 What was the name of Malcolm Campbell's car in which he set the world land speed record on 4 February?

3 Who formulated his "Uncertainty Principle' in 1927?

4 Who was the American dancer strangled by her own scarf in September 1927 when it became entangled in the wheel of her automobile?

5 What was the name of Charles Lindbergh's plane in which he flew solo across the Atlantic in May 1927?

6 What was the name of the 1927 Al Jolson movie which was the first with synchronised sound?

7 Who wrote the music for 'Show Boat' which opened in New York on 27 December 1927?

8 The carving of four US Presidents' heads began on which mountain in 1927?

9 Which future President of Cuba was born in August 1927?

10 The US battle cruisers Lexington and Saratoga were converted in 1927 to what type of vessels?

11 What did Charles Otis, who died in 1927, invent a type of?

12 Who was the author of 'Three Men in a Boat' who died on 14 June 1927?

13 Which actress received a 10-day jail sentence in New York in April 1927 for her production of 'Sex on Broadway'?

14 Who, on Daytona Beach racetrack in Florida broke Malcolm Campbell's land speed record set 7 weeks earlier?

15 Who defeated Jack Dempsey in the famous 'long count' world heavyweight championship contest in 1927?

Answers **1** Bobby Jones **2** Bluebird **3** Werner Heisenberg **4** Isadora Duncan **5** Spirit of St. Louis **6** The Jazz Singer **7** Jerome Kern **8** Mount Rushmore **9** Fidel Casto **10** Aircraft carriers **11** Lift (or elevator) **12** Jerome K. Jerome **13** Mae West **14** Henry Seagrave **15** Gene Tunney

20th Century 1928

1 Disney's world famous mouse appears for the first time in which cartoon?

2 What was the name of the General who launched an attack on northern warlords in China?

3 Who was the woman claiming to be daughter of the murdered Russian Czar Nicholas II?

4 Who discovered a substance to kill bacteria at St Mary's hospital in London?

5 Who formed a cabinet in France that excluded radical socialists?

6 Who abdicated in Afghanistan?

7 What was the name given to the members of the Russian political party arrested in the USSR by OGPU?

8 Which book was completed in Britain after 70 years work?

9 In which country was water skiing invented?

10 Who flew the English Channel in a rotor craft?

11 In Britain, all women of which age are granted the vote?

12 What name was given to the pact outlawing war by 15 nations?

13 In China Beijing's name is changed to?

14 What is the name of the new republican President of the USA?

15 Who is sworn in as President in Mexico?

Answers 1 Steamboat Willie **2** Chiang Kai-Shek **3** Anastasia Chaikovsky **4** Alexander Fleming **5** Raymond Poincare **6** King Amanullah **7** Trotskyists **8** Oxford English Dictionary **9** USA **10** Juan de la Cierva **11** 21 **12** Kellogg Briand **13** Beiping **14** Herbert C. Hoover **15** Emilio Portes Gil

1929 — 20th Century

1 What name was given to the Wall Street crash of 24 October 1929?

2 Which Nobel Prize was won by Frank Kellogg in 1929?

3 Who wrote 'A Farewell to Arms' in 1929?

4 Who was the actress dubbed 'the Jersey Lily' who died on 12 February?

5 What famous event took place in Chicago on 14 February?

6 Who was the legendary Marshall of Dodge City who died with his boots off on 13 January 1929?

7 Who was inaugurated as US President on 4 March?

8 Actress Joan Crawford married which 19-year old actor in New York in June 1929?

9 What was significant about the flags and a bunch of roses shown on television in New York on 27 June 1929?

10 Who wrote 'The Good Companions' first published in 1929?

11 Which future Nobel Peace Prize winner, for his work in the civil rights movement was born on 15 January 1929?

12 Who was the inventor of the gramophone disk who died on 3 August 1929?

13 What cartoon character was created by American cartoonist Elzie Segar on 1 July?

14 Which ill-fated British airship made her maiden voyage over London on 14 October?

15 On 13 September, who told the Congress for Sexual Reform in London: "As a playwrite I am an expert on sex appeal"?

Answers **1** Black Thursday **2** Peace **3** Ernest Hemingway **4** Lillie Langtry **5** The Saint Valentine's Day Massacre **6** Wyatt Earp **7** Herbert Hoover **8** Douglas Fairbanks Jr **9** It was the first transmission in colour **10** J.B. Priestly **11** Martin Luther King Jr **12** Emil Berliner **13** Popeye **14** R101 **15** George Bernard Shaw

20th Century 1930

1 Bathysphere was invented by whom?

2 Who was the first woman to fly solo from England to Australia?

3 Who was the creator of Sherlock Holmes, who died aged 81 on 7 July?

4 What invention made refrigerators possible?

5 What was the name given to rich peasants in Russia?

6 Who was the star of Joseph von Sternberg's masterpiece 'The Blue Angel'?

7 What was the name of the Conservative Prime Minister of Britain who died on 19th March?

8 In which US city was the first supermarket opened?

9 What were white women given in South Africa?

10 What was the name of the new planet discovered by Clyde Tombaugh?

11 Who was the American amateur golfer who won the grand slam of golf in 1930?

12 Where in Iraq was a city dated 550 BC found?

13 Which company introduced full-colour film was introduced by whom?

14 Which novelist, author of 'Sons and Lovers' died of tuberculosis at the age of 44?

15 The Prime Minister of Japan was assassinated. What was his name?

Answers **1** Otis Barton **2** Amy Johnson **3** Sir Arthur Conan Doyle **4** Fluorocarbon **5** Kulaks **6** Marlene Dietrich **7** Arthur James Balfour **8** New York **9** The vote **10** Pluto **11** Bobby Jones **12** Ur **13** Technicolour **14** D.H. Lawrence **15** Hamagushi

1931 — 20th Century

1 Who was the 'wonder child' violinist who gave his first London performance in 1931?

2 Alfonso XIII, who in 1931 was forced to flee his country and spend the rest of his life in exile was King of which country?

3 Which inventor died aged 84 at his home in New Jersey on 18 October 1931?

4 On 22 October 1931, for what offence was Al Capone jailed for 11 years?

5 Who wrote 'The Star-Spangled Banner' which became the national anthem of the United States by an Act of Congress on 3 March 1931?

6 Which city was inaugurated as capital of India in 1931?

7 Named after an American President, which major engineering achievement was started in 1931 at Black Canyon on the Colorado River near Las Vegas?

8 Which Russian-born ballet dancer died at her London home aged 52 on 23 January?

9 Which screen tough guy starred in 'The Public Enemy' in 1931?

10 What was the professional name of Helen Porter Mitchell, the Australian opera singer who died in 1931 and gave her name to a type of dessert?

11 Who was the American jazz cornetist who died in 1931 at the age of 28?

12 Which famous zoo in Bedfordshire, England opened in 1931?

13 Who composed 'Mood Indigo' in 1931?

14 What was the world's tallest structure when it opened in New York on 1 May 1931?

15 On 31 December, which Russian composer's music was banned as decadent by Moscow?

Answers **1** Yehudi Menuhin **2** Spain **3** Thomas Alva Edison **4** Tax evasion **5** Frances Scott Key **6** New Delhi **7** The Hoover Dam **8** Anna Pavlova **9** James Cagney **10** Nellie Melba **11** Bix Beiderbecke **12** Whipsnade **13** Duke Ellington **14** The Empire State Building **15** Sergei Rachmaninov

20th Century 1932

1 The city of Zacatecoluca, badly damaged by an earthquake in 1932, is in which Central American country?

2 Who invented the folding wheelchair?

3 Who put the earth's age at 10 billion years?

4 Who became the new President of the United States?

5 What does the world bank call for?

6 Who resigned from being Prime Minister of Germany?

7 And who became the new Chancellor of Germany?

8 Who was appointed Fascist Prime Minister of Portugal?

9 Who dissolved 'The Dail'?

10 Where did the Siamese army seize power?

11 Which country acknowledged the autonomy of Catalonia?

12 Where was the world's longest single-span bridge?

13 Which President of France was assassinated on 6 May ?

14 Which Nazi is elected President of Germany?

15 Which Japanese Prime Minister is assassinated?

Answers **1** El Salvador **2** Harry Jennings **3** Einstein **4** Franklin D. Roosevelt **5** A return to the gold standard **6** Von Papen **7** Kurt von Schleicher **8** Antonia de Oliveira Salazar **9** De Valera **10** Bangkok **11** Madrid **12** Sydney **13** Paul Doumer **14** Herman Goering **15** Ki Inukai

1933 — 20th Century

1 Which monster made his screen debut in March 1933 and proceeded to fall in love with which actress Fay Wray?

2 Who wrote the 1933 novel 'The Case of the Velvet Claws' which featured his creation 'Perry Mason'?

3 On 31 December 1933, Fiorello La Guardia was sworn in as mayor of which city?

4 Which peasant girl, who claimed to have experienced visions of the Virgin Mary at Lourdes was canonized in 1933?

5 Who was the author of 'The Forsyte Saga' who died in 1933?

6 Which island prison in San Francisco Bay was created in 1933?

7 What was the name of the political police force created in Germany in 1933 by Hermann Goring?

8 Who defeated Dorothy Round to win her sixth Wimbledon tennis title in July 1933?

9 Which film partnership made their debut in 'Flying Down to Rio' in 1933?

10 Who was the Italian boxer who beat Jack Sharkey to become world heavyweight boxing champion on 29 June?

11 Which English-born actor won the 1933 Academy Best Actor award for his performance in the title role of 'The Private Life of Henry VIII'?

12 Which German President appointed Adolf Hitler Chancellor in 1933?

13 What was the nickname of the first heavyweight boxing champion under the Queensbury rules, James J. Corbett who died in 1933?

14 On becoming Chancellor of Germany in 1933, who did Hitler appoint as his Deputy?

15 What was invented in 1870 by the US industrialist Robert Chesebrough who died on 8 September 1933?

Answers **1** King Kong **2** Erle Stanley Gardner **3** New York **4** Saint Bernadette **5** John Galsworthy **6** Alcatraz **7** The Gestapo **8** Helen Wills Moody **9** Fred Astaire and Ginger Rogers **10** Primo Carnera **11** Charles Laughton **12** Paul von Hindenburg **13** Gentleman Jim **14** Rudolf Hess **15** Vaseline

20th Century 1934

1 Name the country that is to be called Iran, by Government decree, in Tehran on 27 December?

2 Which German engineer flies his prototype helicopter?

3 Which actress, born Lily Chauchoin in 1905, apeared as Cleopatra in 1934?

4 What was the name of Stalin's aide, a rising star in the Communist Party, who was murdered giving rise to a purge by Stalin?

5 Who dismissed the entire Italian cabinet?

6 What was the purge of the Fascist party called in Germany?

7 Which countries were united in Italian East Africa?

8 What was the name of the composer of 'The Planets'?

9 What famous outlaw couple were killed in a police ambush?

10 Which country captured the Yemeni city of Hodeida?

11 Where was martial law declared as the government resigns?

12 In Nicaragua which General was gunned down?

13 In Germany who was appointed head of the concentration camps?

14 Germany signs a ten year pact with which country?

15 Where was Martial Law declared in Spain?

Answers **1** Persia **2** Heinrich Focke **3** Claudette Colbert **4** Sergei Kirov **5** Mussolini **6** 'The Night of the Long Knives' **7** Eritrea and Somaliland **8** Gustav Holst **9** Bonnie and Clyde **10** Saudi Arabia **11** Madrid **12** Augusto Sandino **13** Heinrich Himmler **14** Poland **15** Catalonia

1935 — 20th Century

1 Who wrote the opera 'Porgy and Bess' which opened in 1935 in New York?

2 What was the name of the historic 6,000-mile journey by Chinese Communists and the Red Army led by Chiang Kai-Shek throughout 1935?

3 What is the copyrighted name of a professional athletic competition between two teams on roller skates which was introduced in the United States in 1935?

4 What method of detecting aeroplanes was patented in December 1935 by Sir Robert Watson-Watt?

5 King George II was restored to the throne of which country after 12 years in exile?

6 Which British adventurer and author, who led an Arab revolt against the Ottoman Empire in World War I, died in 1935?

7 Which country was invaded by Italy in October 1935?

8 What invention by Percy Shaw was first used on Britain's roads in April 1935?

9 What was the profession of Frenchman Auguste Escoffier, who died in 1935?

10 The American humorist Will Rogers was killed in a plane crash piloted by which famous aviator, who was also killed?

11 Which US Senator was assassinated in September 1935?

12 On 18 September, which US General was appointed to organise the new Philippine army?

13 Who starred in 'A Night at the Opera' in 1935?

14 Which rock and roll star was born in Tupelo, Mississippi on 8 January 1935?

15 Who in 1935 became the first woman to fly across the Pacific Ocean?

Answers **1** George Gershwin **2** The Long March **3** Roller Derby **4** Radar **5** Greece **6** T.E. Lawrence (Lawrence of Arabia) **7** Abyssinia (now Ethiopia) **8** Cat's eyes **9** He was a famous chef **10** Willy Post **11** Huey Long **12** Douglas McArthur **13** The Marx Brothers **14** Elvis Presley **15** Amelia Earhart

20th Century 1936

1 Colour film is put on the market for amateurs, what is it called?

2 Which country is in the grip of civil war?

3 Which leader was kidnapped in China?

4 Who shattered two sprint records in the Olympic Games in Germany?

5 Who made his abdication speech in Britain?

6 Which Spanish writer died shortly after his arrest in Spain, aged 37?

7 Which ruler died in Egypt and is succeeded by the 16-year-old Prince Farouk?

8 Who announces an anti-Communist axis with Germany?

9 What is the name of the Ethiopian capital which fell to the Italians?

10 Who is crowned King of Britain?

11 Who was the British writer, most famous for his series of novels about a priest-sleuth called Father Brown', died on 14 July ?

12 Which Spanish rebel lands at Cadiz?

13 Which South American country set up a Fascist regime?

14 Who comes to power in Baghdad?

15 Which President is ousted in Bolivia?

Answers **1** Kodachrome **2** Spain **3** Chiang Kai-Shek **4** Jesse Owens **5** Edward VIII **6** Federico Garcia Lorca **7** King Fuad **8** Mussolini **9** Addis Ababa **10** George VI **11** G. K. Chesterton **12** General Franco **13** Paraguay **14** Iraqi Kentalists **15** Tejada Sorzano

1937 — 20th Century

1 Whose play 'Of Mice and Men' opened in New York on 23 November?

2 Who won the Pulitzer Prize in 1937 for her book 'Gone With the Wind'?

3 Which actress, whose husbands have included Roger Vadim and Ted Turner was born on 21 December?

4 What did Joseph Schick, who died in 1937, invent a type of?

5 What did Chester F Carlson invent in 1937?

6 Who was the composer of 'Bolero' who died at the age of 62 in 1937?

7 Which fortified building for housing the US gold reserve was completed in 1937?

8 Who did Wallis Simpson marry on 3 June 1937?

9 Who, in 1937, wrote 'The Hobbit'?

10 Which airship crashed in a ball of fire in New Jersey on 6 May?

11 Who was the 'Empress of the Blues' who died after an automobile accident in 1937?

12 Who was elected premier of Eire in 1937?

13 Who was the inventor of the first radio-signalling system and Nobel Laureate, who died in 1937?

14 Who wrote 'Death on the Nile' in 1937?

15 Released in 1937, what was Walt Disney's first feature-length cartoon?

Answers **1** John Steinbeck **2** Margaret Mitchell **3** Jane Fonda **4** Razor **5** Xerography **6** Maurice Ravel **7** Fort Knox **8** The Duke of Windsor (the former King Edward VIII) **9** J R R Tolkein **10** The Hindenburg **11** Bessie Smith **12** Eamon De Valera **13** Marconi **14** Agatha Christie **15** Snow White and the Seven Dwarfs

20th Century 1938

1 Who does the Vatican recognise as leader of Spain?

2 Who constructed the first binary calculator or digital computer?

3 Which country annexes the southern part of Slovenia and Ruthenia?

4 Who was arrested after the Nazis seized his bank in Vienna on 7th April?

5 In 1938, which tennis player became the first to achieve a grand slam?

6 Who invented jet propulsion?

7 What was the name give to the 'people's car', produced in Germany?

8 Who was Eire's first President?

9 Which Chinese town falls to the Japanese?

10 Who is the new Prime Minister of Japan?

11 Who is the Caliph of Islam?

12 What percentage (to the neareset ten per cent) of Germans were in favour of Hiutler's annexation of Austria?

13 New gun comes into service in Britain?

14 Which concentration camp was used for Jews?

15 Which vivid radio production by Orson Welles caused widespread panic in the USA?

Answers **1** Franco **2** Konrad Zuse **3** Hungary **4** Rothschild **5** Don Budge **6** Frank Whittle **7** Volkswagen Beetle **8** Douglas Hyde **9** Guangzhou **10** Baron Hiranuma **11** King Farouk **12** 99.75% **13** Bren **14** Dachau **15** War of the Worlds

1939

20th Century

1 Who was baseball's 'Iron Horse' who had to retire prematurely due to ill health in 1939?

2 What did Gerard Fokker, who died in 1939, design and manufacture?

3 King Zog, who fled in April 1939 after his country was invaded by Italy, was king of which country?

4 Which Nobel Prize was not awarded in 1939?

5 Who was the heroin of Christopher Isherwood's 1939 work 'Goodbye to Berlin', which was later adapted as the musical 'Cabaret'?

6 On what day in 1939 did Britain declare war on Germany?

7 Which part was played by Ray Bolger in the 1939 movie 'The Wizard of Oz'?

8 Who recorded 'In the Mood' on 1 August?

9 Robert Menzies was elected Prime Minister of which country on 24 April?

10 What name was given to baseball developed in the US in 1939 for girls and boys aged nine to 12?

11 Which country was invaded by Germany on 15 March 1939?

12 Who, in 1939, wrote 'The Big Sleep'?

13 What type of books were written by Zane Grey, who died in 1939?

14 Who was the founder of psychoanalysis who died in 1939?

15 Which German battleship was scuttled in the River Plate on 17 December 1939?

Answers **1** Lou Gehrig **2** Aircraft **3** Albania **4** Peace **5** Sally Bowles **6** 3 September **7** The Scarecrow **8** Glenn Miller **9** Australia **10** Little League Baseball **11** Czechoslovakia **12** Raymond Chandler **13** Westerns **14** Sigmund Freud **15** The Graf Spee

20th Century — 1940

1 Who masterminded the liberty cargo ships?

2 Which two low-lying countries did Hitler invade after heavy bombing of an airfield?

3 The Soviet Red Army marched into which neighbouring republic?

4 Which African border did Italian troops cross?

5 Which rival to Stalin was assassinated?

6 Roughly how many men escaped to Britain from Dunkirk?

7 Where did the 'Luftwaffe' carry out its first raid on Britain?

8 Which country revolted against Italian occupation?

9 German troops enter which French city?

10 Germans occupy which islands?

11 Italy declare war on which two countries?

12 Who was the leader of the British division of fascists arrested in Britain?

13 Who is the new Prime Minister of Britain?

14 Which country surrenders to Germany?

15 What was the name for the evacuation of Dunkirk?

Answers **1** Henry J. Kaiser **2** Holland and Belgium **3** Lithuania **4** The border between Ethiopia and British Somaliland **5** Leon Trotsky **6** Nearly 340,000 **7** Kent **8** Albania **9** Paris **10** Channel **11** Britain and France **12** Sir Oswald Mosley **13** Winston Churchill **14** Belgium **15** Dynamo

1941 — 20th Century

1 How did the novelist Virginia Woolf die in March 1941?

2 On what date in 1941 did Japan bomb Pearl Harbour?

3 What instrument did jazz-man Jelly Roll Morton, who died in 1941, play?

4 Which city and port in Libya was besieged and bombed by the Germans under Erwin Rommel in 1941?

5 What was declared a public holiday in the US on 4 July 1941?

6 Which German actress became a US citizen on 4 January?

7 Who wrote his autobiographical 'Father of the Blues' in 1941?

8 Who, in 1941, starred in 'The Maltese Falcon'?

9 Who was born Robert Zimmerman on 24 May?

10 Which 'unsinkable' German battleship was sunk in the Atlantic on 27 May 1941?

11 For which movie about an American war hero did Gary Cooper win an Academy Award in 1941?

12 Who, in June 1941, called the Nazis 'international outlaws' engaged in 'piracy for world conquest'?

13 The song 'Take the 'A' Train' became whose theme song in 1941?

14 Who was the founder of the Boy Scouts who died in 1941?

15 Who was the author of 'Finnegans Wake' who died on 13 January?

Answers **1** She drowned herself in the River Ouse at Sussex, England **2** 7 December **3** Piano **4** Tubruq **5** Independence Day **6** Marlene Dietrich **7** W C Handy **8** Humphrey Bogart **9** Bob Dylan **10** Bismarck **11** Sergeant York **12** President F.D. Roosevelt **13** Duke Ellington **14** Robert Baden-Powell **15** James Joyce

20th Century — 1942

1 What was the weight of the German V2 rocket?

2 Where was the first atomic pile improvised?

3 USA started work on which weapon?

4 China defeated Japan in a ten-day battle at which town?

5 Four Japanese aircraft carriers were trounced by USA at which island?

6 Which town in Germany received 100,000 bombs in one hour?

7 Britain captures which town in Madagascar?

8 Where was Montgomery's great victory?

9 Which fleet was scuttled after the German moved into Toulon?

10 Which island did the British capture on 23 September, its capital being Antanamarivo?

11 Which South American country declared war on Germany and Italy?

12 US Marines land on which island in the Pacific on 7 August?

13 Which island did the Japanese invade, lay siege to and surrender?

14 Which city was bombed by USA?

15 Which German Gestapo leader was assassinated?

Answers **1** 13 tons **2** In a squash court in Chicago **3** The atomic bomb **4** Changsha **5** Midway **6** Dusseldorf **7** Antananarivo **8** El Alamein **9** French **10** Madagascar **11** Brazil **12** Solomon Island **13** Singapore **14** Tokyo **15** Heydrich

1943 — 20th Century

1 Which building housing the US Department of Defense was completed in 1943?

2 Which French actress was born Catherine Dorleac on 22 October?

3 First performed in 1943, what was the first musical written by Rodgers and Hammerstein?

4 What, in 1943, was invented by Emile Gagnan and Jacques Cousteau?

5 Who was made supreme commander of the Allied Forces in Europe in December 1943?

6 Boris III, reported assassinated by German agents in 1943, was king of which country?

7 Which actor, who played Ashley Wilkes in 'Gone With the Wind' was killed in 1943, when his transport plane was shot down over the Bay of Biscay?

8 Which European dictator was deposed in July 1943?

9 Which American folk singer and guitarist, who travelled throughout the USA during the Great Depression and became his era's almost legendary spokesman for the downtrodden, published his autobiography, 'Bound for Glory', in 1943?

10 Who was the author of 'The Tale of Peter Rabbit' who died in 1943?

11 Who was the future Polish trade union leader and Prime Minister of Poland born on 29 September 1943?

12 In Britain what work was done by 'Bevin Boys' who were first called up in 1943?

13 What was the last remaining Italian held city of Mussolini's African empire to fall to Allied troops in January 1943?

14 Who was the notorious head of the Nazi police forces who Hitler appointed minister of the interior in 1943?

15 Who wrote his first book 'The Gremlins' in 1943?

Answers **1** The Pentagon **2** Catherine Deneauve **3** Oklahoma **4** The aqualung **5** Dwight D. Eisenhower **6** Bulgaria **7** Leslie Howard **8** Mussolini **9** Woodie Guthrie **10** Beatrix Potter **11** Lech Welesa **12** Work in coal mines **13** Tripoli **14** Heinrich Himmler **15** Roald Dahl

20th Century 1944

1 What piece of medical equipment did William Kolff invent?

2 What was the name given to the world's first computer?

3 Which European capital was liberated by the Allies?

4 Which people were fighting the Japanese in Burma?

5 Allied troops landed by glider 200 miles behind Japanese lines in which country?

6 Where was the landing in France by USA and British troops?

7 Who, in 1944, wrote the musical 'On TheTown'?

8 Which Yugoslavian leader escaped to the hills as the Germans captured his Bosnian headquarters?

9 Which was De Valera's party in Eire?

10 What was the name of the world's largest warship, launched on 29th January?

11 From where did Germany start to deport Jews as they began to occupy the country?

12 Who did Hitler make dictator of the City of Berlin when he suspended all laws?

13 What was the name of the new chief of staff of the Japanese army?

14 Which countries did Stalin tell to declare war on Germany?

15 Which country did Japan give up to the USA?

Answers **1** Kidney Dialysis machine **2** Colossus **3** Rome **4** The Chindits **5** Burma **6** Normandy **7** Leonard Bernstein **8** Tito **9** Fianna Fail **10** USS Missouri **11** Hungary **12** Goebbles **13** Hideki Tojo **14** Bulgaria, Rumania, Hungary **15** New Guinea

1945 — 20th Century

1. Whose novel 'Animal Farm' was published?
2. Which German Admiral presided over Germany's surrender to the Allies in 1945?
3. Who was the US General "Old Blood and Guts' who died after a car crash in December 1945?
4. Which former British Prime Minister, described by Winston Churchill as 'the greatest Welshman since the Tudor Kings' died on 26 March 1945?
5. Mount Surabachi, on which US Marines famously hoisted the Stars and Stripes on 23 February, is the highest point on which island?
6. Who was the composer of musicals including 'Show Boat' and 'Roberta' who died in 1945?
7. Whose mistress, Clara Petacci, was executed in April 1945?
8. Which British film director, in 1945, directed: 'This Happy Breed', 'Blithe Spirit' and 'Brief Encounter'?
9. William Joyce, tried for treason in 1945, was better known by what name?
10. Which Swedish actress starred in 'Spellbound' in 1945?
11. Who was the composer of 'Cavalleria Rusticana' who died in 1945?
12. How was Maria Eva Duarte, who married an influential figure in 1945, better known?
13. Who returned to the Philippines in 1945?
14. What nationality was composer Bela Bartok, who died on 26 September?
15. Which was the second Japanese city destroyed by an atom bomb in August 1945?

Answers **1** George Orwell **2** Karl Doenitz **3** George S. Patton **4** Lloyd George **5** Iwo Jima **6** Jerome Kern **7** Mussolini **8** David Lean **9** Lord Haw Haw **10** Ingrid Bergman **11** Pietro Mascagni **12** Evita (or Eva Peron) **13** Douglas MacArthur **14** Hungarian **15** Nagasaki

20th Century 1946

1 In the Pacific, which country set up a Republic?

2 Where was the first fast reactor built?

3 Who invented 'action painting'?

4 Civil war broke out in which far eastern country?

5 Who created the bikini?

6 Which camera was developed?

7 In which country was a Proclamation of a Communist People's Republic set up on 11 January?

8 The inaugural session of which organisation took place in London on 30th January?

9 Which Eastern European country became a Republic?

10 In the USA, what did Churchill warn would happen across Europe, involving the USSR?

11 France recognised which Communist Republic?

12 Who was the new President of Argentina?

13 Where was the first atomic test?

14 How many of the top Nazis were executed after Nuremberg?

15 Hostilities open in which country between the French and Ho Chi Minh?

Answers **1** Philippines **2** Los Alamos, New Mexico **3** Jackson Pollock **4** Greece **5** Louis Reard **6** Polaroid **7** Albania **8** UN General Assembly **9** Hungary **10** The spread of the iron curtain (Communism) **11** Vietnam **12** Peron **13** Bikini Atoll **14** Ten **15** Vietnam

1947

20th Century

1 Which fashion designer's 'New Look' was launched in 1947?

2 Whose play 'A Streetcar Named Desire' was premiered in New York on 4 December?

3 The sighting of which phenomena was first purportedly reported in 1947?

4 Who wrote the opera 'Peter Grimes' in 1947?

5 Which French mime artist created his character Bip in 1947?

6 Al Capone, who died in 1947, was known by what nickname?

7 Who wrote 'Annie Get Your Gun' which opened in London in June 1947?

8 Who was the writer of 'Carrie' and 'The Shining' who was born in Portland, Maine on 21 September 1947?

9 The earliest form of which mechanical contrivance was patented in 1891 by Jesse W. Reno, who died in 1947?

10 What was the name of the huge invisible white rabbit which first followed James Stewart around on stage in 1947?

11 What vessel designed to operate at great ocean depths was invented in 1947 by Auguste Piccard?

12 Who led his 'Kon-Tiki' expedition in 1947?

13 Who patented the geodesic dome in America in 1947?

14 What first was achieved by American test pilot Chuck Yeager on 14 October 1947?

15 Whose diary 'Het Achterhuis' ('The House Behind') was published in 1947?

Answers **1** Christian Dior **2** Tennessee Williams **3** UFO **4** Benjamin Britten **5** Marcel Marceau **6** Scarface **7** Irving Berlin **8** Stephen King **9** Escalator **10** Harvey **11** Bathyscaphe **12** Thor Heyerdahl **13** R. Buckminster Fuller **14** He broke the sound barrier **15** Anne Frank

20th Century 1948

1 Who was responsible for the giant telescope at Mount Palomar?

2 What was the latest development in the recording industry?

3 A Greek civil war attempt to establish a Socialist state was suppressed by whom?

4 Which country besides Ceylon (Sri Lanka) became an independent state?

5 Who was assassinated in India?

6 What was the name of the US plan for aid to Europe?

7 What did William Shockley invent at the Bell Laboratories?

8 Which three countries signed the Benelux pact, a 50-year trade agreement?

9 Where in America was the 5-M/200-in Hale reflector telescope installed?

10 What was the outcome of the first Arab-Israeli war?

11 What was the purpose of the Allied airlift from Britain?

12 Which much-loved national organisation came into effect in Britain?

13 Which far eastern country proclaimed a Republic?

14 Rebellion was crushed in which state in India?

15 In America, what new important organisation was formed?

Answers **1** George Ellery Hale **2** Plastic Vinyl LP **3** Royalists **4** Burma **5** Gandhi **6** The Marshall Plan **7** The transistor **8** France, Benelux, Britain **9** Mount Paloma, California **10** Israel annexed more territory **11** To beat the Soviet blockage of Berlin **12** National Health Service **13** South Korea **14** Hyderabad **15** Organisation of American States

1949

20th Century

1 Sir Robert Gordon Menzies became Prime Minister of which country in 1949?

2 For his performance in the title role of which film did Laurence Olivier win Best Actor Oscar in 1947?

3 Which treaty was signed by 12 nations in Washington on 4 April?

4 Who, in 1949, wrote the musical 'Kiss Me Kate'?

5 The American folk singer Huddie Ledbetter, who died in 1949, was better known by what name?

6 Which boxer, who announced his retirement 1 March 1949, was known as 'The Brown Bomber'?

7 Which film duo made their farewell starring appearance in 'The Barclays of Broadway' in 1949?

8 Which Hollywood actress married the Aly Khan in June 1949?

9 Who was Count Maurice Maeterlinck who died on 6 May 1949?

10 Who was 'Gorgeous Gussie' who shocked Wimbledon with her lace-trimmed panties in June 1949?

11 What was the name of the world's first jet airliner which made its first flight in June 1949?

12 Who directed his father, William, in 'The Treasure of the Sierra Madre' in 1949?

13 Which Nobel Prize was won in 1949 by William Faulkner?

14 What was the title of George Orwell's 'Big Brother' novel, written in 1949?

15 Nereid, discovered in 1949, is the second satellite of which planet?

Answers **1** Australia **2** Hamlet **3** The North Atlantic Treaty **4** Cole Porter **5** Leadbelly **6** Joe Louis **7** Fred Astaire and Ginger Rogers **8** Rita Hayworth **9** A Belgian author **10** Gussie Moran, an American tennis player **11** De Havilland Comet **12** John Huston **13** Literature **14** Nineteen Eighty-Four **15** Neptune

20th Century 1950

1 Which company announced the new disc brake?

2 What was the name of the new drug developed for heart disease?

3 What was the title of the first Japanese film to be shown in the West?

4 Which country invaded South Korea?

5 What was the name of the first credit card launched by Ralph Schneider?

6 Which prolific American writer published his first science-fiction novel 'Pebble in the sky' in 1950?

7 With whom did USSR sign a 30-year alliance?

8 Who annexed Arab Palestine?

9 Where were early hominid fossils found by Louis Lockey?

10 Who entered the war in Korea?

11 What was the name of the Tibetan leader who fled from the Chinese invasion?

12 Who recognises Ho Chi Minh's regime in Vietnam?

13 In Vietnam whose regime was also recognised?

14 Where did the Chinese nationalists set up a government in exile?

15 Who was proclaimed President of nationalistic China?

Answers **1** Dunlop **2** Beta Blockers **3** Rashomon **4** North Korea **5** Diners Club **6** Isaac Asimov **7** China **8** King Abdulla of Jordan **9** Tanzania **10** China **11** Dalai Lama **12** USSR **13** Bao Dai's Saigon regime **14** Formosa **15** Chiang Kai-Shek

1951

20th Century

1 Which newspaper tycoon who built an empire on "a diet of lurid crime, sex and scandal" died in Beverly Hills on 14 August 1951?

2 Basil Spence won a competition in August 1951 to design which new English cathedral?

3 Which American President fired General Douglas MacArthur because 'he wouldn't respect the authority of the President' in 1951?

4 What was the name of 'Little Mo' who at 16 became the youngest ever winner of the US Tennis Championships in 1951?

5 Which composer of 'The Student Prince' and 'The Desert Song' died in 1951?

6 Who was the American entertainer portrayed by Barbra Streisand in 'Funny Girl' who died in 1951?

7 Who is the Australian future ladies Wimbledon tennis champion born on 31 July 1951?

8 Who, in 1951, became the first woman to swim the English Channel in both directions?

9 Who were the two British diplomats who 'went missing' in June 1951 after spying for Russia?

10 Who, in 1951, won an Academy Award for his role as the jungle tramp in 'The African Queen'?

11 Who were the married couple sentenced to death in the US is April 1951 for spying?

12 In America what provision regarding the Presidency was made by The 22nd Amendment in 1951?

13 Which King of Belgium abdicated in 1951?

14 Which North African country gained independence from Britain in 1951?

15 Who was the US breakfast-cereal tycoon and statesman who died on 6 October 1951?

Answers **1** William Randolph Hearst **2** Coventry **3** Harry S. Truman **4** Maureen Connolly **5** Sigmund Romberg **6** Fanny Brice **7** Evonne Goolagong **8** Florence Chadwick **9** Burgess and MacLean **10** Humphrey Bogart **11** The Rosenberg's (Julius and Ethel) **12** That no person be elected President more than twice **13** Leopold III **14** Libya **15** William Kellogg

20th Century 1952

1 USA explodes first 'H' bomb, where?

2 Who invented the first artifical heart valve?

3 Who wrote 'Theatre of the Absurd'?

4 Where did the occupation of Germany by the Allied forces end?

5 Which two countries joined the NATO group?

6 Who attacked the colonists in Kenya?

7 Which two cities served as departure and arrival points for the first passenger jet service?

8 Which British King died?

9 Who overthrew the President of Cuba?

10 Where did the first clinical test of a pacemaker for the heart take place?

11 Where did an anti-apartheid rally take place?

12 Which Egyptian leader was ousted in an army coup by Muhammad Neguib on 26 July?

13 Who became King of Jordan?

14 Where was the first British 'A' bomb test carried out?

15 Which country was united with Ethiopia?

Answers **1** Eniwetok Atoll **2** Charles Hufnagel **3** Harold Pinter **4** West Germany **5** Greece and Turkey **6** The Mau Mau **7** London and Johannesburg **8** George VI **9** Batista **10** Boston USA **11** South Africa **12** King Farouk I **13** Hussein **14** Monet Bello **15** Entrea

1953 — 20th Century

1 Who married Jacqueline Bouvier on 12 September 1953?

2 Which Welsh poet and short-story writer whose works include 'Under Milk Wood' died in 1953?

3 Which golfer won both the US and British Open Championships in 1953?

4 Who on 7 April 1953 was elected Secretary-General of the United Nations?

5 What was introduced to radio by Harry Secombe, Peter Sellers, Michael Bentine and Spike Milligan in 1953?

6 Which Nobel Prize was won by Winston Churchill in 1953?

7 To what in June 1953 was Sherpa Tensing referring when he said: "We done the bugger"?

8 Which former occupant of 10 Rillington Place, London, went on the run in March 1953?

9 Dr Jonas E Salk developed a vaccine against which disease in 1953?

10 For which novel did Ernest Hemingway win a Pulitzer Prize in 1953?

11 Which Soviet leader who adopted a name meaning 'a man of steel' died in 1953?

12 Whose first starring role was the 1953 film 'Gentlemen Prefer Blondes'?

13 Born in 1891, who was the Russian composer of 'Peter and the Wolf' who died in 1953?

14 Who in 1953, as Chairman of the Senate subcommittee on investigations carried out his probe of alleged Communist activities in the US?

15 Who won an Academy award in 1953 for Best Supporting Actor in 'From Here to Eternity'?

Answers **1** John F. Kennedy **2** Dylan Thomas **3** Ben Hogan **4** Dag Hammarskjöld **5** The Goon Show **6** Literature **7** The conquest of Everest **8** John Christie **9** Polio **10** The Old Man and the Sea **11** Joseph Stalin **12** Marilyn Monroe **13** Sergey Prokofiev **14** Joseph McCarthy **15** Frank Sinatra

20th Century 1954

1 Where was the first nuclear reactor built?

2 Who invented non-stick frying pans?

3 Which pact was formed between USSR and Eastern European states?

4 Security forces in Kenya launch a big security drive against whom on 24 April?

5 The battle of Dien Bien Phu in North Vietnam marked the end of French control of which country?

6 A US backed military coup halted nationalisation and land reform in which country?

7 Who made his first rock and roll recordings in Memphis Tennessee?

8 Where in Africa did a war of independence take place?

9 What was the title of William Golding's first novel?

10 Who became USSR first secretary?

11 Which English athlete became the first person to run a mile in under four minutes?

12 Britain agrees to withdraw troops from where in Egypt?

13 An international agreement was reached by oil-using nations on which country's oil?

14 Signed in Manila, what was the SEATO mean?

15 Which country rejects European defence treaty?

Answers **1** Obninsk in Russia **2** Marc Gregoire **3** The Warsaw Pact **4** Mau Mau **5** Indo-China **6** Guatemala **7** Elvis Presley **8** Algeria **9** Lord of the Flies **10** Khrushchev **11** Roger Bannister **12** Suez Canal **13** Iran **14** South East Asian Defence Treaty Organisation **15** France

1955

20th Century

1 What is the motto of the United States which became obligatory to appear on all US currency in 1955?

2 On 3 April in Paris, football representatives from eight countries set up which new soccer contest?

3 In January 1955, which snooker champion made the first televised 147 maximum break?

4 In 1955, an American rock and roll singer born Elias Bates McDaniel adopted what name meaning, in black slang, 'a mischievous child'?

5 On 20 December 1955, which city became the capital of Wales?

6 Which 1955 book by Vladimir Nabokov featured the character Humbert Humbert?

7 What first was achieved by the American controlato, Marian Anderson at New York's Metropolitan Opera House in 1955?

8 Which Spanish artist painted 'The Sacrament of the Last Supper' in 1955?

9 Which James Bond novel written in 1955 features a villain called Hugo Drax?

10 In October, of whom did Princess Margaret 'like it to be known that she had decided not to marry'?

11 Which actor and teen hero died in a car crash in Los Angeles on 30 September?

12 At which race track, on 11 June 1955, were eighty spectators killed when three cars crashed ?

13 Who was the 'femme fatale' sentenced to hang on 21 June for shooting her lover David Blakely in a crime of passion?

14 Which American folk singer who wrote 'If I had a Hammer' and 'Turn, Turn, Turn' was investigated by the House Committee on 'un-American' activities in 1955?

15 In which 1955 movie did Marilyn Monroe's skirt take off in the breeze?

Answers **1** In God We Trust **2** The European Cup **3** Joe Davis **4** Bo Diddley **5** Cardiff **6** Lolita **7** The first performance of a black soloist with the Met **8** Salvador Dali **9** Moonraker **10** Captain Peter Townsend **11** James Dean **12** Le Mans **13** Ruth Ellis **14** Pete Seeger **15** The Seven Year Itch

20th Century 1956

1 What is incorporated into the second generation computers?

2 What new television improvement was invented by Ampes of California?

3 What new feature connected Britain with the USA?

4 What was built at Sellafield in the North of England?

5 Which three African countries became independent of France?

6 What was discovered by Clyde Cowan and Fred Reines?

7 What building in New York did Ludwig Mies van der Rohe design?

8 Who wrote 'Look Back in Anger'?

9 Where did the Soviet troops crush an uprising?

10 Between which two nations did a second war break out?

11 Who directed the film 'The Seventh Seal'?

12 Which Cypriot leader was exiled?

13 Stalin denounced by whom?

14 Which great waterway did Nasser nationalise?

15 Who was Poland's new Prime Minister?

Answers **1** Transistors **2** Video recorder **3** Transatlantic telephone cable **4** Nuclear reactor **5** Morocco, Sudan and Tunisia **6** The Neutrino **7** The Seagram building **8** John Osborne **9** Hungary **10** Arabs and Israelis **11** Ingmar Bergman **12** Makarios **13** Khruschev **14** Suez Canal **15** Gomulka

1957 — 20th Century

1 On 20 July, which British Prime Minister said: 'You have never had it so good'?

2 The title of which Ismaelite spiritual leader fell to a 20 year old Harvard student on the death of his grandfather on 12 July?

3 Which American black tennis player and golfer was named woman athlete of the year in America in 1957?

4 Name the capital of the newly independent Federation of Malaya in 1957?

5 John George Diefenbecker became Prime Minister of which country in 1957?

6 Name the Russian dog that orbited the earth in space in November 1957?

7 Which rock and roll star said: "Don't knock the rock", in 1957?

8 Which Nobel Prize was won in 1957 by Lester Pearson?

9 All nationals of which European country were expelled from Indonesia?

10 Who starred with Audrey Hepburn in 'Funny Face' in 1957?

11 Which King of Jordan foiled a coup of 14 April?

12 What was created by the Treaty of Rome on 25 March?

13 On which island were the remains of the Bounty discovered in 1957?

14 American broadcaster Lawrence Harvey Zeiger when he went on air for the first time in 1957. What professional name did he adopt?

15 Who was President Eisenhower's Vice-President sworn in for a second term on 20 January 1957?

Answers **1** Harold McMillan **2** Aga Khan **3** Althea Gibson **4** Kuala Lumpur **5** Canada **6** Laika **7** Bill Haley **8** Peace **9** Dutch nationals (The Netherlands) **10** Fred Astaire **11** King Hussain **12** The Common Market **13** Pitcairne Island **14** Larry King **15** Richard Nixon

20th Century 1958

1 Which new object for the long-term storage of food and other merchandise was developed by the USA

2 What new safety feature did the latest space craft have incorporated?

3 Who was assassinated in Iraq ion 14 July before a Republic was proclaimed?

4 Where was the first telescopic dish erected in Britain?

5 What was the name of the very first satellite launched into space?

6 Who invented the rotary petrol engine?

7 Who produced the musical 'West Side Story'?

8 The structure of RNA was determined, what was its full name?

9 Who invented ultrasound for medical institutes?

10 Which Brazilian footballer appeared in his first World Cup competition?

11 Which Pope succeeded Pope Pius XII?

12 Which two countries formed the United Arab Republic?

13 Which belt of radiation was discovered by US physicist?

14 Who, in 1958, composed the music for the film 'Gigi'?

15 In which Asian country was there a military coup?

Answers **1** Aluminium can **2** Silicon solar panel **3** King Faisal **4** Jodrell Bank **5** Sputnik **6** Felix Wankel **7** Leoonard Bernstein **8** Ribonucleic acid **9** Ian Donald **10** Pele **11** Pope John XXIII **12** Egypt and Syria **13** James Van Allen **14** Frederick Loewe **15** Pakistan

1959 — 20th Century

1 Which golfer turned professional in 1959 after winning the United States amateur championship?

2 What was originated by an American comedian Harry Fox, who died in 1959, in his 1913 Ziegfeld Follies routines?

3 Who, on 8 January 1959, was inaugurated as first President of the Fifth Republic?

4 Which city was replaced by Rawalpindi as the capital of Pakistan in 1959?

5 First constructed in 1959, who was the invetor of the hovercraft?

6 Who did Sweden's Ingemar Johansson defeat to win the World Heavyweight Boxing Championship in 1959?

7 Jazzman Sidney Bechet, who died in 1959, was a virtuoso on which instrument?

8 Who published her autobiography, "Goodness Had Nothing to Do with It' in 1959?

9 Which exiled King of Egypt became a citizen of Monaco in 1959?

10 Of which country did Lee Kuan Yew become first prime minister in 1959?

11 Who directed 'Some Like It Hot' in 1959?

12 What became the US 49th state on 3 January 1959?

13 Which actor was the star of 'Twelve Angry Men' in 1959?

14 What was the nickname of America's most famous tap dancer, Bill Robinson who died in 1959?

15 Which Cuban leader fled from the country on 1 January 1959 after Fidel Castro assumed power?

Answers **1** Jack Nicklaus **2** The dance, the Fox-Trot **3** Charles De Gaulle **4** Karachi **5** Christopher Cockerell **6** Floyd Patterson **7** Saxophone **8** Mae West **9** King Faruk **10** Singapore **11** Billy Wilder **12** Alaska **13** Henry Fonda **14** Bojangles **15** Fulgencio Batista

20th Century 1960

1 What in the pharmaceutical world was 'Norethynudrel'?

2 What did Theodore Maman invent?

3 For what purpose was Echo I satellite launched?

4 A right-wing coup took place in which eastern country?

5 What happened at Sharpeville, South Africa?

6 What was the first weather satellite called?

7 What were the names given to two new minor tranquilizers?

8 What was the name of Harold Pinter's new play?

9 Which President resigned in South Korea?

10 What was the name of the USA reconnaisance plane shot down in USSR?

11 In Cape Town, who made the 'wind of change' speech?

12 Who became the new President of USA on 9h November?

13 Which country was controlled by the army under Mobuto?

14 Who was the first woman to be the Prime Minister of Ceylon?

15 Which country outlaws the A.N.C ?

Answers **1** Oral contraceptive pill **2** Laser beam **3** Telephone communications **4** Laos **5** 69 anti-apartheid demonstrators were massacred by police **6** Tiros I **7** Valium, Librium **8** The Caretaker **9** Syngman Rhee **10** U-2 **11** MacMillan **12** Kennedy **13** Congo **14** Sirimavo Bandaranaike **15** South Africa

1961

20th Century

1 What name was given to the unsuccessful attempt to overthrow Fidel Castro's government in Cuba by United States-backed Cuban exiles?

2 Who was moved from his tomb in Red Square on 30 October?

3 How was the American painter Anna Mary Robinson, who died in 1961 aged 101, better known?

4 Who was sentenced to death in Jerusalem on 15 December for the murder of millions of Jews during the Nazi occupation of Europe?

5 Which of the Marx brothers was Leonard, who died in 1961?

6 Which organisation dedicated to the release of 'prisoners of conscience' was founded in 1961?

7 Who in 1961 said of the Beatles: "I want to manage those four boys, it wouldn't take me more than two half-days per week"?

8 Which figure did the US congress adopt as a national symbol in 1961?

9 Which city was renamed Volvograd on 10 November 1961?

10 Who in 1961, wrote 'The Prime of Miss Jean Brodie'?

11 Which writer killed himself with his 12-bore shot gun early on the morning of 2 July 1961?

12 Which Russian ballet dancer defected to the West on 16 June?

13 Who was the creator of detective 'Sam Spade' who died in 1961?

14 Which American made a 15-minute sub-orbital flight on 5 May?

15 Which city became the capital of Sierra Leone in 1961?

Answers **1** Bay of Pigs Invasion **2** Stalin **3** Grandma Moses **4** Adolf Eichmann **5** Chico **6** Amnesty International **7** Brian Epstein **8** Uncle Sam **9** Stalingrad **10** Muriel Spark **11** Ernest Hemingway **12** Rudolf Nureyev **13** Dashiell Hammett **14** Alan B. Shepard **15** Freetown

20th Century 1962

1 In which Central American country did Soviet missiles threaten nuclear war with the US?

2 Political Independence was granted to which country after she rejected membership to the Federation of the West Indies?

3 In Massachusetts General Hospital, what did two surgeons do for the first time using micro surgery?

4 There were clashes on which part of the Indian border?

5 In which constellation was an x-ray source discovered?

6 Which American mathematician invented fractal images?

7 Who was the first man to orbit the earth in space?

8 What was the name of the first live television transmission sent by satellite between the US and Europe?

9 Which naturalist drew attention to the effects of pesticides?

10 Which US actress starred in her last film 'The Misfits'?

11 Which volcanic island erupted?

12 Where in Africa was a republic formed with Julius Nyerere as President?

13 Where the Marines sent in to oppose Communist pathey LAO?

14 From whom did India annexe Goa?

15 Who produced paintings of green Coca-Cola bottles and of Marilyn Monroe in 1961?

Answers **1** Cuba **2** Jamaica **3** Grafted the right arm on a boy **4** Sino-Indian **5** Scorpius **6** Benoit Mandelbrot **7** John Glenn in Friendship 7 **8** Telstar **9** Rachel Carson **10** Marilyn Monroe **11** Tristan da Cunha **12** Tanganyika **13** Laos **14** Portugal **15** Andy Warhol

1963 — 20th Century

1 Who, on 26 June, declared: "Ich bin ein Berliner"?

2 What sporting event was won by Charles 'Chuck' McKinley in July 1963?

3 In which city did Martin Luther King make his 'I have a dream' speech on 28 August 1963?

4 What was the name of Cape Kennedy prior to 1963?

5 Which organisation won the third of its Nobel peace prizes in 1963?

6 What crime took place at a secluded spot at Cheddington, Bucks England on 8 August?

7 On what date in November was President Kennedy assassinated in Dallas?

8 Which Pope died on June 30, 1963?

9 Whose son was released by kidnappers in Los Angeles in December 1963 after his father paid a $24,000 ransom?

10 Who was the satirist turned mystic, and author of 'Brave New World' who died in Hollywood on 22 November?

11 Who on 22 November said: "I will do my best, that is all I can do. I ask for your help and God's"?

12 Which American country singer died in a plane crash at the height of her fame in 1963?

13 In what 1963 affair were Dr Stephen Ward and Christine Keeler central characters?

14 Who was Sylvia Plath married to, until her death in 1963?

15 Who was the first woman in space who circled the earth in June 1963?

Answers **1** John F. Kennedy **2** He won the Wimbledon Men's Singles title **3** Washington **4** Cape Canaveral **5** The Red Cross **6** The Great Train Robbery **7** 22 November **8** John XXIII **9** Frank Sinatra **10** Aldous Huxley **11** Lyndon B. Johnson **12** Patsy Cline **13** The Profumo Affair **14** Ted Hughes **15** Valentina Tereshkova

20th Century 1964

1 What was the name of the first bullet train in Japan?

2 What did the IBM 360 series computer have for the first time?

3 Under which name did Tanganyika and Zanzibar unite?

4 Which black leader was jailed for life in South Africa on 14 June?

5 The PLO was formed in 1964, what do the letters stand for?

6 War was declared between two neighbouring south eastern countries?

7 What elementary chemical particle did Murray Gell-Mann and George Zweig discover in the USA?

8 What did David Hockney paint for the first time?

9 Who became World Heavyweight boxing champion?

10 Name the first Prime Minister of independent India who died in New Delhi on 27 May?

11 who becomes the new Prime Minister of Southern Rhodesia?

12 With which country did the USA start retaliatory bombing on 4 August?

13 USSR dismisses which leader?

14 Who was Britain's new Prime Minister?

15 Which East African country becomes a Republic, with a former leader of the Mau Mau rebellion as her first President?

Answers **1** Shinkansen **2** Silicon chips **3** Tanzania **4** Nelson Mandela **5** Palestine Liberation Organisation **6** Indonesia and Malaysia **7** The quark **8** A swimming pool **9** Cassius Clay **10** Jawaharlal (Pandit) Nehru **11** Smith **12** N. Vietnam **13** Khrushchev **14** Wilson **15** Kenya

1965 — 20th Century

1 President Sukarno survived an attempted coup in October 1965 in which country?

2 Who, on 30 December, was sworn in as sixth president of the Philippines?

3 Which fashion model known as 'The Shrimp', helped to popularise the mini-skirt in 1965?

4 Which 1965 movie about professional card players and gamblers starred Steve McQueen and Edward G. Robinson?

5 Who was the 'Saint of Lambarene' who died in 1965?

6 Who painted a 'Campbell's Soup Can' in 1965?

7 Which author who wrote 'Of Human Bondage' and 'The Moon and Sixpence' died aged 91 in 1965?

8 Who directed 'Dr. Zhivago' in 1965?

9 Who in 1965 played an unscrupulous hired killer in 'For a Few Dollars More'?

10 Who wrote the 1965 film 'What's New Pussycat'?

11 What creature was Goldie, who escaped from London Zoo in March 1965?

12 Thomas Arthur Jefferson, who died on 23 February at the age of 74 was better known by what professional name?

13 Which former British colony became Africa's smallest independent state on 17 February?

14 Which American poet and dramatist on whose works the musical 'Cats' is based died on 4 January 1965?

15 Who was the actress wife of Roald Dahl who he nursed back to health after a stroke in 1965?

Answers **1** Indonesia **2** Ferdinand Marcos **3** Jean Shrimpton **4** The Cincinnati Kid **5** Albert Schweitzer **6** Andy Warhol **7** W. Somerset Maugham **8** David Lean **9** Clint Eastwood **10** Woody Allen **11** A Golden Eagle **12** Stan Laurel **13** Gambia **14** T S Eliot **15** Patricia Neal

20th Century 1966

1 Which two Asian countries ended their three-year war?

2 Which European country left NATO?

3 Who harassed the artists and academics in China?

4 Which black activist party was formed in USA by Huey Newton and Bobby Seale?

5 Where in Europe was a large oil deposit found?

6 Around the world, special areas were established for the protection of what??

7 Which state in America introduced legislation to limit air pollution by cars?

8 Which rock group collaborated with artist Andy Warhol on shows in New York?

9 Which US song writer had a massive hit with 'Highway 61 Revisited'?

10 The soundtrack of which very popular film starring Julie Andrews was released in USA?

11 Name South Africa's pro-apartheid Prime Minister, who was stabbed to death on 6 September?

12 The world's first electronic exchange opened in which US state?

13 Who designed the mini skirt?

14 Which three African countries became independent members of the Commonwealth?

15 Where was the first tidal barrage built in France?

Answers **1** Malaysia & Indonesia **2** France **3** Red Guards **4** Black Panthers **5** North Sea **6** Animals and plants **7** California **8** The Velvet Underground **9** Bob Dylan **10** The Sound of Music **11** H. F Verwoerd **12** New Jersey **13** Mary Quant **14** Guyana, Botswana and Lesotho **15** Brittany

1967

20th Century

1 Who did Priscilla Beaulieu marry in May 1967?

2 Which lone yachtsman did the Queen of England knight in July 1967 after sailing round the world?

3 How was Albert De Salvo, recaptured on 25 February by US police after escaping from a prison mental ward, better known?

4 Nicolae Ceaucescu became premier of which country on 9 December 1967?

5 Which group urged the world 'Let's Go To San Francisco' in 1967?

6 How did Louis Washkansky make history in December 1967? (similar to q 14 1966. Ck year)

7 Which Argentine-born revolutionary was shot dead by troops in the jungle of Bolivia on 10 October?

8 On 23 August the Belgian, Eddy Merckx became world champion at which sport?

9 The six-day war of June 1967 was fought between the Arab countries against which other nation?

10 Who in 1967 was 'Cool Hand Luke'?

11 Who on 16 May declared a resounding 'Non!' to Britain joining the European Common Market?

12 Bert Lahr, who died in 1967 played which character in 'The Wizard of Oz'?

13 Who became the first woman since 1939 to win the triple crown of singles, doubles and mixed doubles in both the British and American tennis championships?

14 Harold Holt who drowned while swimming in the sea near his holiday home in December 1967 was Prime Minister of which country?

15 The musical 'Half a Sixpence' which premiered in London on 21 December 1967 was based on which Rudyard Kipling novel?

Answers **1** Elvis Presley **2** Sir Francis Chichester **3** The Boston Strangler **4** Rumania **5** Flowerpot Men **6** He was the first heart transplant patient **7** Che Guevara **8** Cycling **9** Israel **10** Paul Newman **11** Charles De Gaulle **12** The Cowardly Lion **13** Billie Jean King **14** Australia **15** Kipps

20th Century 1968

1 What water sport equipment did Jim Drake and Hoyle Schweiter invent?

2 Which island in the Indian Ocean gained political independence from Britain, becoming a constitutional monarchy, with the British Queen as head of state?

3 Where was there a massacre of up to 500 civilians during the Tet offensive by US troops?

4 Which city in Vietnam received a prolonged attack by the Vietcong?

5 Which black rights leader was assassinated in Memphis on 9 April??

6 Who was Canada's new Prime Minister?

7 Students 'month of the barricades' in which country?

8 In which city was Robert Kennedy fatally wounded?

9 Who was overthrown in Czechoslovakia by the Warsaw Pact invasion on 20th August?

10 President Johnson orders the end of the US bombing of which country?

11 Who was inaugurated as the new President of the USA?

12 What was orbited in space for the first time?

13 Rodolfo in 'La Boheme' is among the most famous roles of which opera singer, with which he made his debut in 1968 with the Metropolitan Opera in New York?

14 Which country flew, for the first time, the world's first supersonic airliner, the TU-144?

15 Where were British Asians deprived of their trading licences?

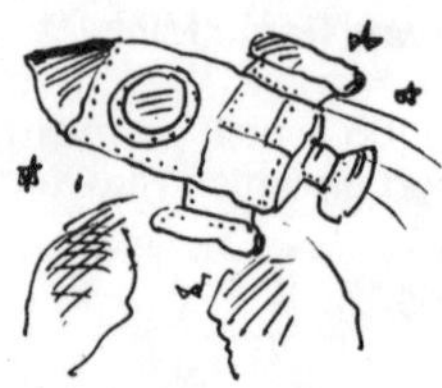

Answers 1 The sailboard **2** Mauritius **3** My Lai, Vietnam **4** Saigon **5** Martin Luther King **6** Trudeau **7** France **8** Los Angeles **9** Dubcek **10** North Vietnam **11** Nixon **12** Moon **13** Luciano Pavarotti **14** USSR **15** Kenya

1969 — 20th Century

1 Who were Charles Conrad and Alan Bean who attracted the world's attention in November 1969?

2 What did the US airforce stop investigating in 1969?

3 Ho Chi Minh, who died in 1969, was the Communist leader of which country?

4 Which new Nobel prize category was created by Sweden, to commemorate its 300th anniversary, in 1969?

5 Who was the leader of a cult 'The Family' whose chilling act shocked America and the world in 1969?

6 Paul Anka wrote the words to which Frank Sinatra recording which was a smash hit in 1969?

7 Brian Jones who drowned in his swimming pool at East Sussex, England on 2 July was a member of which rock group?

8 Which actor, born William Pratt in 1887, died on 2 February?

9 Which group made the 1969 album 'Tommy', a rock opera written by their leader Pete Townshend?

10 Who, on 21 July 1969, said: "That's one small step for man, one giant leap for mankind"?

11 Which married couple had a 'bed-in' for peace in March 1969 with the message 'Make love not war'?

12 What was the name of John Wayne's character in the 1969 movie 'True Grit'?

13 Who was the 34th President of the United States who died in 1969?

14 Which woman became Israeli Premier in 1969?

15 Who was jailed in Memphis for 99 years on 10 March for the murder of Martin Luther King?

Answers **1** The second team of US astronauts to walk on the moon? **2** UFOs **3** North Vietnam **4** Economics **5** Charles Manson **6** My Way **7** The Rolling Stones **8** Boris Karloff **9** The Who **10** Neil Armstrong **11** John Lennon and Yoko Ono **12** Rooster Cogburn **13** Dwight D Eisenhower **14** Golda Meir **15** James Earl Ray

20th Century 1970

1 Which system used 21 navigation satellites?

2 Who succeeds Gomulka when he resigns after riots in Poland?

3 What was the name of the first Jumbo jet?

4 Where in Canada was a state of insurrection proclaimed on 16 October?

5 Who became the new President of Chile?

6 What was name of the Cambodian Prince, overthrown in 1970?

7 What was the name of the USSR space probe which took photographs of the Moon's surface?

8 Where did the PLO agree to evacuate strongholds in Egypt on 27 September?

9 Ian Smith declares a Republic in which country?

10 To which country did US troops fly in order to attack Communist bases?

11 What was the name of Britain's new Prime Minister?

12 In which country did Palestinians blow up three planes?

13 Which controversial Arab president, died in Cairo on 28 September?

14 Who became the new President of Egypt?

15 Who is the architect of France's Fifth Republic and twice her President, who died on 9 November?

Answers **1** Global positioning system **2** Edward Gierek **3** Boeing 747 **4** Quebec **5** Salvadore Allende **6** Sihanouk **7** Lunokhod **8** Cairo **9** Rhodesia **10** Cambodia **11** Heath **12** Jordan **13** Nasser **14** Sadat **15** De Gaulle

1971

20th Century

1 Which Austrian diplomat was appointed UN Secretary-General on 21 December 1971?

2 Which German statesman won the Nobel Peace prize in 1971?

3 Which French fashion designer whose name became synonymous with French chic died, aged 89, on 10 January?

4 Which province of Pakistan became a country in its own right in 1971?

5 In which 1971 movie did Clint Eastwood first play tough cop Harry Callahan?

6 Who was premier of the USSR from 1958-64 who died on 11 September 1971?

7 Who was found guilty of murdering 20 Vietnamese at the 'My lai Massacre', on 29 March 1971?

8 Born in 1893, who was the straight-faced silent film comedian who died in March 1971?

9 Who wrote 'The Female Eunuch' which was published in the United States in 1971?

10 Who appointed himself President of Uganda in 1971?

11 Where did David Scott and James Irwin go for a drive on 31 July 1971?

12 Which city became the capital of the independent state of Qatar in 1971?

13 Who made his first solo album, 'Got to Be There' in 1971?

14 Who wrote 'A Clockwork Orange' which was made into a controversial 1971 movie?

15 On 10 July King Hassan crushed a coup attempt in which country?

Answers **1** Kurt Waldheim **2** Willie Brandt **3** Coco Chanel **4** Bangladesh **5** Dirty Harry **6** Nikita Khrushchev **7** Lieutenant William Calley **8** Harold Lloyd **9** Germaine Greer **10** Idi Amin **11** On the moon **12** Doha **13** Michael Jackson **14** Anthony Burgess **15** Morocco

20th Century 1972

1 Computerised cargo handling came into operation for the first time at which airport?

2 In which city wasa the 1,353-foot high, twin-towered World Trade Centre was completed?

3 Where was the first digital watch made?

4 After the Soviet space craft SALYUT-1 was placed in orbit, the USA followed with the second. What was it called?

5 Who did Acheampong oust when he seized power in Ghana?

6 Which other country besides Britain, Norway and Denmark signed the EEC treaty?

7 What was the name of the scan pioneered by Godfrey Hounsfield, first used on a human brain?

8 Who was the new Prime Minister of Australia?

9 The USA bombed which North Vietnamese City?

10 Ceylon changed its name to what?

11 Brezhnev and Wilson sign SALT-1 in which city?

12 The British Army killed 13 demonstrators in Northern Ireland. What has that day become known as?

13 Who expelled British Asians from Uganda?

14 USA troops withdraw from which country?

15 Who stormed the Israeli compound at the Munich Olympics?

Answers **1** Heathrow **2** New York **3** Dallas, Texas **4** Skylab **5** Busia **6** Ireland **7** CAT scan **8** Whitlem **9** Hanoi **10** Sri Lanka **11** Moscow **12** Bloody Sunday **13** Idi Amin **14** South Vietnam **15** Arab guerillas

1973 — 20th Century

1 Who was the President of Ireland, the world's oldest head of state, who resigned aged 90 in June 1973?

2 Who, in 1973, became the first foreign-born citizen to hold the post of Secretary of State in the US?

3 Who, in 1973, became the first US Vice-President to resign because of criminal charges?

4 Name the author of 'The Hobbit' who died in 1973?

5 Who said in 1973: "There will be no whitewash at the White House"?

6 The 1971 Frederick Forsyth best-seller 'The Day of the Jackal' was about the attempted assassination of which political figure?

7 Pablo Cassals, who died in 1973 aged 96, was a virtuoso performer on which instrument?

8 Which country became a republic in 1973 after it's ruler King Constantine III was deposed?

9 Who was the President of Chile killed in a military coup on11 September?

10 Who wrote the musical 'A Little Night Music' in 1973?

11 Which rock and roll singer, known as 'The Boss' made his first album 'Greetings from Asbury Park' in 1973?

12 Whose ragtime composition 'The Entertainer' was used in the 1971 movie 'The Sting'?

13 Which pesticide was banned in the US in 1973 except for use in extreme health emergencies?

14 What, in 1973, was won in record time by 'Secretariat' at Churchill Downs?

15 In 1973 a suspension bridge was opened at Istanbul linking the Asian and European shores of which strait?

Answers **1** Eamon de Valera **2** Henry Kissinger **3** Spiro Agnew **4** J.R.R. Tolkien **5** Richard Nixon **6** Charles de Gaulle **7** Cello **8** Greece **9** Salvador Allende **10** Stephen Sondheim **11** Bruce Springsteen **12** Scott Joplin **13** DDT **14** The Kentucky Derby **15** Bosporus

20th Century — 1974

1 What 'mathematical toy' became a craze in 1974?

2 What did the USA begin to research as a possible form of energy?

3 What scandal led to the downfall of President Nixon?

4 What immigration policy was abolished in Australia?

5 What was found at Laetoli in Ethiopia?

6 What was the cause of a 3-day working week in Britain?

7 Who formed a minority Labour government in Britain?

8 Who was electe new Prime Minister for Israel?

9 Who replaced Brand as Chancellor in Germany?

10 Who became France's new President?

11 Which two-times President of Argentina died in Buenos Aires?

12 Who did the Turks invade?

13 Who was the USA's new President?

14 Which scandal was Richard Nixon talking about when he made his: 'There can be no whitewash in the Whitehouse' speech?

15 Where was the Human Rights pact signed?

Answers **1** The Rubik cube **2** Solar power **3** Watergate **4** That only white people were allowed into Australia – immigration became open to all **5** Footprints of a hominid called 'Lucy', 3-7 million years old **6** Miner's strike **7** Wilson **8** Rabin **9** Schmidt **10** Valery Giscard d'Estaing **11** Peron **12** Cyprus **13** Ford **14** Watergate **15** Helsinki

1975 — 20th Century

1 Who had a smash hit with 'Bohemian Rhapsody' in 1975?

2 Who co-founded Microsoft in 1975 with Paul Allen?

3 Who was the creator of 'Bertie Wooster' and 'Jeeves', who died in 1975?

4 Which Czechoslovakian tennis champion defected to the West on 9 September 1975?

5 Who did Lynette 'Squeaky' Fromme attempt to assassinate in September 1975?

6 Which 'king of soccer' signed a 3-year contract with the New York Cosmos for $7 million on 3 June 1975?

7 Who was Britain's leading woman sculptor killed in a fire in her studio at St. Ives on 21 May?

8 Who won substantial damages from the BBC in May 1975, over a programme linking him to the Mafia?

9 Who was the last Emperor of Ethiopia, and 'Lion of Judah', who died in 1975?

10 After a 30-year break from movies, which American comedian returned to the big screen in 1975 and won an Oscar for his performance in 'The Sunshine Boys'?

11 Which successful 1975 Steven Spielberg movie was adapted from a novel by Peter Benchley?

12 Who was Georges Carpenter, who died in 1975?

13 Who became King of Spain in 1975?

14 Who was the King of Saudi Arabia assassinated by his nephew in March 1975?

15 Who did Agatha Christie kill off in her 1975 novel 'Curtain'?

Answers **1** Queen **2** Bill Gates **3** P G. Wodehouse **4** Martina Navratilova **5** President Gerald Ford **6** Pele **7** Barbara Hepworth **8** Frank Sinatra **9** Haile Selassie **10** George Burns **11** Jaws **12** A French heavyweight boxer who fought Jack Dempsey in 1921 **13** Juan Carlos I **14** King Faisal **15** Hercule Poirot

20th Century 1976

1 In which troubled country was a women's peace movement launched?

2 Which leading official died in China?

3 Who won the Canadian Quebex election?

4 In which South African township were there riots?

5 Who raided Entebbe in Uganda?

6 Who was the new President of Mexico?

7 Which Chinese city was destroyed by a massive earthquake?

8 What did the Sex Pistols make popular in Britain?

9 Which plane made the transatlantic crossing in three hours?

10 In the Malay archipelago, which country, which had declared independence on Portugal's withdrawal, was annexed by Indonesia?

11 Which two countries were reunited as a Socialist Republic?

12 In which European country were free elections held for the first time in 50 years?

13 Where did Cuba-backed MPLA gain control of nation's key points?

14 Who was new President of Argentina?

15 Name the new Prime Minister in Britain?

Answers **1** Northern Ireland **2** Mao Zedong **3** Parti Quebecois **4** Soweto **5** The Israelis **6** Portillo **7** Tangshan **8** Punk **9** Concorde **10** East Timor **11** N and S Vietnam **12** Portugal **13** Angola **14** Videla **15** Callaghan

1977

20th Century

1 Which asteroid was discovered in 1977 in an eccentric orbit between Saturn and Uranus?

2 Which Greek soprano, and one time lover of Aristotle Onassis, died of a heart attack aged 53 on 17 September?

3 Who was found dead at Graceland on 16 August?

4 Which organisation received the 1977 Nobel Peace Prize for 'its efforts on behalf of defending human dignity against violence and subjugation'?

5 Which spacecraft made its maiden flight in February 1977 on top of a Boeing 747 aircraft?

6 Which one of the Marx brothers was Julius, who died in 1977?

7 Which actress, born in 1908 as Lucille le Sueur, died in May 1977?

8 Who, in 1977, was 'Annie Hall'?

9 Zulkfikar Ali Bhutto was ousted as Prime Minister of which country in July 1977?

10 In which country, in July 1977, were the 'Gang of Four' expelled from the Communist Party?

11 Carl XVI Gustaf became King of which country in 1977?

12 Who defeated Ernie Shavers to retain his World Boxing heavyweight title on 29 September 1977?

13 Who played the title role in the 1977 Ken Russell film 'Valentino'?

14 Which Austrian driver became World Motor Racing champion in October 1977?

15 Which rock singer and leader of 'T Rex' was killed in a car crash on 16 September 1977?

Answers **1** Charon **2** Maria Callas **3** Elvis Presley **4** Amnesty International **5** The Space Shuttle **6** Groucho **7** Joan Crawford **8** Diane Keaton **9** Pakistan **10** China **11** Sweden **12** Muhammed Ali **13** Rudolf Nureyev **14** Niki Lauda **15** Marc Bolan

20th Century — 1978

1 Dr Robert Edwards pioneered the birth of what?

2 Where was the Middle-East peace agreement determined?

3 Who was elected as the new President of Kenya on 10 October?

4 What was the name of the Pope, who died after just one month in office?

5 Which pop group, formed in 1978, by its lead singer Sting, had a chart success that same year with their first single 'Roxanne'?

6 Which planet did Pioneer probes 1 and 2 reach?

7 Where did tons of oil get spilled from Amoco Cadiz?

8 What new innovation for recording and playing sound was first demonstrated?

9 Which Italian terrorist organisation assassinated Italy's Prime Minister Aldo Moro?

10 Where was President Daoud killed?

11 Which great Kenyan leader died on 27 August?

12 Martial law was implemented in which country after millions march against the Shah?

13 Who is the new Prime Minister in South Africa?

14 Who became the first non-Italian Pope for 450 years and where was he from?

15 Which two men shared the Nobel Peace Prize?

Answers **1** The test-tube baby **2** Camp David, USA **3** Moi **4** John Paul **5** The Police **6** Venus **7** Off the coast of Brittany **8** Compact Disc **9** Red Brigade **10** Afghanistan **11** Kenyatta **12** Iran **13** Botha **14** Karol Wojtyla from Poland **15** Begin and Sadat

1979

20th Century

1 Which French film director, and son of a famous painter, died in 1979?

2 Who, in 1977, starred in 'The Deer Hunter'?

3 Which 'living saint' won the 1977 Nobel Peace Prize?

4 Born Gladys Marie Smith in 1893, who was America's Sweetheart who died in 1979?

5 Who won Academy Award for best actor in the 1979 movie 'Kramer vs Kramer'?

6 In which country is the island of Lomblen, where a tidal wave killed 750 people on 22 July?

7 Which dictactor was overthrown in 1979 by an invasion force from Tanzania, eventually finding refuge in Saudi Arabia?

8 The 1977 Normal Mailer novel 'The Executioner's Song' was about the execution of which murderer in the US in 1979?

9 In July 1979 the Sandinista rebels gained control of which Central American country?

10 What distinctive feature was displayed by the Israeli statesman and soldier Moshe Dayan, who played an important role in negotiating the peace treaty with Egypt in 1979?

11 Which country, formerly under the control of Denmark, voted for home rule in 1979?

12 Which science fiction writer published a two-volume autobiography 'In Memory Yet Green?

13 A revolution in January 1979 caused the downfall of the 'Peacock Throne' in which country?

14 Where in Pennsylvania in March 1979 did an atomic leak take place at a nuclear power station?

15 Which country did the Soviet Union invade on 27 December 1979?

Answers **1** Jean Renoir **2** Robert De Niro **3** Mother Theresa **4** Mary Pickford **5** Dustin Hoffman **6** Indonesia **7** Idi Amin **8** Gary Gilmore **9** Nicaragua **10** He had a black eyepatch over his left eye **11** Greenland **12** Isaac Asimov **13** Iran **14** Three Mile Island **15** Afghanistan

20th Century 1980

1 What did IBM in the USA and NEC in Japan perfect?

2 Who perfected the program for IBM desk top computers?

3 What did two American students invent as a training device?

4 Rhodesia became independent. What was its new name?

5 1980 saw the start of which war, where 1 million people were to die?

6 Which killer disease was eradicated throughout the world?

7 Which killer disease was first recognised in USA?

8 Japanese car production overtook that of which country?

9 Which country launched the first wind assisted commercial ship for half a century?

10 Which mountain erupted in Washington State USA?

11 Which President of Egypt was assassinated?

12 Which Mediterranean country joined the European community?

13 Which former film star became President of USA?

14 Which Communist leader died in Yugoslavia?

15 Which politician was killed in a plane crash in India?

Answers **1** Bar codes **2** Microsoft **3** Roller blades **4** Zimbabwe **5** Iran-Iraq **6** Smallpox **7** AIDS **8** USA **9** Japan **10** Mount St. Helens **11** Sadat **12** Greece **13** Ronald Reagan **14** Tito **15** Sanjay Gandhi

1981

20th Century

1 Who did Turkish gunman, Mehmet Ali Agca, shoot and wound on 13 May?

2 Which Jamaican Rastafarian reggae singer died in May, aged 36?

3 Which American actress's 'Workout Book' was a best-seller in 1981?

4 Who, after being shot on 30 March by John Hinckley III, said to his wife, "Honey, I forgot to duck"?

5 Which actress made her Broadway debut at the age of 49 in the revival of Lillian Hellman's 'The Little Foxes'?

6 Hosni Mubarak was chosen to be the next President of which country?

7 Who came out of a 20-year retirement to play in the movie 'Ragtime'?

8 Who, in 1981, directed 'Raiders of the Lost Ark'?

9 Who ended Bjorn Borg's run of five consecutive Wimbledon titles?

10 Which Australian-born media magnate acquired the 'London Times' and 'Sunday Times' in 1981?

11 In which church did Lady Diana Spencer and the Prince of Wales marry?

12 Who became the first Socialist President of the Fifth Republic in France?

13 Of which country did Dr. Garret Fitzgerald become Prime Minister?

14 What was the name of Fred Astaire's sister and former partner who died?

15 Who became Ronald Reagan's Vice-President?

Answers **1** Pope John Paul II in St. Peter's Square **2** Bob Marley **3** Jane Fonda **4** Ronald Reagan **5** Elizabeth Taylor **6** Egypt **7** James Cagney **8** Steven Spielberg **9** John McEnroe **10** Rupert Murdoch **11** St. Paul's Cathedral **12** Francois Mitterand **13** The Republic of Ireland **14** Adele **15** George Bush

20th Century 1982

1 What was the name of the new Chancellor of Germany?

2 What home-filming equipment did Sony launch?

3 What was the new type of oral contraceptive pill developed in the UK?

4 Which European country joined NATO?

5 Which island was the cause of the war between Argentina and Britain?

6 Where were there massacres in Palestinian refugee camps?

7 The new chemical element 109 was synthesized in which country?

8 In which German city were gene databases established?

9 One of King Henry VIII's sunken warships was discovered. What was it called?

10 Who succeeded Brezhnev as Leader of USSR on 12 November?

11 Which nation withdrew from Sinai?

12 Who was King of Saudi Arabia crowned on 13 June?

13 Which political group did Israel oust in Beirut?

14 Who was Lebanon's new President?

15 Who became the new President of Spain?

Answers **1** Kohl **2** Camcorder **3** Morning after pill **4** Spain **5** Falklands **6** Lebanon **7** Germany **8** Heidelberg **9** Mary Rose **10** Andropov **11** Israel **12** Fahd **13** PLO **14** Gemayal **15** Gonzalez

1983 20th Century

1 Who became Prime Minister of Australia in 1983?

2 What first was achieved in June 1983 by Sally Ride?

3 Which actor, who also wrote the best-selling autobiography, 'The Moon's a Balloon', died on 30 July?

4 Which Pole was the 1983 winner of the Nobel Peace Prize?

5 Who was the notorious wartime SS chief of Lyons, arrested in Bolivia on 19 January?

6 Which European golfer won the Masters at Augusta, Georgia for the second time in 1983?

7 Who starred in, directed and produced the film 'Yentl' in 1983?

8 On 19 October 1983, the Senate in Washington approved a bill to make whose birthday a national holiday?

9 Who won the fifth of his United States Open Tennis Championships in 1983?

10 A suicide mission by Shia terrorists killed 241 US Marines and 58 French paratroopers in which Middle East city on 23 October?

11 Which Israeli Prime Minister stepped down from power in 1983?

12 Who said in 1983: "I am extraordinarily patient, providing I get my own way in the end"?

13 Wat was the name of George Gershwin's brother and lyric writer who died in 1983?

14 Who had a hit with 'Uptown Girl' in 1983?

15 Which ex-US President made his acting debut in the soap opera 'Dynasty' in December 1983?

Answers **1** Bob Hawke **2** America's first female astronaut **3** David Niven **4** Lech Walesa **5** Klaus Barbie **6** Severiano Ballesteros **7** Barbra Streisand **8** Martin Luther King **9** Jimmy Connors **10** Beirut **11** Menachem Begin **12** Margaret Thatcher **13** Ira **14** Billy Joel **15** Gerald Ford

20th Century **1984**

1 What was the name of the computer that Apple launched?

2 Where did 2,600 people die when poisonous gas was released?

3 What did China request be handed over in1997?

4 In which country did a famine spark a worldwide aid effort?

5 Which native race of Australia was given legal protection?

6 Who was the French philosopher who analysed the structure of power in society, who died?

7 A vaccine for which disfiguring illness was developed?

8 Who was the USSR's new leader?

9 Which British industry went on strike?

10 Troops storm which Sikh temple in India?

11 Who is the new Prime Minister for Canada?

12 Which conference was bombed by the IRA?

13 Which female politician was assassinated in India?

14 From where did Western peace-keeping force withdraw?

15 Who was Israel's new Prime Minister?

Answers **1** Macintosh **2** Bhopal, India **3** Hong Kong **4** Ethiopia **5** Aborigines **6** Michael Foucalt **7** Leprosy **8** Chernenko **9** The Miners **10** Golden Temple **11** Mulroney **12** The Conservative Party **13** Mrs. Gandhi **14** Lebanon **15** Peres

1985

20th Century

1. How old was Boris Becker when be became the youngest ever Wimbledon Men's Champion in 1985?
2. Who captained the victorious European Ryder Cup team at 'The Belfry' in September 1985?
3. What was the television talk show 'A.M. Chicago' renamed in 1985?
4. The movie 'Sweet Dreams' (1985) with Jessica Lange told the story of which country music singer?
5. Which Welsh-born fashion empress died in September 1985 after falling down the stairs in her home?
6. Which 1985 film, set in Kenya, starred Meryl Streep and Robert Redford?
7. What was the name of the Italian cruise ship hijacked off the Mediterranean coast of Egypt on 7 October 1985 by members of the Palestine Liberation Front?
8. Who launched his pedal-powered tricycle C5 in January 1985?
9. Which tyrant resigned as Khmer Rouge commander in 1985?
10. Who was the author of 'I Claudius' who died in 1985?
11. On 13 July, the US Live Aid concert was held in the JFK Stadium in which city?
12. What was the name of the Greenpeace vessel blown up by French agents in Auckland harbour on 10 July?
13. In West Germany, on 8 July, the originators of whose diaries were jailed for forgery?
14. For what sport did Katarina Witt win a world title in 1985?
15. Which singer appeared in 'Desperately Seeking Susan' in 1985?

Answers **1** 17 **2** Tony Jacklin **3** The Oprah Winfrey Show **4** Patsy Cline **5** Laura Ashley **6** Out of Africa **7** Achille Lauro **8** Sir Clive Sinclair **9** Pol Pot **10** Robert Graves **11** Philadelphia **12** Rainbow Warrior **13** The 'Hitler' Diaries **14** Figure skating **15** Madonna

20th Century 1986

1 What was the name of the 'arms for hostages' scandal in USA?

2 Which two neighbouring countries joined the EC?

3 Which Middle East country did the USA bomb

4 Who was the new President for the Philippines?

5 In the USSR what does Perestroika and Glastnost mean?

6 Where was there an accident in a nuclear reactor in the Ukraine?

7 What electrical discovery was made?

8 What was the name of the space shuttle which exploded after take off?

9 On which planet were six new moons discovered?

10 Which world famous cricketer becomes captain of the West Indies?

11 Who was the leading politician ousted in Haiti?

12 Which former leader of the Philippines was forced to flee?

13 Who became the new President of Austria?

14 Who is the American cyclist who won the first Tour de France in 1986, and went on to win the event twice more, in 1989 and 1990?

15 Which Soviet 'internal exile' was freed in the USSR?

Answers **1** Irangate **2** Spain and Portugal **3** Libya **4** Corazon Aquino **5** Reform and Openness **6** Chernobyl **7** First high-temperature superconductor **8** Challenger **9** Uranus **10** Viv Richards **11** Baby Doc Duvalier **12** President Ferdinand Marcos **13** Kurt Waldheim **14** Gregory LeMond **15** Sakharov

1987

20th Century

1 Who, in 1987, was 'Crocodile Dundee'?

2 For her leading role in which movie did Cher win an Academy Award in 1987?

3 What name was given to 19 October 1987, the day on which stock market prices in the United States plummeted?

4 Which fomer Nazi, and long time prisoner at Spandau Prison, West Berlin, died in 1987?

5 Whose painting 'Irises' sld for $53.9 million at New York on 11 November?

6 Who was the Archbishop of Canterbury's envoy kidnapped in Beirut in January 1987?

7 Whose third novel, 'Patriot Games' was published in 1987?

8 Who was the US actor and comedian, born David Daniel Kaminski in 1913, who died in March 1987?

9 Who recorded his concert performance of his 'Graceland' album in Harare, Zimbabwe in 1987?

10 Who defeated Anatoly Karpov to win the World Chess Championship in December 1987?

11 Who is the American economist who Ronald Reagan appointed Chairman of the Federal Reserve Board in 1987?

12 Who was the film director, whose movies include 'The African Queen' and 'The Maltese Falcon', who died in 1987?

13 Who was the Lieutenant-Colonel involved in the Irangate hearing in 1987?

14 Which controversial book by Peter Wright was eventually published in 1987?

15 Where did a 19-year old West German, Mathias Rust, land a Cessna aircraft in 1987?

Answers **1** Paul Hogan **2** Moonstruck **3** Black Monday **4** Rudolf Hess **5** Van Gogh **6** Terry Waite **7** Tom Clancy **8** Danny Kaye **9** Paul Simon **10** Gary Kasparov **11** Alan Greenspan **12** John Huston **13** Oliver North **14** Spycatcher **15** Red Square, Moscow

20th Century 1988

1 What was the name of the fast breeder nuclear reactor, which became operational in France?

2 Where was a wave-power device erected?

3 What new heart device came into being?

4 Where in Palestine was there an uprising?

5 Where in the USSR was the Army sent in to quell unrest?

6 On which British territory were three IRA members gunned down by the SAS?

7 What was the name of the oil rig where fire killed over 150 workers?

8 Which Middle east war was halted after 8 years?

9 In which country were 20 million reported homeless after severe floods?

10 Who was Pakistan's new Prime Minister?

11 Which nation became the world's largest debtor owing $532 billion.

12 Over where in Scotland did a US passenger aircraft blow up?

13 Between which two Asian nations was a nuclear treaty signed?

14 What was the name of the Soviet Space shuttle launched from the rocket Energiya?

Answers **1** Super Phoenix **2** Offshore Scotland **3** Pacemaker **4** Gaza/West Bank **5** Azerbaijan **6** Gibralter **7** Piper Alpha **8** Iran/Iraq **9** Bangladesh **10** Benazir Bhutto **11** USA **12** Lockerbie **13** India & Pakistan **14** Buran

1989 — 20th Century

1 Which supertanker ran aground in Alaska on 25 March 1989, causing the worst oil spillage in US history?

2 Where in China was the scene of student-led pro-democracy demonstrations?

3 Which former Monty Python star went 'Around the World in 80 Days'?

4 The playwright Vaclav Havel became President of which country?

5 Who in 1989 said: "We have become a grandmother"?

6 David Dinkins achieved which 'first' in November 1989?

7 Which exiled leader of Tibet won the Nobel Peace Prize?

8 Who was elected President of Argentina?

9 Who resigned as Prime Minister of South Africa?

10 Triton, pictures of which were beamed to earth by Voyager 2 in August 1989, is a moon of which planet?

11 Which gymnast, and star of the 1980 Moscow Olympic Games, defected from Romania to the United States?

12 Who became Emperor of Japan on 7 January 1989?

13 Which author did Iran's Ayatollah Khomeini condemn to death?

14 Who became US Vice-President in 1989 under George Bush?

15 Who won a Golden Globe in 1989 for his role in the movie 'Rain Man'?

Answers **1** Exxon Valdez **2** Tianammen Square **3** Michael Palin **4** Czechoslovakia **5** Margaret Thatcher **6** He was elected New York's first black mayor **7** The Dalai Lama **8** Carlos Menem **9** P.W. Botha **10** Neptune **11** Nadia Comaneci **12** Akihito **13** Salman Rushdie **14** Dan Quayle **15** Dustin Hoffman

20th Century 1990

1 What did the shuttle Atlantis place into space?

2 What new innovation was introduced in medicine?

3 Bells Labs. created a robotic experiment. What was it called?

4 What sort of car was there a race to develop in the motor industry?

5 What 's the name given to shopping by computer?

6 What was the name of the new building in Tokyo in which all functions, such as lighting and security, were controlled by computers?

7 Who won the Burmese elections and was then placed under house arrest by a military dictatorship?

8 Which rich oil-producing country did Iraq invade?

9 Which European country, segregated after World War II, was reunified?

10 Protests about which new tax led to riots in Britain?

11 Name Britain's new Tory Prime Minister?

12 What new computer Software did Microsoft release?

13 Approximately how many motor vehicles were on the road worldwide?

14 Who won the Women's Wimbledon Singles title for a record number of times?

15 Which two parts of a Middle Eastern country were unified?

Answers 1 Hubble telescope **2** Genetic engineering **3** Virtual reality **4** Electric car **5** Cyber shopping **6** 'Super Tower' **7** Aung San Suu Kyi **8** Kuwait **9** Germany **10** Poll tax **11** John Major **12** Windows 3 **13** 550 million **14** Martina Navratilova **15** North and South Yemen

1991 — 20th Century

1 Which former Indian Prime Minister was assassinated by a suicide bomber in May 1991?

2 What was the name of the operation which launched the Gulf War in January 1991?

3 Which actress made her directorial debut with 'Little Man Tate' ?

4 Who was Martha Graham who died in New York City on 1 April at the age of 97?

5 Who was the author of 'Our Man in Havana' and "Brighton Rock' who died in April 1991?

6 Which hostage, whose then girlfriend Jill Morrell campaigned long and hard for his release, was freed from captivity in Lebanon in August 1991?

7 Which long-surviving athletics record was broken in August 1991 by Mike Powell?

8 In Oliver Stone's 1991 film 'The Doors' which part was played by Val Kilmer?

9 What instrument was played by jazz musician Miles Davis, who died in 1991?

10 Who became the first popularly elected President of Russia?

11 Who in 1991 said: "The great, the jewel and the mother of all battles has begun"?

12 What nationality is Aung San Sun Kizi who won the Nobel Peace Prize?

13 Which legendary American jockey was paralysed in an car accident?

14 Of where did Edith Cresson become Prime Minister?

15 Which major world leader was toppled by a coup on 19 August?

Answers **1** Rajiv Gandhi **2** Desert Storm **3** Jodie Foster **4** An American choreographer and dancer **5** Graham Greene **6** John McCarthy **7** Long Jump **8** Jim Morrison **9** Trumpet **10** Boris Yeltsin **11** Sadam Hussain **12** Burmese **13** Willie Shoemaker **14** France **15** Mikhail Gorbachev

20th Century 1992

1 Civil war broke out in which eastern European country?

2 What did Philips launch in 1992 to play multi-media program for home use?

3 Found in Washington, USA, what is the name of the largest organism so far discovered in the world?

4 In which country, where there was there a civil war and famine, did US intervene under the umbrella of the United Nations?

5 What was the world's first propeller-less ship called?

6 Europe launched an unsuccessful satellite. What was it called?

7 Who replaced the Communists to rule in Afghanistan?

8 What did the Cobe satellite discover?

9 Who were acquitted on charges of beating black motorist Rodney King during riots?

10 Where was the earth summit conference held?

11 Which international treaty caused an E C crisis because an agreement could not be reached?

12 Which African country voted for majority rule?

13 What financial system did Britain drop out of?

14 Who was the rioting between in India?

15 Who said: "There is nothing wrong with America, that can be cured by what is right with America"?

Answers **1** Yugoslavia **2** CD-1 Compact Disc (player or disc) **3** Honey Fungus **4** Somalia **5** Yamato **6** Hipparcos **7** Muslims **8** Ripples from the Big Bang **9** Los Angeles police officers **10** Rio de Janeiro, Brazil **11** Maastricht **12** South Africa **13** European Monetary System **14** Muslims and Hindus **15** Bill Clinton

1993

20th Century

1 Who is the actor, best known as Perry Mason, who died in September 1993?

2 Who, in 1993, became the 45th Vice-President of the United States?

3 To what position in the US government was Janet Reno appointed in 1993?

4 Who was the Italian film director whose films include 'La Dolce Vita' who died in November 1993?

5 In which 1993 movie did Bill Murray wake up every morning to find that it's the same day?

6 Which Canadian athlete was banned for life in March 1993 for doping?

7 Which jazz trumpeter and one of the leading lights of bebop, instantly recognisable by his ballooning cheeks, died in January 1993?

8 Danial Arap Moi became President of which country in January 1993?

9 Which former chief of staff of the US Armed Forces was awarded an honorary knighthood by Queen Elizabeth II in September 1993?

10 For which movie did Emma Thompson win Best Actress Oscar in 1993?

11 Which tennis player was stabbed during a match in April 1993?

12 Who shared the Nobel Peace Prize with South Africa's President de Klerk?

13 Who was the King of Belguim who died in July 1993?

14 Benazir Bhutto was returned to power in which country in October 1993?

15 Who was the author of 'A Clockwork Orange' who died on 22 November 1993?

Answers **1** Raymond Burr **2** Al Gore **3** Attorney General **4** Frederico Fellini **5** Groundhog Day **6** Ben Johnson **7** Dizzy Gillespie **8** Kenya **9** Colin Powell **10** Howard's End **11** Monica Seles **12** Nelson Mandela **13** King Baudouin **14** Pakistan **15** Anthony Burgess

20th Century 1994

1 Which country took over presidency of the EU?

2 Name the tall, debonair US actor who played 'The Joker' in TV's 'Batman' series who died?

3 Which two Eastern European countries agreed to a ceasefire?

4 The name of the editor of 'The Sun', who resigned?

5 Which couple won the European Ice Dancing Championship?

6 Who was the former Manchester United football manager and survivor of the 1958 Munich air crash who died in 1994?

7 An oil tanker Brack spilled 100 million litres of oil off which islands?

8 On which island was there an earthquake measuring 6.5 on the Richter scale?

9 Which organisation took over London Weekend Television?

10 Which female American singer died?

11 Which Indonesian leader resigned?

12 Which British athlete set up a world record in the 60-metre hurdles?

13 Where did Government forces seize the Khmer Rouge Headquarters?

14 Two war lords of which country sign a peace pact in Nairobi?

15 What communication devices are banned in Iran?

Answers **1** Greece **2** Cesar Romero **3** Bosnian and Croatian **4** Kelvin MacKenzie **5** Torvill and Dean **6** Matt Busby **7** Shetland Islands **8** Sumatra **9** Granada **10** Dinah Shore **11** Suharto **12** Colin Jackson **13** Cambodia **14** Somalia **15** Satellite Dishes

1995 — 20th Century

1 Which Japanese city was devastated by an earthquake in January 1995?

2 In which country in January 1995 did 'Tamil Tigers' offer to drop their demand for separate homeland in exchange for autonomy?

3 In February 1995 the space shuttle Discovery had a rendezvous with which space station?

4 In April 1995 Australians celebrated a century of which 'unofficial' anthem?

5 In which city in March 1995, did members of the 'Supreme Truth' cult release deadly nerve gas on the subway system?

6 Who struggled with incriminating gloves at his murder trial in Los Angeles in June 1995?

7 Nick Leeson, arrested in March 1995, bankrupted which bank?

8 Who was the leader of the group 'The Grateful Dead' who died in August 1995?

9 Which Canadian province voted to remain part of Canada on 30 October?

10 Which Israeli Prime Minister was assassinated on 4 November 1995?

11 The Galileo space probe had a close encounter with which planet in December 1995?

12 To which royal couple did Queen Elizabeth II write in December 1995 stating that an early divorce was desirable?

13 Detective Eddie Egan, who died on 10 November in the US, was the inspiration for which movie?

14 Who, in September, succeeded James Molyneux as leader of the Ulster Unionists?

15 Who was the Kennedy clan matriarch who died, aged 104, in January 1995?

Answers **1** Kobe **2** Sri Lanka **3** Mir **4** Waltzing Matilda **5** Tokyo **6** O.J. Simpson **7** Barings Bank **8** Jerry Garcia **9** Quebec **10** Yitzhak Rabin **11** Jupiter **12** Charles and Diana **13** The French Connection **14** David Trimble **15** Rose Kennedy

20th Century 1996

1 What was the name of Edvard Munch's most famous painting which was stolen in 1996?

2 Who became the new Greek Prime Minister?

3 Which organisation took over the Forte hotel chain?

4 The name of the creator of comic book hero 'Superman' who died in 1996?

5 Where did a Boeing 757 crash in the Pacific?

6 Who was the new President of Palestine authority?

7 In which European country did conscription end?

8 Which sea mammal was declared an endangered species?

9 What was the name of the Serb General indicted for war crimes?

10 Which British driver won the Australian Grand Prix?

11 President Clinton places an embargo on goods to which country?

12 Who swept the mid-west primaries?

13 Which fast-food restaurant in Britain banned beef from hamburgers?

14 What was banned as a component in animal feed in Britain?

15 Who beat Leeds United 3-0 to win the Coca-Cola Cup final?

Answers **1** The Scream **2** Costas Simitis **3** Granada **4** Jerry Siegel **5** Dominican Republic **6** Yassir Arafat **7** France **8** Black whale **9** Djordje Djukie **10** Damon Hill **11** Cuba **12** Bob Dole **13** McDonalds **14** Meat and bonemeal **15** Aston Villa

1997 — 20th Century

1 Which territory passed back to China from Britain at midnight on 30 June 1997?

2 Who was the former Prime Minister and self-styled President of Malawi who died in November 1997?

3 Volcanic eruptions caused mass evacuation of which British island colony in August 1997?

4 Who was Elton John's co-writer of the 1997 best-selling tribute to Diana, Princess of Wales, 'Candle in the Wind'?

5 Who, in September 1997, visited Robben Island and the prison in which he spent 20 years, to declare it a national heritage site?

6 Who drove the car in which the Princess of Wales was killed in Paris in August 1997?

7 Who, in Cambodia in July 1997, was arrested and put on trial by his former Khmer Rouge colleagues?

8 In which 1997 movie, starring John Travolta and Nicolas Cage, do a terrorist and an undercover agent swap identity and faces?

9 The Labour Party victory in the UK May 1997 election ended how many years of Conservative rule?

10 Chaim Herzog, who died on 17 April 1997, was President of which country from 1983-93?

11 Who was the former Irish President who was appointed the new UN High Commissioner for Human Rights in June 1997?

12 Which weather phenomenon affected weather globally in 1997?

13 Who did Sister Nirmala succeed in the Calcutta-based Catholic Missionaries of Charity in September 1997?

14 In December 1997 Jenny Shipley became the first woman Prime Minister of which country?

15 An earthquake in which Middle Eastern country killed 2,400 people in May 1997?

Answers **1** Hong Kong **2** Hastings Banda **3** Montserrat **4** Bernie Taupin **5** Nelson Mandela **6** Henri Paul **7** Pol Pot **8** Face Off **9** 18 years **10** Israel **11** Mary Robinson **12** El Nino **13** Mother Theresa **14** New Zealand **15** Iran

20th Century — 1998

1 Which Asian country asked for $20 billion loan from the IMF?

2 Who won the Australian golf tournament?

3 Who won the Turner prize?

4 Which television personality was proven to be the father of Paula Yates?

5 Which disease appeared in Britain for the first time?

6 Name the TV personality Anthea Turner's husband and manager, who she left for lover Grant Bovey?

7 Which island did the Pope visit for the first time?

8 Where were the Winter Olympic Games held?

9 Who did the MCC reject for membership admission to Lords?

10 Which two cities were declared to have the largest population in the world of over 10 million people?

11 Which US film star and father of actors Jeff and Beau died?

12 Who bought the Los Angeles Dodgers?

13 Who beat Newcastle United 2-0 to win the 1998 FA Cup Final?

14 The body of a 5,000 year-old man was found where?

15 Which man, associated with a famously fast, expensive car, died in Austria?

Answers 1 South Korea **2** Lee Westwood **3** Gillian Wearing **4** Hughie Green **5** Meningitis **6** Peter Powell **7** Cuba **8** Japan **9** Women **10** Sao Paolo, Brazil and Seoul, South Korea **11** Lloyd Bridges **12** Rupert Murdoch **13** Arsenal **14** Italian Alps **15** Ferdinand Porche

1999 — 20th Century

1 Who was the King of Jordan who died in February 1999?

2 Name the American baseball player, and former husband of Marilyn Monroe, who died in March 1999?

3 Which movie stars Bruce Willis as a therapist to a boy who talks to dead people?

4 Which American Ryder Cup golfer died in a bizarre plane crash in 1999?

5 What was the name of the computer bug that threatened disaster at the end of 1999?

6 For what athletic event did Tomas Dvorak of the Czech Republic break the world record in 1999?

7 Who was the velvet-voiced American jazz singer and composer, who died aged 75 in June 1999?

8 Which coupled were married at St Georges Chapel, Windsor, England on 19 June?

9 The body of which mountaineer, who disappeared in 1924, was found near the summit of Mount Everest on 3 May 1999?

10 Who wrote the 1999 best-selling book 'The Art of Happiness' which tells readers how to bring peace and purpose to their lives?

11 Who was the Yugoslav President involved in the 1999 Kosovo crisis against NATO forces?

12 Who was the 'Godfather' author who died in July 1999?

13 Who died in a plane crash with his wife Carolyn and sister-in-law Lauren Bessette on 16 July 1999?

14 Who was the US film maker and director of 'A Clockwork Orange' who died on 7 March 1999?

15 Who won a 1999 Golden Globe for directing the movie 'Saving Private Ryan'?

Answers **1** King Hussein **2** Joe Di Maggio **3** The Sixth Sense **4** Payne Stewart **5** Y2K **6** Decathlon **7** Mel Torme **8** Prince Edward and Sophie Rhys-Jones **9** George Mallory **10** The Dalai Lama **11** Slobodan Milosevic **12** Mario Puzo **13** John F. Kennedy Jr **14** Stanley Kubrick **15** Steven Spielberg

SECTION 2

Alphabet

Alphabet — Quiz 1

A Name the Roman Wall, built in AD142, which ran from the Forth estuary to the Clyde

B Name of the former royal family of Portugal and Brazil?

C Port in southern Spain raided by Sir Francis Drake in 1587?

D One time fight manager of Mohammed Ali, Angelo ------?

E The supreme Allied commander in World War II?

F Who translated the 'Rubaiyat of Omar Khayam'?

G Republic on the northern coast of South America?

H Who said: "blessed are the young for they will inherit the national debt"?

I In Greek mythology, who is the son of Daedalus, whose wings melted when he flew too near the sun?

J Shrub whose berries are used to flavour gin?

K Drummer of the swing band era played in a 1959 movie by Sal Mineo?

L Type of sugar present in milk?

~Answers 1 Antonine **2** Braganza **3** Cadiz **4** Dundee **5** Eisenhower **6** Fitzgerald **7** Guyana **8** Hoover **9** Icarus **10** Juniper **11** Krupa **12** Lactose

Quiz 1 — Alphabet

M What, in ancient times, was known as Balearis Major?

N A tide occurring at the first and third quarters of the moon?

O Which pop group's first single was 'Supersonic' in 1994?

P Intel's fifth generation of high-speed microprocessors, whose name means the fifth-element?

Q -------- is another name for a monocle?

R Of what was Sir Robert Watson-Watt a pioneer in the 1930s?

S Whose hometown was on the planet Vulcan in Shikahr?

T Who wrote 'Vanity Fair'?

U What word means hook-shaped?

V Flemish painter who gave his name to a type of beard?

W Arthur ---------, was the Duke of Wellington?

Z City of northern Croatia on the Sava River?

Answers cont **13** Majorca **14** Neap **15** Oasis **16** Pentium **17** Quizzing **18** Radar **19** Spock **20** Thackeray **21** Unciform **22** Vandyke **23** Wellesley **24** Zagreb

Alphabet — Quiz 2

A A rampart of felled trees?

B A three-masted ship?

C The name in the USA for Canadians?

D Payment for delay in unloading goods?

E Restraining the movement of goods?

F What is a musical term signifying 'loud'?

G Famous Hindu Spiritual leader?

H One third of this country is below sea level?

I African antelope?

J Name for a sleeveless jacket?

K Paraffin distillation from petrol?

L Nonsense or humorous stanza?

Answers **1** Abatis **2** Brquentine **3** Canucks **4** Demurrage **5** Embargo **6** Forte **7** Gandhi **8** Holland **9** Impala **10** Jerkin **11** Kerosene **12** Limerick

Quiz 2 Alphabet

M Mohammedan priest?

N He roams from place to place?

O Glass-like lava used for knives in prehistoric times?

P The Greek name for Neptune?

Q Chewing tobacco?

R Pieces of stewed meat and vegetables?

S A broad-brimmed hat of felt or straw?

T Thin transparent muslin fabric?

U Person chosen to enforce rules?

V Slanting line to make divisions of words?

W French speaking population in Belgium?

Z Comically idiotic?

Answers cont **13** Mufti **14** Nomad **15** Obsidian **16** Poseidon **17** Quid **18** Ragout **19** Sombrero **20** Tarlatan **21** Umpire **22** Virgule **23** Walloons **24** Zany

Alphabet — Quiz 3

A Marine snail whose shells are used in the manufacture of decorative objects?

B British inventor who designed the first computing machine?

C Russian title derived from the word Caesar?

D In law, illegal compulsion to force someone to commit an act they would not otherwise do?

E Mary Baker ----------, the founder of Christian Science?

F Baking company which lent its name to a type of sport in the 1950s because of the shape of its pie tins?

G 18th century artist whose works include 'The Blue Boy' (1779)?

H Who said; "as you walk down the fairway of life you must smell the roses, for you only get to play one round"?

I Breed of miniature English greyhound believed to have originated in Asia Minor 2000 years ago?

J The --------- was the nickname of O.J. Simpson in his football playing days?

K Which people of Kenya led a campaign of terrorism against British rule in the 1950s led by Jomo Kenyatta?

L An expert in the collection of butterflies and moths?

Answers **1** Abalone **2** Babbage **3** Czar **4** Duress **5** Eddy **6** Frisbie **7** Gainsborough **8** Hogan **9** Italian **10** Juice **11** Kikuyu **12** Lepidopterist

Quiz 3 Alphabet

M Who accepted the surrender of Japan on Septèmber 2, 1945?

N Who was the wise and aged counsellor in Homer's epics?

O What is the name of the Greek national airline?

P Which concert pianist was Prime Minister of Poland?

Q Independent state that borders on Saudi Arabia?

R French statesman called the Red Eminence who held control over King Louis XIII?

S Who created the 'Peanuts' comic strip?

T Who was the second Emperor of Rome?

U A device for measuring rainfall?

V A vegetarian who avoids all animal products?

W Who was known in the 15th Century as the Kingmaker?

Y The name of the brothers who were part of the Jesse James outlaw gang?

Answers cont **13** macarthur **14** Nestor **15** Olympic **16** Paderewski **17** Qatar **18** Richelieu **19** Shultz **20** Tiberius **21** Udometer **22** Vegan **23** Warwick **24** Younger

Alphabet — Quiz 4

A Zeus's shield?

B Britain's most common large bird?

C Rodents known as guinea pigs?

D He wrote 'The Three Musketeers'?

E Large American antelope?

F Small cask for liquids?

G Tail-less water bird?

H Screw-shaped coil?

I A narrow neck of land in sea?

J A glossy black varnish or lacquer?

K The German form of the word Caesar?

L A West Indian dance?

Answers **1** Aegis **2** Buzzard **3** Cavies **4** Dumas **5** Eland **6** Firkin **7** Grebe **8** Helix **9** Isthmus **10** Japan **11** Kaiser **12** Limbo

Quiz 4 Alphabet

M A kind of veil over the head?

N A sentimental longing for times gone by?

O Shakespeare's 'King of the Fairies'?

P Science devoted to the study of diseases?

Q A city at the mouth of the St Lawrence River?

R A disease affecting cattle?

S Sweet substance from coal tar?

T Two-wheeled vehicle for carrying ammunition?

U A long loose overcoat?

V Patron saint of dancers?

W Small fish related to cod and haddock?

X Musical instrument of flat narrow bars?

Answers cont **13** Mantilla **14** Nostalgia **15** Oberon **16** Pathology **17** Quebec **18** Rinderpest **19** Saccharin **20** Tumbrel **21** Ulster **22** Vitus **23** Whiting **24** Xylophone

Alphabet — Quiz 5

A A character from the Arabian Nights, the son of Mustafa the tailor?

B Type of fern, also called the Brake plant?

C Ancient Roman name for the country north of the firths of Forth and Clyde in Britain?

D A small silvery fish of the minnow family?

E What does the 'e' stand for in e-mail?

F The 'First Lady of Jazz'?

G Stridulation is the name of the shrill grating chirp of which creature?

H Used on the Nile, what is a dahabia a type of?

I In the Bible, who was the Hebrew patriach and the son of Abraham and Sarah?

J Who said: "Information is the currency of democracy"?

K Helen -------- was known as the Boop-a-Doop girl whose theme song was 'I Wanna be Loved by You'?

L Who in mythology swam the Hellespont nightly to see Hero, but was eventually drowned in a storm?

Answers **1** Aladdin **2** Bracken **3** Caledonia **4** Dace **5** Electronic **6** Fitzgerald **7** Grasshopper **8** Houseboat **9** Isaac **10** Jefferson **11** Kane **12** Leander

Quiz 5 — Alphabet

M Molton rock formed by the partial melting of the earth's mantle?

N Which Japanese city was destroyed by an atomic bomb on August 9, 1945?

O Reference sign in the shape of a dagger used to indicate footnotes?

P --------- Valley was the former name of the city of Hollywood?

Q Title of a magistrate in ancient Rome?

R What was the name of the husband and wife team executed for spying in the United States in 1953?

S Which actor was six-times winner of the Mr Olympia title in the 1970s?

T Famous 1950s recording by Debbie Reynolds?

U The study of flying saucers?

V A cycle-racing arena?

W Dragon with wings and a serpent's tail?

Z Who invented Esperanto?

Answers cont **13** Magma **14** Nagasaki **15** Obelisk **16** Paradise **17** Quaestor **18** Rosenberg **19** Schwarzenegger **20** Tammy **21** Ufology **22** Velodrome **23** Wyvern **24** Zamenhof

Alphabet — Quiz 6

A What is the capital of Paraguay?

B Small round sweet cake made with light dough?

C The largest species of vulture?

D Monetary unit of Iraq?

E The French word for a star?

F A river mouth?

G Low flat-decked ship driven by oars?

H The offspring of a stallion and a she ass?

I An image or a statue?

J Doleful prophet?

K A water sprite of Scottish folklore?

L A Biblical sea monster?

Answers **1** Asuncion **2** Brioche **3** Condor **4** Dinar **5** Etoile **6** Firth **7** Galley **8** Hinny **9** Icon **10** Jeremiah **11** Kelpie **12** Leviathan

Quiz 6 — Alphabet

M Infantry soldier's light gun?

N Scientific name for threadworms?

O Loose hemp and rope?

P A bathing pool, especially in Roman times?

Q Twentieth part of a ream?

R To copy or make two of?

S Old language of India?

T An opening in a mine?

U A poisonous tree from Java?

V An enclosed space containing no matter?

W Largest animal of the weasel family?

Y A sweet potato?

Answers cont **13** Musket **14** Nematodes **15** Oakum **16** Piscine **17** Quire
18 Replicate **19** Sanskit **20** Thirl **21** Upas **22** Vacuum **23** Wolverine
24 Yam

Alphabet — Quiz 7

A Empress of Russia murdered by the Bolsheviks in 1918?

B Benjamin Disraeli was the 1st Earl of ________?

C What is likely to be contained in a Salmanzar?

D The longest river of Australia?

E Porous type of pottery, usually fired at the lowest kiln temperatures?

F American high jumper who, in the 1960s, perfected a technique known as 'the flop'?

G What is defied by levitation?

H In computer science, a system for retrieving and referencing related documents?

I Popular holiday island in the Balearics?

J Which playwright is buried in Westminster Abbey in a sitting position due to lack of space?

K Japanese city which was the country's capital from 794 to 1868?

L Constellation in the northern sky between Cygnus and Hercules?

Answers **1** Alexandra **2** Beaconsfield **3** Champagne **4** Darling **5** Earthenware **6** Fosbury **7** Gravity **8** Hypertext **9** Ibiza **10** Jonson **11** Kyoto **12** Lyra

Quiz 7

Alphabet

M Perennial plant cultivated as a culinary herb called oregano?

N Who invented the steam engine?

O Wild type of ass living in central Africa?

P Who was the Greek philosopher and mathematician whose doctrines strongly influenced Plato?

Q Settlement in Palestine near where the Dead Sea scrolls were found in 1947?

R Who wrote a history of the world while imprisoned in the Tower of London?

S The seventh largest island in the world?

T --------- Grange was the Linton family estate in Emily Bronte's novel 'Wuthering Heights'?

U What, in 1871, was discovered by William Herschel?

V What is the capital of Liechtenstein?

W An unauthorized independent program that penetrates a computer and replicates itself?

Z Sword-shaped?

Answers cont **13** Marjoram **14** Newcomen **15** Onager **16** Pythagoras **17** Qumran **18** Raleigh **19** Sumatra **20** Thrushcross **21** Uranus **22** Vaduz **23** Worm **24** Xiphoid

Alphabet — Quiz 8

A Declaration under oath?

B A badge worn on the arm in uniform?

C A liquer of spirits and peel of oranges?

D The skin under the throat of oxen?

E A state of balance?

F A person guilty of a crime more serious than a misdemeanour?

G Chess opening moves?

H The capital of North Vietnam?

I An inexperienced young girl?

J A Muslim spirit?

K The monetary unit of Iceland?

L Short leather trousers with braces?

Answers **1** Affidavit **2** Brassard **3** Curacao **4** Dewlap **5** Equipoise **6** Felon **7** Gambit **8** Hanoi **9** Ingenue **10** Jinn **11** Krona **12** Lederhosen

Quiz 8 — Alphabet

M The wild card or joker used in draw poker?

N South American ostrich?

O Prognostication of a future event?

P A small reddish-brown British bat?

Q One who aids the enemy?

R Casting a flood of light?

S Vigorous musical composition?

T Type of gig for two?

U Excessively or submissively fond of a wife?

V A type of llama from South America?

W Monitor lizard?

Z White metallic element?

Answers cont **13** Mistigris **14** Nandu **15** Omens **16** Pipistrelle **17** Quisling **18** Refulgent **19** Scherzo **20** Tilbury **21** Uxorious **22** Vicuna **23** Worral **24** Zinc

Alphabet — Quiz 9

A Who was the Roman soldier who fell in love with Cleopatra?

B The name of a Monarchist country of southern Central Asia in the eastern Himalayas?

C Frank ________, Italian-born racketeer and member of the Cosa Nostra under Lucky Luciano?

D Distinctive looking dog, whose name in German means 'badger dog'?

E Swedish tennis player whose wins include the Men's singles at Wimbledon in 1988 and 1990 and the US Open in 1991?

F Seaport near Nicosia in Cyprus which was occupied by Turkish forces in 1974?

G What is the common name for a type of hyacinth also known as Muscari?

H What is the common name for two species of flatfish related to the flounder?

I One of two or more species of atom having the same atomic number?

J In the Bible, who was the son of Obed and father of David?

K Long loose Japanese robe secured by a wide sash?

L The bobcat is a member of which family of wild carnivores?

Answers **1** Antony **2** Bhutan **3** Costello **4** Dachsund **5** Edberg **6** Famagusta **7** Grape **8** Halibut **9** Isotope **10** Jesse **11** Kimono **12** Lynx

Quiz 9 — Alphabet

M Who is the central character of the 'Threepenny Opera' and the subject of the song 'Mack the Knife'?

N In Greek mythology, the nymphs of brooks, springs and fountains?

O What is the name given to Asian countries and the east in general?

P Which silent film star said: 'The thing that we call failure is not falling down, but the staying down'?

Q What is the name of the London home of M in the James Bond stories?

R Animal which walks on the soles of the its feet with the heels touching the ground, similar to the practice of bears and humans?

S Great desert of NW Australia?

T Who, in 1899, invented the vacuum cleaner?

U The second largest country in Europe, after Russia?

V In Norse mythology, who were the messengers of Odin who selected heroes to die in battle?

W Who invented the steam-power brake device?

Z Diamond-like mineral used as a gemstone?

Answers cont **13** macheath **14** Naidds **15** Orient **16** Pickford **17** Quarterdeck **18** Raccoon **19** Sandy **20** Thurman **21** Ukraine **22** Valkyries **23** Westinghouse **24** Zircon

Alphabet — Quiz 10

A Remote group of islands in the Atlantic?

B A short gun with large bore?

C The lowest ranking suit at bridge?

D Training a horse in obedience?

E Belonging to the Christian church?

F A small face of a diamond?

G Birth stone for January?

H Famous escapologist (1874-1926)?

I 15th day in March in ancient Rome?

J Another name for the god Jupiter?

K New Zealand parrot?

L An open-air swimming pool?

Answers **1** Azores **2** Blunderbus **3** Clubs **4** Dressage **5** Ecumenic **6** Facet **7** Garnet **8** Houdini **9** Ides **10** Jove **11** Kea **12** Lido

Quiz 10 — Alphabet

M A mixture of clay and chalk?

N The capital of Tennessee USA?

O Small opening?

P Portable fan in India?

Q The minimum number of persons required to render a meeting valid?

R Large black birds, synonymous with the Tower of London?

S What is the name given to the harem of a Turkish Sultan?

T A surveyor's instrument?

U Natural dark brown pigment?

V Part of an arch?

W A salad plant grown in watery places?

Z A word that describes the figure '0'?

Answers cont **13** Malm **14** Nashville **15** Orifice **16** Punkah **17** Quorum **18** Ravens **19** Seraglio **20** Theodolite **21** Umber **22** Voussoir **23** Watercress **24** Zero or zilch

Alphabet — Quiz 11

A Famous theatre in the Harlem district of New York City?

B Number system which plays an important role in computer technology?

C Type of music made famous by Harry Belafonte?

D Term applied to a politician who takes a soft line in foreign policy matters?

E Who said: “As far as the laws of mathematics refer to reality, they are not certain, as far as they are certain, they do not refer to reality”?

F Type of acid secreted by red ants in the sting?

G The most southerly of the Windward Islands in the East Caribbean?

H What is the meaning of the prefix crypto?

I Author of ‘Hedda Gabler‘ (1890)?

J Roman satirical poet on who many later writers such as Jonathan Swift and Samuel Johnson modelled their work?

K Maori greeting meaning good health or good luck?

L Composer who wrote ‘My Fair Lady’ with Alan Jay Lerner?

Answers **1** Apollo **2** Binary **3** Calypso **4** Dove **5** Einstein **6** Formic **7** Genada **8** Hidden **9** Ibsen **10** Juvenal **11** Kiaoro **12** Loeure

Quiz 11 — Alphabet

M Who made her 'Blond Ambition' concern tour in 1990?

N Pauvo ---------, was a great Olympian of the 1920s whose statue stands outside the Helsinki Olympic Stadium?

O A mountain nymph in Greek mythology?

P Mountain range of South West Europe?

Q What is the name of the pole used for pushing a punt?

R River between Italy and Gaul in ancient times which was crossed by Julius Caesar in 49 BC?

S Which military leader said "War is a profane thing"?

T Who was the Roman goddess of Earth?

U In the Bible, who was the husband of Bathsheba, sent to death in battle by David?

V Singer whose life story formed the basis of the 1987 movie 'La Bamba'?

W Where did a 51-day stand-off between law enforcement officers and members of the Branch Davidian cult take place in 1993?

X One of the noble gases, discovered in 1898?

Answers cont **13** Madonna **14** Nurmi **15** Oread **16** Pyrenees **17** Quant **18** Rubicon **19** Schwarzkopf **20** Tellus **21** Uriah **22** Valens **23** Waco **24** Xenon

Alphabet — Quiz 12

A Luminous streamers of light in the sky in the polar regions?

B Fear of needles?

C A small rounded roof dome?

D Name of Scotland's Aberdeen airport?

E Meet by chance?

F Lively Spanish dance?

G A young French working class woman?

H Author of 'Far from the Madding Crowd'?

I A triangle in which two sides are equal?

J Caretaker of a building?

K A baby doll with a top knot of hair sold at a County Fair?

L A ball game played with a long-handled netted stick?

Answers Aurora **2** Belonemania **3** Cupola **4** Dyce **5** Encounter **6** Fandango **7** Grisette **8** Hardy **9** Isosceles **10** Janitor **11** Kewpie **12** Lacrosse

Quiz 12 — Alphabet

M Austrian composer of 'Don Giovanni'?

N The lower regions of the body?

O The branch of medicine dealing with pregnancy?

P Paralysis of the lower part of the body?

Q A game bird similar to a partridge?

R One of the muscles of the human body that is straight?

S The indigenous religion of Japan?

T A brownish-grey colour?

U A chamber in the inner ear?

V The Spanish word for a window?

W A name given to the whole of the sky?

Y A ship's small boat?

Answers cont **13** Mozart **14** Nether **15** Obstetrics **16** Paraplegia **17** Quail **18** Rectus **19** Shinto **20** Taupe **21** Utricle **22** Ventana **23** Welkin **24** Yawl

Alphabet — Quiz 13

A Greek philosopher and scientist?

B The type of automobile which Isadora Duncan was driving when she was strangled by her own scarf in 1927?

C Lizard which is capable of changing colour?

D Inventor of the pneumatic tyre?

E In the electromagnetic spectrum, what does the letter E stand for in the abbreviations ELF and EHF?

F Gambling card game named from the picture of an Egyptian Ruler on one of the cards in the original French pack?

G Term for the effect the atmosphere has in keeping warm the Earth's surface?

H Instrument used to measure atmospheric humidity?

I Wading bird with long curved bill, native to tropical regions?

J Adjective relating to the god or the planet Jupiter?

K The capital of Saint Vincent and the Grenadines?

L US fashion designer famous for styles such as 'prairie look' and 'frontier fashion'?

Answers **1** Aristotle **2** Bugatti **3** Chameleon **4** Dunlop **5** Extremely **6** Faro **7** Greenhouse **8** Hygrometer **9** Ibis **10** Jovian **11** Kingstown **12** Lauren

Quiz 13 Alphabet

M Carlton C ---------- invented the parking meter in 1935?

N What did Johanne Galle discover in 1846?

O An upholstered divan without arms or a back?

P US commander of Pulitzer Prize for History winner, known as 'Black Jack'?

Q A flower shape with four leaflets or petals?

R Who said: "To the artist there is never anything ugly in Nature"?

S What is the language of Tanzania?

T For what did Henry Mill obtain the first patent in 1714?

U The capital of Mongolia, formerly Urga?

V Relating to a fox, or fox-like?

W Who invented the rotary engine?

Z City in which the Irish novelist James Joyce is buried?

Answers cont **13** Magee **14** Neptune **15** Ottoman **16** Pershing **17** Quatrefoil **18** Rodin **19** Swahili **20** Typewriter **21** Ulaan-baatar **22** Vulpine **23** Wankel **24** Zurich

Alphabet — Quiz 14

A In Greek legend a race of warrior women?

B He wrote 'Pilgrims Progress'?

C Dried Eastern flower used as a spice?

D Windless belt in the sea near the Equator?

E A young eel?

F Aromatic gum resin from trees used for incense?

G A goblin accused of vexing airmen?

H Japanese poem, usually comical, in three lines of 5, 7, 5 syllables?

I Native, not imported?

J A pier for ships to berth?

K Fear of motion?

L The seed of the flax plant yields an oil?

Answers **1** Amazons **2** Bunyan **3** Clove **4** Doldrums **5** Elver **6** Frankincense **7** Gremlin **8** Haiku **9** Indiginous **10** Jetty **11** Kinesomania **12** Linseed

Quiz 14 — Alphabet

M A native American's blanket?

N Light and quick in motion?

O Russian seaport on the Black Sea?

P The science of fruits?

Q A golden green parrot from Central America with long tail feathers?

R Edible pasta cases with savoury fillings?

S Wading bird of the ibis family?

T A sheep or a doe in its second year?

U To reproach or chide?

V A Spanish herdsman?

W Instrument for boring holes?

Z Wheel of life?

Answers cont **13** Mackinaw **14** Nimble **15** Odessa **16** Pomology **17** Quetzal **18** Ravioli **19** Spoonbill **20** Teg **21** Upbraid **22** Vasquero **23** Wimble **24** Zoetrope

Alphabet — Quiz 15

A Chester Alan -----------, the 21st President of the US?

B French card game, dating from end of 15th century, played in casinos?

C New York concert-hall, former home of the New York Philharmonic?

D Cigar-shaped steerable airship?

E Rising to 4,399m (14,432 feet) in Lake County, Colorado, which Mount is the highest peak in the Rocky Mountains?

F Prison in California which was the setting of the 1954 movie 'Riot in Cell Block II'?

G Who said, "I could prove God statistically"?

H Group of five chemical elements; chlorine, bromine, fluorine, iodine and astatine?

I The capital of Pakistan?

J ---------- Gatsby was the hero of F. Scott Fitzgerald's novel 'The Great Gatsby'?

K Director of 'A Clockwork Orange' (1971)?

L The science of valid reasoning and argument?

Answers **1** Arthur **2** Baccarat **3** Carnegie **4** Dirigible **5** Elbert **6** Folsom **7** Gallop **8** Halogens **9** Islamabad **10** Jay **11** Kubrick **12** Logic

Quiz 15 Alphabet

M On which island in the Cyclades, Greece, was the Venus de Milo sculpture discovered in 1820?

N In the Bible, who was the vineyard owner stoned to death because he would not sell it to Ahab?

O Charles Boyle, who commissioned a model of the solar system now named after him, was the fourth Earl of -----------?

P What device was invented by Louis S Lenormand in France in 1783?

Q What word describes the position of a planet or the Moon when the angular distance from the Sun, as measured from the Earth, is 90 degrees?

R Who discovered X-rays?

S Who, in her poem 'Sacred Emily' wrote 'A rose is a rose is a rose is a rose'?

T Another name for the constellation Gemini?

U President of the German Democratic Republic from 1960-1973?

V Dynasty that ruled France from 1328 to 1589?

W Who wrote 'The Complete Angler'?

Z Who produced 'The Sound of Music' and 'The Longest Day'?

Answers cont **13** Melos **14** Naboth **15** Orrery **16** Parachute **17** Quadrature **18** Roentgen **19** Stein **20** Twins **21** Ulbricht **22** Valois **23** Walton **24** Zanuck

Alphabet

Quiz 16

A Large snake from South America?

B Pistol which makes a low report?

C A conceited showy person?

D Monetary unit of Yugoslavia?

E Lasting only one day?

F A bassoon?

G An opera hat?

H A sandbank?

I The hip bone?

J The Japanese quince?

K A three-stringed fiddle?

L South American mammal related to camel?

Answers **1** Anaconda **2** Barker **3** Coxcomb **4** Dinar **5** Ephemeral **6** Fagotto **7** Gibus **8** Hurst **9** Ilium **10** Japonica **11** Kit **12** Llama

Quiz 16

Alphabet

M Cattle plague?

N An idiot?

O Fear of vehicles?

P Animals and plants floating in sea?

Q A punting pole?

R A drowned valley?

S A butcher-bird allied to the sparrow, a passerine bird?

T Famous Italian conductor born 1867?

U The Canadian porcupine?

V An Indian stringed instrument?

W A Maori woman?

Z The sixth letter of the Greek alphabet?

Answers cont **13** Murrain **14** Nidget **15** Ochomania **16** Plankton **17** Quant
18 Ria **19** Shrike **20** Toscanini **21** Urson **22** Vina **23** Wahine **24** Zeta

Alphabet — Quiz 17

A King of the Huns, called the Scourge of God?

B Another name for apiculture?

C Winged celestial beings similar to angels?

D Computer slang for finding and correcting an error in a program?

E Species of African animal which includes the largest type of antelope?

F Which Germanic name means peaceful ruler?

G The main protein of wheat?

H Who wrote in 'The Garden of Eden' that "happiness in intelligent people is the rarest thing I know"?

I In Egyptian mythology, the goddess of motherhood and fertility?

J British Commander in the Battle of Jutland in 1916?

K Desert of Southern Africa?

L Of what invention is Charles H. Townes a pioneer?

Answers **1** Attila **2** Beekeeping **3** Cherubim **4** Debug **5** Eland **6** Frederick **7** Gluten **8** Hemingway **9** Isis **10** Jellico **11** Kalahari **12** Laser

Quiz 17

Alphabet

M What is enjoyed by a mycophile?

N What is another name for Lake Malawi in South Eastern Africa?

O The oldest book in the Old Testament consisting of one Chapter of 21 verses?

P Who was the wife of Elvis Presley from 1967 to 1972?

Q What was the name of the alliance formed by Britain, Russia, Austria and Portugal after the fall of Napoleon in 1818?

R Type of professor at a British university whose chair was established by royal grant?

S In the 'Muppet Show' whose uncle owns the theatre in which 'The Muppets' perform?

T Who said: "If you want something said, ask a man; if you want something done, ask a woman"?

U In mythology the personification of the Heaven and father of Titans?

V Who is the hero of Victor Hugo's 'Les Miserables'?

W Duke, also known as the 'Good King', who became the Patron Saint of Bohemia and Czechoslovakia, and has his feast day on 28th September?

Z Who was the Mexican revolutionary who fought alongside Pancho Villa?

Answers cont **13** Mushrooms **14** Nysas **15** Obadiah **16** Priscilla **17** Quadruple **18** Regius **19** Scooter **20** Thatcher **21** Uranus **22** Valjean **23** Wenceslas **24** Zapata

Alphabet — Quiz 18

A A planet's furthest point from the sun?

B A wild hog found in Celebes?

C Line of animals fastened together?

D Irish sausage made with sheep's blood?

E Nest of an eagle?

F A grave-digger?

G Grain eating?

H Pistol case?

I The holm oak?

J A stamped metal counter?

K Old liquid measure?

L A hare in its first year?

Answers **1** Aphelion **2** Babiroussa **3** Coffle **4** Drisheen **5** Eyrie **6** Fossor **7** Granivorous **8** Holster **9** Ilex **10** Jetton **11** Kilderkin **12** Leveret

Quiz 18

Alphabet

M West African baboon?

N Feeling of sickness?

O The florentine iris?

P The name given to the study of soil?

Q Unit of currency in Albania?

R Scale for measuring earthquakes?

S Walled palace of a sultan?

T A tract of ground?

U Light cavalryman?

V A guy rope?

W A sea monster shaped like a man?

Z Ancient Greek waist belt?

Answers cont **13** Mandrill **14** Nausia **15** Orris **16** Pedology **17** Qintar **18** Richter **19** Seraglio **20** Terrain **21** Uhlan **22** Vang **23** Wasserman **24** Zoster

Alphabet — Quiz 19

A Instrument used in performing arithmetic calculations?

B The capital of China, formerly Peking?

C Science dealing with the communication and control systems in living organisms, machines and organisations?

D Metal stringed, trapeziform-shaped type of zither?

E Type of tree whose berries are used for making wines and jellies?

F Who is the patron saint of firemen?

G American economist, advisor to Presidents Nixon and Ford and supporter of President Clinton's deficit-reduction Programmes?

H In the Bible, the brother of Abraham and father of Lot?

I Muslim scholar and prayer leader?

J People who invaded Britain in 449 led by two brothers Hengist and Horsa?

K Hardy variety of cabbage with curly leaves?

L Building created in mythology by Daedalus as a prison for The Minotaur?

Answers **1** Abacus **2** Beijing **3** Cybernetics **4** Dulcimer **5** Elder **6** Florian **7** Greenipan **8** Haran **9** Iman **10** Jutes **11** Kale **12** Labryinth

Quiz 19 — Alphabet

M City of southern Netherlands which gave its name to the Treaty for European Unity signed there in 1991?

N What is the name of the plane which went missing carrying Glenn Miller in 1944?

O Which Roman poet was noted for his humorous legends about The history of the world?

P What law states that properties of elements are functions of their atomic weights?

Q What, in the Book of Exodus, were said to have supplied food to the Israelites in the Wilderness?

R Who became ruler of Monarco in 1949?

S Who, in 1892, invented the toothpaste tube?

T Bead-like granules of cassava-root stock?

U Port in Germany on the Danube river where Napoleon defeated the Austrians in 1805?

V United States Secretary of State from 1977-80?

W Which film producer said, in 1927, “Who the hell wants to hear actors talk”?

Z Belgian ferry port, scene of the ‘Herald of Free Enterprise’ disaster in 1987?

Answers cont **13** Maastricht **14** Norseman **15** Ovid **16** Periodic **17** Quail **18** Rainier **19** Sheffield **20** Tapioca **21** Ulm **22** Vance **23** Warner **24** Zeebruger

Alphabet — Quiz 20

A A crane-like bird the golden breasted trumpeter?

B Enclosure for slaves?

C Club-shaped?

D Earthenware made in Holland?

E Like or belonging to a red deer?

F Small North African fox?

G A full set of chromosomes?

H South American tree yielding rubber?

I The letter 'z' in words?

J An Indian common soldier?

K A Japanese lord or god?

L A gleam of light?

Answers **1** Agami **2** Barracoon **3** Clavate **4** Delft **5** Elaphine **6** Fennec **7** Genome **8** Hevea **9** Izzard **10** Jawan **11** Kami **12** Leam

Quiz 20

Alphabet

M A grinding tooth?

N A Muslim Prince or nobleman in India?

O A gad fly?

P Large cask 70-120 gallons?

Q A stone hand mill?

R Old variety of apple?

S Study of Chinese language?

T Glossy silk material for ball gowns?

U Part of the throat?

V Having a protruding stomach?

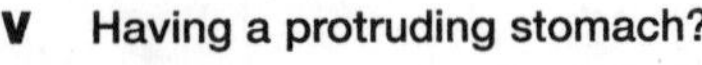

W A dirk?

X Sword-shaped?

Answers cont **13** Molar **14** Nawab **15** Oestrus **16** Punchion **17** Quern **18** Rennet **19** Sinology **20** Taffeta **21** Uvula **22** Ventricose **23** Whinger **24** Xiphoid

Alphabet — Quiz 21

A Lower of two cavities into which the diaphragm divides the human body?

B Knife named after a famous frontiersman?

C The highest dignitary of the Roman Catholic Church after the Pope?

D Noise reduction system devised originally for professional tape recording?

E The outer shell of the atmosphere from which light gases can escape?

F Thorny evergreen shrub also known as gorse?

G Soviet President from 1985-8?

H Legendary American film director whose works include 'The Maltese Falcon', 'The African Queen' and 'Prizzi's Honor'?

I The scientific study of fishes?

J Who, in 1796, discovered the vaccination for smallpox?

K The group of advisors to US President Andrew Jackson were known as the ---------- Cabinet?

L Tree which bears yellow flowers and produces poisonous seeds?

Answers **1** Abdomen **2** Bowie **3** Cardinal **4** Dolby **5** Exosphere **6** Furze **7** Gromyko **8** Huston **9** Ichthyology **10** Jenner **11** Kitchen **12** Laburnum

Quiz 21 — Alphabet

M The Greek god of sleep and dreams?

N Crescent shaped island in the Atlantic Ocean which is near to, and part of, Massachusetts?

O Greek business tycoon who made his fortune in shipping?

P College from which US Presidents James Madison and Woodrow Wilson graduated and J.F. Kennedy attended for a short time?

Q What were first classified as 'up', 'down' and 'strange', their name taken from James Joyce's 'Finnegan's Wake'?

R In the Muppets, what was the name of Kermit the Frog's five-year-old nephew?

S 1954 hit song co-written by Charlie Chaplin?

T What word is derived from Genghis Khan's fierce Mongol Hordes?

U Distinctive bird with curving crests of erectile feathers?

V Island of British Columbia in the Pacific Ocean?

W Which cartoonist created Calvin & Hobbes?

Z Greek philosopher who devised the paradox of Achilles and the Tortoise?

Answers cont **13** Morpheus **14** Nantucket **15** Onassis **16** Princeton **17** Quarks **18** Robin **19** Smile **20** Tartar **21** Umbrella **22** Vancouver **23** Waterson **24** Zeno

Alphabet — Quiz 22

A Registrar or clerk in Insurance company?

B Ancient German chant which incited war?

C Word for sky blue?

D Czech composer born 1841?

E Phantom or apparition?

F An Italian flask?

G Orchestral instrument?

H To comb out?

I An Indian of Peru?

J Unit of energy?

K Striped antelope of Africa?

L German carriage?

Answers **1** Actuary **2** Bardit **3** Cerulian **4** Dvorak **5** Eidolon **6** Fiasco **7** Glockenspiel **8** Heckle **9** Inca **10** Joule **11** Koodoo **12** Landau

Quiz 22 — Alphabet

M An old wine in England?

N A Xmas carol?

O Genus of antelopes?

P A rope fastened to a boat?

Q Formerly in the UK a hundred weight?

R A yacht meeting?

S Highland war cry?

T A third?

U Iniquitous interest on a loan?

V An obsolete term for a hit in fencing?

W North American stag?

X The woody tissue of plants?

---

13 Malmsey **14** Noel **15** Oryx **16** Painter **17** Quintal **18** Regatta
19 Slogan **20** Terce **21** Usury **22** Venue **23** Wapiti **24** Xylem

Alphabet — Quiz 23

A Free-reed musical instrument invented in Berlin in 1822?

B Pete ----------, the Beatles' drummer fired in 1963 and replaced by Ringo Starr?

C Which author, born Leslie Charles Bowyer Yin, is best known as the creator of Simon Templar 'The Saint'?

D In Biblical history, the flood of water described in Genesis which inundated the earth?

E Egg-laying mammal, also known as the spiny anteater?

F Arthur --------- (1894-1999), American conductor and director of the Boston Pops Orchestra?

G Any mollusc of the class which includes snails and slugs?

H Composer of the opera 'Hansel and Gretel'?

I Queen of Spain who sponsored the voyages of Christopher Columbus?

J Site near Chesapeake Bay, Virginia, of the first successful British settlement in America?

K Who was the British Secretary of State for war in World War I who was lost at sea in 1916?

L Legendary King of Britain after who the city of Leicester is named?

M A champagne bottle of eight times the normal capacity?

Answers **1** Accordian **2** Best **3** Charteris **4** Deluge **5** Echidna **6** Fielder **7** Gastropod **8** Humperdinck **9** Isabella **10** Jamestown **11** Kitchener **12** Lear

Quiz 23 Alphabet

N Who invented logarithms?

O Egg-shaped wind instrument whose name in Italian means 'little goose'?

P Which composer was also organist at Westminster Abbey?

Q Which city was the capital of the Philippines from 1948 to 1976?

R Which town in Kent was the home of Charles Dickens?

S St Crispin is the patron saint of which occupation?

T A jug in the shape of a man wearing a three-cornered hat?

U Region of central Italy which contains Lake Trasimero, the largest lake in Italy?

V Group of islands in the Pacific Ocean formerly known as New Hebrides?

W Who became the oldest fighter to win the heavyweight title when he defeated Eggard Charles in 1951 at the age of 37?

Z What is another name for a courgette?

Answers cont **13** Methuselah **14** Napier **15** Ocarina **16** Purcell **17** Quezon **18** Rochester **19** Shoemakers **20** Toby **21** Umbria **22** Vanuatu **23** Walcott **24** Zucchini

Alphabet — Quiz 24

A Extinct vulcano near Naples?

B Indian fig tree?

C Pertaining to twilight?

D An old small French silver coin?

E A team in motor racing?

F Latin countryside god with horns and tail?

G A dish of veal or poultry fillets?

H Long-legged wading bird?

I Part of the small intestine?

J Temporary mast raised in place of one lost?

K Long single-edged Samurai sword?

L A list of candidates for office?

M Australian river?

Answers **1** Avernus **2** Banyan **3** Crepuscular **4** Denier **5** Equipe **6** Faun **7** Grenadine **8** Heron **9** Ileum **10** Jurymast **11** Katana **12** Leet

Quiz 24 — Alphabet

N Native well in Australia?

O Likeness for a particular food?

P The evergreen oak?

Q A game in which a ring is thrown over a peg?

R To retract?

S The third Sunday before Lent?

T The most Southerly island in the West Indies?

U Existence everywhere?

V Lively?

W A short distance?

Z A genus of eared seals?

Answers cont **13** Murray **14** Namma Hole **15** Opsomania **16** Pinus **17** Quoits **18** Recant **19** Septagesima **20** Trinidad **21** Ubiquity **22** Vivo **23** Wee **24** Zalophus

Alphabet — Quiz 25

A The science of sound?

B Plant of the genus Ranunculus?

C Small symbol (^) found over the sixth key on a computer keyboard?

D American boxer who was known as the 'Manassa Mauler'?

E Gaelic name of the Republic of Ireland?

F British novelist who wrote 'A Passage to India'?

G French dance for a circle of couples which remained in vogue until the French Revolution?

H Pueblo Indian group of Arizona whose name means 'peaceful ones'?

I Professional name of John Henry Brodribb, who, in 1895, was the first actor to be knighted?

J The academic study of law?

K Two-masted for-and-aft-rigged sailing vessel?

L Dutch portrait painter Sir Peter ----------, original Pieter van der Faes?

Answers **1** Acoustics **2** Buttercup **3** Caret **4** Dempsey **5** Eire **6** Forster **7** Gavotte **8** Hopi **9** Irving **10** Jurisprudence **11** Ketch **12** Lely

Quiz 25 — Alphabet

M Territory on the South East coast of China, which Portugal returned to China in 1999?

N The SI unit of force?

O ---------- Bay, a town on Long Island, New York, where President Theodore Roosevelt had his 'Summer White House'?

P The capital of Tahiti?

Q Adjective which means recurring daily?

R Which political humorist who talked to his audience while he performed rope tricks was killed in a plane crash in 1935?

S Who is the advertising executive who spearheaded Margaret Thatcher's 1979 election campaign?

T Which vehicle was invented by Benjamin Hill in 1900?

U In mythology, the muse of astronomy?

V In mathematics, a quantity having both magnitude and direction?

W Wild pig of Africa which has two pairs of tusks?

Z Chemist who won the Nobel Prize for chemistry in 1963 for his work in the development of plastics?

Answers cont **13** Macan **14** Newton **15** Oyster **16** Papeeta **17** Quotidian **18** Rogers **19** Saatchi **20** Tractor **21** Urania **22** Vector **23** Warthog **24** Ziegler

Alphabet — Quiz 26

A Combination of nitrogen and hydrogen?

B A secret method of voting?

C A ravine or lava flow?

D A ten-footed crustacean?

E The study of words?

F Lancet for bleeding horses?

G A halo or glory?

H Praise to God?

I A confused heap?

J A tiny flea that burrows under the skin?

K A small anchor?

L Diseased person such as a leper?

Answers **1** Ammonia **2** Ballot **3** Coulee **4** Decapod **5** Etymology **6** Fleam **7** Gloriole **8** Hosanna **9** Imbroglio **10** Jigger **11** Killick **12** Lazar

Quiz 26 — Alphabet

M A mauve plant with soft downy leaves?

N Ribbon-shaped pasta?

O Of the coast?

P Motion of a horse over same ground?

Q A distant star possibly related to a black hole?

R A piece of good humoured ridicule?

S Position of an animal sitting?

T Language of Sri Lanka?

U A small four-stringed guitar?

V Stone shaped by wind blown sand?

W A final defeat?

Y A ship turning out of line?

Answers cont **13** Mallow **14** Noodle **15** Orian **16** Passade **17** Quasar **18** Raillery **19** Sejant **20** Tamil **21** Ukulele **22** Ventifact **23** Waterloo **24** Yaw

Alphabet — Quiz 27

A Arm of the Mediterranean Sea between Greece and Asia Minor?

B Alloy of copper and tin?

C Chester F ---------- was the inventor of copying?

D Science of the structure, functions and diseases of the skin?

E A unit of time used in Geology as a subdivision of a period?

F Colourful butterfuly which has yellow-brown wings with black markings?

G Argentine revolutionary leader executed in Bolivia in 1967?

H City of New Jersey and birthplace of Frank Sinatra?

I Belgian racing driver who won the Le Mans 24-hour race a record six times?

J Mountain range straddling the border between France and Switzerland?

K What in Japanese is literally 'divine wind'?

L The general name for the Eastern shores of the Mediterranean Sea?

Answers **1** Aegean **2** Bronze **3** Carlson **4** Dermatology **5** Epoch **6** Fritillery
7 Guevara **8** Hoboken **9** Ickx **10** Jura **11** Kamikaze **12** Levant

Quiz 27 — Alphabet

M A fractional or decimal part of a logarithm?

N Who was the British motor magnate who developed Morris Cars?

O Mammal of the giraffe family, native to Zaire?

P The 14th President of the United States?

Q Romantically idealistic, as a Cervantes hero?

R Who wrote the light operas 'Student Prince' and 'Desert Song'?

S Who, in the 1950s developed an oral vaccine for polio?

T Who was the Roman god of boundaries and landmarks?

U A function in computer science which reverses the last act performed?

V The most sacred literature of Hinduism whose name in Sanskrit means 'knowledge'?

W Famous circus high-wire act, two members of which were killed in a fall at the Detroit Coliseum in 1962?

Z A soft gentle breeze from the west?

Answers cont **13** Mantissa **14** Nuffield **15** Okapi **16** Pierce **17** Quixotic **18** Romberg **19** Sabin **20** Terminus **21** Undo **22** Veda **23** Wallendas **24** Zephyr

Alphabet — Quiz 28

A Garlic-flavoured mayonnaise?

B A thorny shrub with yellow flowers and orange or red berries, cultivated as a hedge plant?

C Belonging to the body?

D A British seaweed, found on rocks with edible red fronds?

E To take by storm?

F Association of Irishmen in New York?

G The capital of Botswana?

H Theatrical plot or business?

I To put in one's purse?

J American brothers with robbed banks and trains during the 1870's?

K A bucket of a draw well?

L Plaintive?

Answers **1** Alioli **2** Barberry **3** Corporeal **4** Dulse **5** Expugn **6** Fenian **7** Gaberones **8** Hokum **9** Imburse **10** James **11** Kibble **12** Lagrimoso

Quiz 28 Alphabet

M The Greek god of riches?

N A small bunch of flowers sometimes worn in a buttonhole or an a dress?

O River that flows in South Africa into the Atlantic?

P Card game played with 32 cards?

Q The 4 aces and picture cards of each suit?

R Having the form of a net?

S Framework of a cell?

T American fresh water tortoise?

U An open-skin boat manned by women?

V Another name for kelp?

W Whose real name was Marion Michael Morrison?

Y Monetary unit of China?

Answers cont **13** Mammon **14** Nosegay **15** Orange **16** Piquet **17** Quatorze **18** Retiform **19** Stroma **20** Terrapin **21** Umiak **22** Varec **23** Wayne **24** Yuan

Alphabet — Quiz 29

A Voluntary written statement sworn before an officer qualified to administer an oath?

B Collective designation of Belgium, Netherlands and Luxembourg?

C The oldest form of stringed keyboard and predecessor of the piano?

D The earliest of the five main orders of classical architecture?

E Pen name of British novelist Marian Evans?

F Name given to methane occurring in coal mines?

G In mythology, the beautiful boy who was successor to Hebe as cupbearer of the gods?

H Monsters in mythology with heads of women and bodies of birds?

I Number system which is assigned to every newly published book?

J Red variety of chalcedony?

K The compulsive impulse to steal object?

L What street is London's equivalent of Wall Street?

Answers **1** Affidavit **2** Benelux **3** Clavicord **4** Doric **5** Eliot **6** Firedamp
7 Ganymede **8** Harpies **9** ISBN **10** Jasper **11** Kleptomania **12** Lombard

Quiz 29

Alphabet

M Who names the Pacific Ocean because of its calmness?

N Timbuktu in Africa stands on which river?

O Who did the Warran report conclude 'acted alone'?

P What was the name of writer Ernest Hemingway's 40-foot vessel named after a character in 'For Whom the Bell Tolls'?

Q Large brightly coloured bird of Central and South America whose feathers were used for decoration

R Who in the Bible was the wife of Isaac?

S In 'Gone With the Wind' what is the name of Scarlett O'Hara's youngest sister?

T What did the Aztecs use for their fine mosaic art, where it became known as chalchihuith?

U The common name applied to any hoofed mammal?

V The brightest star in the northern hemisphere?

W Whose epitaph is: 'If you seek his monument, look about you'?

Y Plant cultivated for its edible tubers?

Answers cont **13** Magellan **14** Niger **15** Oswald **16** Pilar **17** Quetzal **18** Rebecca **19** Suellen **20** Turquoise **21** Ungulate **22** Vega **23** Wren **24** Yam

Alphabet — Quiz 30

A Patriotic song?

B Tapestry showing invasion of England by France?

C Red Bordeaux wine?

D The branch of medicine which deals with skin diseases?

E A subsonic tactical missile launched from ship?

F Public room opening onto a lobby?

G Small tropical lizard?

H Shakespearean term for winter?

I The property contained by a body at rest?

J A worthless fellow in Old English?

K Commonest of British hawks?

L What famous statue is found on Bedloe's island?

Answers **1** Anthem **2** Bayeux **3** Claret **4** Dermatology **5** Exocet **6** Foyer **7** Gecko **8** Hiems **9** Inertia **10** Javel **11** Kestrel **12** Liberty

Quiz 30

Alphabet

M Former name for Iraq?

N Dancing woman from India?

O The study of birds?

P Light porous rock from volcanoes?

Q Character in 'Hunchback of Notre Dame'?

R A small song bird, a visitor to the British Isles. The male has a black throat, an orange-brown tail and breast and grey back?

S Type of harpsichord in 17th century?

T African fly which spreads the fatal disease, 'sleeping sickness'?

U Fruit, cross between an orange and tangerine?

V A rare, toxic silvery metallic element which is difficult to melt and is used in steel alloys?

W Fish with sharp, venomous dorsal spines capable of wounding humans?

Y A gate or door?

Answers cont **13** Mesopotamia **14** Nautch **15** Ornithology **16** Pumice **17** Quasi-Modo **18** Redstart **19** Spinet **20** Testes **21** Ugli **22** Vanadium **23** Weever **24** Yett

Alphabet — Quiz 31

A Province of Western Canada?

B Second wife of King David and mother of King Solomon?

C The first Christian Emperor of Rome?

D In economics the act of reducing the rate at which one currency is exchanged for another in international currency markets?

E Welsh national music festival whose name means 'a sitting of learned men'?

F Japanese floor matress used as a bed?

G In computer science, one billion bytes?

H Painter of 'A Rake's Progress' (1735)?

I River, which rises in Tibet and flows into the Arabian Sea 1,700 miles later?

J Roman god of gates and doors, represented with two opposite faces?

K Which almost real-life TV star said: 'Time's fun when you're having flies'?

L American chat show host who said: 'The New England Journal of Medicine reports 9 out of 10 doctors agree that 1 out of 10 doctors is an idiot'?

Answers **1** Alberta **2** Bathsheba **3** Constantine **4** Devolution **5** Eisteddfod **6** Futon **7** Gigabyte **8** Hogarth **9** Indus **10** Janus **11** Kermit **12** Leno

Quiz 31 Alphabet

M The channel separating the isle of Anglesey from the Welsh Mainland?

N Who in Greek mythology is the goddess of victory?

O River in Canada linked to Lake Ontario by the Rideau Canal?

P Who, in 1608, saved the life of Capt John Smith?

Q Where would you find Toowoomba, the Great Dividing Range, Cooper Creek and Mount Bartle Frere?

R Who in 1988 controversially published 'The Satanic Verses'?

S Which aristocratic Jewish party was denounced by Jesus Christ in the phrase 'beware the leaven'?

T John Buchan, the author of 'The Thirty-Nine Steps' was 1st Baron -------?

U Island of Alaska, and largest of the Aleutian Islands?

V Who painted the 'Adoration of the Magi'?

W Who wrote 'Brideshead Revisited'?

Y Where did the final campaign of the US War of Independence take place?

Answers cont **13** Menai **14** Nike **15** Ottowa **16** Pocahontas **17** Queensland **18** Rushdie **19** Sadducees **20** Tweedsmuir **21** Unimak **22** Velasquez **23** Waugh **24** Yorktown

Alphabet — Quiz 32

A The zodiacal sign of the ram?

B Woman's small private room?

C Lobster-like crustacean?

D The scum off molten metal?

E Inscription upon a stone?

F Member of weasel family?

G The fire opal?

H Composer of the water music?

I A line on a map joining places with the same atmospheric pressure?

J Lying flat, sluggish?

K Dance of Northern India that tells a story?

L Capital of Peru?

Answers **1** Aries **2** Boudoir **3** Crayfish **4** Dross **5** Epigraph **6** Ferret **7** Girasol **8** Handel **9** Isobar **10** Jacent **11** Kathak **12** Lima

Quiz 32

Alphabet

M Venomous African snake?

N Hurtful?

O Author of 'Animal Farm'?

P A heathen?

Q A case for carrying arrows?

R Rambling meaningless talk?

S The sheath of a sword?

T Cards for fortune telling?

U Rust in plants?

V Prophetic?

W A male witch?

Y A language spoken asw a vernacular by Jews in Europe?

Answers cont **13** Mamba **14** Nocuous **15** Orwell **16** Paynim **17** Quiver **18** Rigmarole **19** Scabbard **20** Tarot **21** Uredo **22** Vatic **23** Warlock **24** Yiddish

Alphabet

Quiz 33

A Republic of Western North Africa?

B Canadian-born British newspaper publisher Lord ----------, born William Maxwell Aitken?

C Ancient water-clock which measured time by the flow of water through a small orifice?

D Canadian Prime Minister from 1957-1963?

E Type of work written by Thomas Gray?

F 16th century French chateau used by Napoleon as his imperial palace?

G Actress born Caryn Jones in New York City and winner of an Academy Award for her supporting role in Ghost (1990)?

H World boxing heavyweight champion from 1978-1985?

I Site of the 1964 and 1976 Winter Olympics?

J Queen of the Netherlands from 1948-80?

K The nickname which Anne Frank gave to her diary, in which she always began: 'Dear ----------'?

L Edwin ----------, invented the Polaroid camera?

Answers **1** Algeria **2** Beaverbrook **3** Clepsydra **4** Diefenbaker **5** Elegy **6** Fontainbleau **7** Goldberg **8** Holmes **9** Innsbruck **10** Juliana **11** Kitty **12** Land

Quiz 33

Alphabet

M Which poet wrote ‘revenge, at first though sweet, bitter ‘ere long, back on itself recoils’?

N Which radioactive metallic element is named after the inventor of dynamite?

O In Egyptian mythology, the god of the underworld and judge of the dead?

P The smallest resolved unit of a video image?

Q The Battle of ---------- Heights took place in 1812 in present day Ontario?

R Of where is Kigali the capital?

S American film actor known as Sly?

T Which British mathematician was a pioneer in the theories of computer logic?

U Author of ‘The Witches of Eastwick’?

V Who was the woman who, according to legend gave Jesus her Veil to wipe his face as he bore the cross to Calvary?

W What is the SI unit of magnetic flux?

Y The longest river of Asia?

Answers cont **13** Milton **14** Nobelium **15** Osiris **16** Pixel **17** Queenston **18** Rwanda **19** Stallone **20** Turing **21** Updike **22** Veronica **23** Weber **24** Yangtze

Alphabet — Quiz 34

A Channel for carrying water over distances?

B A strong leather high shoe?

C Highland freebooter or robber?

D Tyrant governor?

E Who composed 'Pomp and Circumstance Marches'?

F Lock of hair above the forehead?

G Narrow boat used on canals of Venice?

H Soft felt hat?

I Language of the people of a country?

J Plant used to make hessian?

K General Gordon was killed here?

L Vital urge?

Answers **1** Aqueduct **2** Blucher **3** Cateran **4** Despot **5** Elgar **6** Forlock **7** Gondola **8** Homburg **9** Idiom **10** Jute **11** Khartum **12** Libido

Quiz 34

Alphabet

M Common breed of South American duck?

N Adjective used to describe aquatic plants floating on the water?

O Personal magnetism?

P An important official of the Ottoman Empire or in modern Egypt?

Q Hollow stem of a feather?

R Another term for hydrophobia?

S Breed of wire-haired terrier?

T Another name for lockjaw?

U Without feudal superior?

V Puffed up with conceit?

W A castaway?

Y A state of Mexico and a centre of Mayan civilization?

Answers cont **13** Muscovy **14** Natant **15** Oomph **16** Pasha **17** Quill
18 Rabies **19** Sealyham **20** Tetanus **21** Udal **22** Ventose **23** Weft
24 Yucatan

Alphabet — Quiz 35

A Multi-millionaire businessman who lost his life when the Titanic sank?

B Powerful and aggressive large African monkey?

C Town in France named after a brandy made there since the 18th century?

D What are 'sumach', 'kermes' and 'annato' types of?

E Capital of the Canadian province of Alberto?

F The first American chess player to win the world Championship?

G Common name for three unrelated American burrowing animals which include the ground squirrel?

H Acclaimed violinist born in Lithuania in 1901 and who became an American citizen in 1925?

I What is a psocid a type of?

J Forces led by Bonnie Prince Charlie in 1745?

K Mary Jo ---------- was killed off Dike Bridge at Chappaquiddick on July 18, 1969?

L French military leader who fought on the side of the colonists in the American Revolution?

Answers **1** Astor **2** Baboon **3** Cognac **4** Dyes **5** Edmonton **6** Fischer **7** Gopher **8** Heifetz **9** Insect **10** Jacobite **11** Kopechne **12** Lafayette

Quiz 35 — Alphabet

M Another name for the blue mineral Azurite?

N Which sports person said 'whoever said: it's not whether you win or lose that counts, probably lost'?

O Who was the head of the atomic laboratory at Los Alamos largely responsible for the development of the atomic bomb?

P Which Egyptian astronomer propounded the theory that the earth was the centre of the universe?

Q Borough of New York City on Long Island?

R Who wrote 'Guys and Dolls'?

S Which icicle-shaped mass of calcium carbonate hangs from the ceilings of caves?

T Who said: 'Facts are stubborn but statistics are more pliable'?

U ---------- are Thummium were, according to the Old Testament, two objects used in divination?

V In mythology, the god of fire?

W Burrowing marsupial native to Australia and Tasmania?

Z Jewish political group who resisted Roman rule in Judea during the 1st century AD?

Answers cont **13** Malachhite **14** Navratilova **15** Oppenheimer **16** Ptolomy **17** Queens **18** Runyon **19** Stalactite **20** Twain **21** Urin **22** Vulcan **23** Wombat **24** Zealots

Alphabet — Quiz 36

A The daughter of Zeus and the Greek goddess of love and beauty?

B French composer of 'Carmen'?

C Venomous hooded snake?

D A pointed tool used for holes for plants?

E To interlace?

F A tall head dress worn in the 17th century?

G An Irish policeman?

H Scottish New Year's Eve celebration?

I An oblique hint?

J English dramatist, author of 'The Alchemist', who developed the 'comedy of humours'?

K An Irish foot soldier?

L A revolving tray, usually on a table for holding condiments?

Answers **1** Aphrodite **2** Bizet **3** Cobra **4** Dibble **5** Entrail **6** Fontage **7** Garda **8** Hogmanay **9** Innuendo **10** Jonson **11** Kern **12** Lazy Susan

Quiz 36

Alphabet

M A public declaration of policy?

N London architect who planned Regent Street?

O The capital of Canada?

P 17 March is which Saint's day?

Q Open tart with savoury filling?

R A river in North America which forms the border between US and Mexico?

S Long-necked Indian musical instrument?

T A series of waves larger than tidal waves?

U The Latin name of Odysseus?

V Nest of wasps?

W A portable cassette player?

Z A branch of the Bantu family of South Africa?

Answers cont **13** Manifesto **14** Nash **15** Ottowa **16** Patrick **17** Quiche **18** Rio Grande **19** Sitar **20** Tsunami **21** Ulysses **22** Vespiary **23** Walkman **24** Zulu

Alphabet — Quiz 37

A The song that Irving Berlin presented to his wife as a wedding gift in 1926?

B God of wine in Greek and Roman mythology?

C The study and use of materials at very low temperatures?

D Actress whose first leading role was in 'The Blue Angel' (1930)?

E A type of what, was invented in 1853 by Elisha Otis?

F Cave situated on the coast of Staffa in the Inner Hebrides whose beauty is celebrated in Mendelssohn's Hebridean overture?

G Name of Nizhaiy Novgorod, city in Russia from 1932-91?

H Hindi of the lowest status, formerly called 'untouchable'?

I Saint, who was Pope from 401-17 and name of ten subsequent Popes?

J Boxer who knocked out Bob Fitzsimmonds to win the World Heavyweight title in 1899?

K Silent film company founded by Mack Sennett?

L Figure of speech in the form on an understatement, as in 'no mean achievement'?

Answers **1** Always **2** Bacchus **3** Cryogenics **4** Dietrich **5** Elevator **6** Fingal's **7** Gorky **8** Harijan **9** Innocent **10** Jeffries **11** Keystone **12** Litotes

Quiz 37 — Alphabet

M A mechanical device which indicates the tempo of a piece of music?

N In the Bible, who was the mighty hunter and son of Cush?

O Mammal, Felis pardalis, of the cat family found from Texas to Peru?

P Gas obtained from petroleum and natural gas used as a fuel and refrigerant

Q Division of geological line in the Cenozoic era?

R Dutch painter whose masterpieces include 'The Blinding of Samson (1636)?

S Prehistoric site on Salisbury Plain?

T Whose recording 'Telstar' became the first British instrumental, in 1962, to top the US pop charts?

U Of where is Tashkent the capital?

V Which group of three Japanese islands in the Pacific include Iwo Jima?

W What is the earlier name for Tungsten?

Y American marsupial also known as the water opossum?

Answers cont **13** Metronome **14** Nimrod **15** Ocelot **16** Propane **17** Quaternary **18** Rembrandt **19** Stonehenge **20** Tornados **21** Uzbekistan **22** Volcano **23** Wolfram **24** Yapok

Alphabet — Quiz 38

A American state of which Montgomery is the capital?

B Famous library in Oxford founded in 1598?

C Open-ended cigar?

D Bird which nests in reeds?

E The Queen of Edward I?

F Temperature scale 32°F - 212°F

G Vandal King of Spain in 419?

H The science of time measurement?

I Large lizard of South America?

J South African town founded in 1886?

K Uncut hair worn by Sikhs?

L Close fitting one piece costume for ballet?

Answers **1** Alabama **2** Bodleian **3** Cheroot **4** Dabchick **5** Eleanor **6** Farenheit **7** Genseric **8** Horology **9** Iguana **10** Johannesburg **11** Kesh **12** Leotard

Quiz 38

Alphabet

M Officer one above a Captain?

N A type of primitive man, not thought to be related to modern humans?

O The British universities of Oxford and Cambridge?

P A flower with scarlet and yellow flowers?

Q A member of the Society of Friends?

R The brother of Remus?

S A slang term for a rumpus or brawl?

T A set of three?

U To hoot or screech?

V A pardonable sin?

W The watery part of milk?

Y A lout or hooligan?

Answers cont **13** Major **14** Neanderthal **15** Oxbridge **16** Poinsettia **17** Quaker **18** Romulus **19** Shemozzle **20** Tern **21** Ululate **22** Venial **23** Whey **24** Yob

Alphabet — Quiz 39

A In law, a person residing in one country while being a citizen of another?

B Adult male of any species of swine?

C Light vessel, armed and built for speed, used by the US coastguard to deal with smugglers?

D Flower related to the narcissus?

E Hebrew prophet who assembled the people of Israel on Mount Carmel to demonstrate the power of God?

F The former name of Taiwan?

G An auk with long pointed bill, also known as 'murre' in the USA?

H A medium-range cannon for firing shells at a steep angle?

I Hormone, whose molecular structure was first determined in 1955 by the British biochemist Frederick Sanger?

J Capital city on the island of Java, formerly called Batavia?

K Light silky plant fibre used as stuffing in pillows and lifebelts?

L Town in Egypt on the site of ancient Thebes?

Answers **1** Alien **2** Boar **3** Cutter **4** Daffodil **5** Elijah **6** Formosa
7 Guillemot **8** Howitzer **9** Insulin **10** Jakarta **11** Kapok **12** Luxor

Quiz 39 — Alphabet

M Tributary of the Hudson River which flows through central New York?

N Pen name of Mrs Hubert Bland, who wrote 'The Railway Children'?

O A general term applied to the isles of the Pacific Ocean?

P Who tried and sentenced Jesus to be executed?

Q The oldest American breed of horse, developed for sprinting a short distance?

R Which is the largest of the Mascarine island group in the Indian Ocean?

S Which novelist was romantically linked with Chopin?

T Who illustrated 'Alice's Adventures in Wonderland'?

U French impressionist painter who suffered from alcoholism?

V Rodent and member of same family as lemming and muskrat?

W What story was broken by Washington Post reporters Bob Woodward and Carl Berneteen?

Y What is the capital of Cameroon?

Answers cont **13** Mohawk **14** Nesbit **15** Oceana **16** Pilate **17** Quarter **18** Reunion **19** Sand **20** Tenniel **21** Utrillo **22** Vole **23** Watergate **24** Yaounde

Alphabet — Quiz 40

A English astronomer who discovered Neptune?

B Order of monks of which St. Augustine was a member?

C Prime Minister of the Irish Republic 1948-51?

D Muslim religious order?

E King of Kent during 6th century?

F A comic strip?

G Small plot of enclosed land?

H 16th century painter of 'The Dance of Death'?

I Eskimo's hut?

J Evergreen resembling gorse?

K A bag strapped on the back or shoulder?

L A city in North West France, where there is an annual motor race?

Answers **1** Adams **2** Benedictines **3** Costello **4** Dervish **5** Ethelbert **6** Fumetto **7** Garth **8** Holbein **9** Igloo **10** Juniper **11** Knapsack **12** Le Mans

Quiz 40 — Alphabet

M In the middle?

N The inventor of dynamite?

O Healing based on manipulation of the bones?

P A room over a church porch?

Q A period of four years?

R A ship with its upper decks removed?

S Republic proclaimed in 1931?

T A variety of rum?

U Official language of Pakistan?

V To make off?

W English dramatist (1580-1625), author of 'Duchess of Malfi'?

Z The hill on which Jerusalem stands?

Answers cont **13** Median **14** Nobel **15** Osteopathy **16** Parvis
17 Quadrennium **18** Razee **19** Spanish **20** Tafia **21** Urdu **22** Vamoose
23 Webster **24** Zion

Alphabet — Quiz 41

A Substance composed of two or more metals?

B The capital of Colombia?

C In Roman mythology, the son of Venus?

D City of Eastern France, famous for its mustard?

E Doctrine propounded by Aristotle which claims that everything has a nature or essence?

F Who said: 'What a distressing contrast there is between the radiant intelligence of the child and the feeble mentality of the average adult'?

G Author of 'The Wind in the Willows'?

H The cloth flap at the back of a cap to protect the neck from sunburn, which was named after a 19th century British General in India?

I Summer resort of central Switzerland which provides a spectacular view of the Jungfrau from its main street?

J Who wrote 'Three Men in a Boat'?

K A peaked, pillbox-shaped, French military cap?

L Who designed the Cenotaph in Whitehall, London?

Answers **1** Alloy **2** Bogota **3** Cupid **4** Dijon **5** Essentialism **6** Freud **7** Graham **8** Havelock **9** Interlaken **10** Jerome **11** Kepi **12** Lutyens

Quiz 41

Alphabet

M The chief seaport of Kenya?

N What, in Buddhism is the attainment of supreme bliss?

O Philosopher known as Doctor Invincibilis (unconquerable Doctor) and Venerabilis Inceptor (worthy initiator)?

P In Greek mythology, the god of the sea?

Q The first dynasty to rule over a united China?

R Common name for either of two South American ostrich-like birds?

S What song composed by George Gershwin was sung by Al Jolson in 'The Jolson Story' and Judy Garland in 'A Star is Born'?

T Who was the Roman playwright whose comedies include 'The Eunoch' and 'The Brothers'?

U --------- Pendragon was, in legend, the father of King Arthur?

V What is the capital of Laos?

W Who, in 1793, invented the cotton gin?

Y Japanese fashion designer who specialises in loose functional clothes?

Answers cont **13** Mombasa **14** Nirvana **15** Ockham **16** Poseidon **17** Qin **18** Rhea **19** Swanee **20** Terence **21** Uther **22** Vientiane **23** Whitney **24** Yamamoto

Alphabet — Quiz 42

A A religious retreat?

B Dark volcanic rock?

C Member of crow family?

D A brand of luminous materials, usually green, pink, yellow and orange?

E A particle with a negative electrical charge?

F An Indonesian island?

G A waiter, especially in France?

H Sweating in excess?

I A solid with twenty plane faces?

J The sap of vegetables?

K A hard paving brick?

L Lithesome?

Answers **1** Ashram **2** Basalt **3** Chough **4** Day-Glo **5** Electron **6** Flores **7** Garcon **8** Hidrosis **9** Icosahedron **10** Juice **11** Klinker **12** Lissom

Quiz 42 — Alphabet

M An island in the Indian Ocean off the east coast of Africa?

N Leavened bread from India and Pakistan?

O A native of the Orkneys?

P Smoked cut of beef?

Q An odd-looking person?

R An American painter and a leading exponent of pop art?

S Mountain breed of British sheep?

T A rapid piece of instrumental music piece for the organ and harpsichord?

U An imaginary place of perfection?

V Italian composer of 'The Four Seasons'?

W President of Poland from 1990-95 and winner of the 1983 Nobel peace prize?

Z A hump-backed ox used as a draught animal in India?

Answers cont **13** Madagascar **14** Nan **15** Orcadian **16** Pastrami **17** Quiz **18** Rauschenberg **19** Swaledale **20** Toccata **21** Utopia **22** Vivaldi **23** Walesa **24** Zebu

Alphabet — Quiz 43

A Name given to the plastic ends of a shoelace?

B The national dance of Spain?

C Weapon, also called the arbaleet?

D Descriptive of the comedy that is considered the greatest work of the Italian poet Dante Alighieri?

E In philosophy, the study of human values and conduct?

F Legendary American dance choreographer whose successes included 'Sweet Charity', 'Cabaret' and 'All That Jazz'?

G English political philosopher who married the author Mary Wollstonecroft in 1797?

H The ancient name for the Dardanelles?

I Gelatini made from the bladders of fish?

J Large artichoke cultivated for its edible tubers?

K Wooden club formerly used as a weapon by South African Zulus?

L What is the name of the British steamship of the Cunard line torpedoed without warning during World War I?

Answers **1** Aglets **2** Bolero **3** Crossbow **4** Divine **5** Ethics **6** Fosse **7** Godwin **8** Hellespont **9** Insinglass **10** Jeruslaem **11** Knobkerrie **12** Lusitania

Quiz 43 — Alphabet

M Which mount in Alaska is known to Indians as Denali, 'the high one'?

N Who was known originally as Lucius Dòmitius Ahenobarbus?

O Large swamp of South Georgia and north eastern Florida?

P Snow capped volcano of south central Mexico?

Q Industrial town of Iran and pilgrimage centre for Shite Muslims?

R Type of jelly fed to all bee larvae until the third day after hatching?

S The two varieties of which foodstuff are called wrinkled, or Savoy and smooth-leaved?

T Which tree is known commercially as Canary or American Whitewood?

U Another name for a sunspot

V French film director who was married to Brigette Bardot and Jane Fonda?

W What did Don Quixote mistake for monsters?

Y Where did the final campaign of the US War of Independence take place?

Answers cont **13** Mckinley **14** Nero **15** Okefenokee **16** Popocatepetl **17** Qom **18** Royal **19** Spinach **20** Tulip **21** Umbra **22** Vadim **23** Windmills **24** Yorktown

Alphabet

Quiz 44

A Latin word meaning 'elsewhere'?

B Small streams in England?

C Sculptor of the Colossus of Rhodes?

D During the day?

E Worn out?

F A smoked fish, especially a pilchard?

G A breakwater?

H The spotted ray fish?

I A broad linen tape?

J A crude Hindu idol of Krishna, worshipped at Puri, Orissa and Bengal and wheeled through the town on a chariot?

K Capital of Zaire?

L British songwriter assassinated by a fan in 1980?

Answers **1** Alibi **2** Bourne **3** Chares **4** Diurnal **5** Epulse **6** Fumado **7** Groyne **8** Homelyn **9** Inkle **10** Juggernaut **11** Kinshasa **12** Lennon

Quiz 44

Alphabet

M Molten rock rising to the surface?

N The old King of Pylos, a Greek hero?

O Egg-shaped in outline?

P Explorer who reached the North Pole in 1909?

Q A Spanish hide riding whip?

R Cardinal, Minister of France 1624-1642?

S The largest butterfly in British Isles?

T A mosaic covering for floors?

U The last syllable of a word?

V A tube or duct, wasp-waisted?

W American engineer who built Dynamos for Niagara Falls?

Z French infantry of great dash?

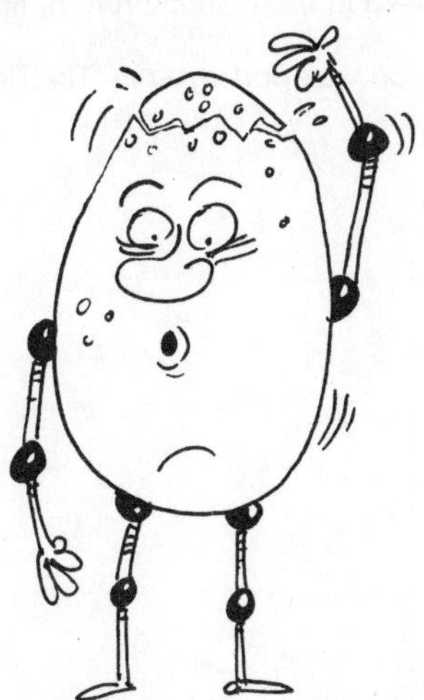

Answers cont **13** Magma **14** Nestor **15** Obovate **16** Peary **17** Quirt **18** Richelieu **19** Swallowtail **20** Terrazzo **21** Ultima **22** Venturi **23** Westinghouse **24** Zouave

Alphabet — Quiz 45

A Small food fish related to the herring?

B The practice of illegally transporting or selling intoxicating liquors?

C American frontier hero who, in 1827, became a member of the US Congress?

D What is a merganser a type of?

E Arctic island in North west Territories, Canada?

F What type of food treatment was invented by Clarence Birdseye in 1924?

G In mythology, the statue of a maiden carved from ivory by Pygmalion and given life by Aphrodite?

H Interjection used in hymns and liturgies which in Hebrew means 'praise the Lord'?

I The correct term for the Eskimo?

J Mouse-like rodent, also know as desert rat?

K Pure soft white clay used in the manufacture of fine porcelain and china?

L Which boxing champion was portrayed in 'The Raging Bull' by Robert de Niro?

Answers **1** Anchovy **2** Bootlegging **3** Crockett **4** Duck **5** Ellesmere **6** Freezing **7** Galetea **8** Hallelujah **9** Inuit **10** Jerbou **11** Koalin **12** Lamotta

Quiz 45 — Alphabet

M Naval battle of 4-6 June 1942 between America and Japan which resulted in the first defeat of the Japanese navy for 500 years?

N Another name for the Hawaiian Goose?

O The King of Norway from 1957-1991?

P Species of the order Cetacea?

Q Principle supply and service organisation of the US army?

R What is the capital of Latvia?

S Colouring material obtained from the crocus?

T Which Italian physicist gave the first description of a barometer?

U Evergreen Malaysian tree whose milky latex is used to make a powerful arrow poison?

V The tenth cranial nerve?

W A document which lists a ship's goods?

Z Which French author wrote his famous 'J'accuse' letter in 1898?

Answers cont **13** Midway **14** Nene **15** Olav **16** Porpoise **17** Quartermaster **18** Riga **19** Saffron **20** Torricelli **21** Upas **22** Vagus **23** Waybill **24** Zola

Alphabet — Quiz 46

A Loss of voice from hysteria?

B Sound made by a car's horn?

C Song like, flowing and expressive?

D Dead, finished, no longer of use?

E The nest of a bird of prey, especially an eagle?

F Curved like a sickle?

G Central American republic?

H A poisonous spotted conifer widely planted in Britain?

I A block of buildings?

J One versed in the science law?

K A rich peasant in Tsarist Russia?

L The space before a kiln fire?

Answers **1** Aphonia **2** Beep **3** Cantabile **4** Defunct **5** Eyrie **6** Falciform **7** Guatemala **8** Hemlock **9** Insula **10** Jurist **11** Kulak **12** Logie

Quiz 46 — Alphabet

M Immediately occurring within a world?

N Cathedral church of Paris?

O Small chapel - a place for private prayer?

P Vegetables boiled with or without meat?

Q An angle, especially of a building?

R Bait used by fishermen?

S Sultan of Egypt who led the Muslims against the Christians in the third crusade

T A disease discovered by Dr. Koch in 1882?

U Female water sprite?

V Mischievous person?

W Reclaiming marshland from a tidal estuary?

Y A year old calf, sheep, or foal?

Answers cont **13** Medial **14** Notre Dame **15** Oratory **16** Pottage **17** Quoin
18 Ragworms **19** Saladin **20** Tuberculosis **21** Undine **22** Varmint
23 Warping **24** Yearling

Alphabet — Quiz 47

A A word that modifies or qualifies a noun or pronoun?

B Wimbledon tennis champion for five consecutive years 1976-80?

C Originally a sailing man-of-war, smaller than a frigate but larger than a sloop?

D In computer science a terminal that does not contain an internal microprocessor?

E Collaboration with Karl Marx and founder of scientific Socialism?

F In mythology, avenging spirits also known as Erinyes or Eumenides?

G The science of the earth as a whole?

H Japanese poem of just 17 syllables?

I Any animal lacking a vertebral column?

J The term used in Islam for 'holy war'?

K The ---------- rat us a squirrel-like rodent native to North America?

L General term for a pain in the lower back?

Answers **1** Adjective **2** Borg **3** Corvette **4** Dumb **5** Engles **6** Furies **7** Geology **8** Haiku **9** Invertebrate **10** Jihad **11** Kangaroo **12** Lumbago

Quiz 47 Alphabet

M What name connects a city in Uraguay and a make of car?

N The Channel Islands were once part of which French region?

O Island of south west Japan and scene of a bitter battle between USA and Japan in World War II?

P Building that houses the US Department of Defence?

Q The pseudonym of US crime fiction writer Frederick Dannay?

R Sally ---------- was the first woman in the American space program to take part in an orbital mission?

S Where would you find the Ahaggar mountains, the Tibesti Massif and the Qattarah Depression?

T Ancient city and capital of ancient Egypt?

U Name of the last King of Italy?

V An ingredient of a 'Bloody Mary'?

W British Major-General who fought behind the Japanese lines in Burma in World War II and whose corps were nicknamed 'Raiders'?

Z A species of what, is named after the 19th century British naturalist William John Burchell?

Answers cont **13** Mercedes **14** Normandy **15** Okinawa **16** Pentagon
17 Queen **18** Ride **19** Sahara **20** Thebes **21** Umberto **22** Vodka
23 Wingate **24** Zebra

Alphabet — Quiz 48

A Frame for counting?

B Yellow butterfly in British Isles?

C A cornfield weed called wild mustard?

D A Baltic city and port of Poland?

E An architrave?

F The name for a German leader, especially applicable to Adolf Hitler while he was Chancellor?

G Great water-colourist of the 18th century?

H Flock of sheep under care of one shepherd?

I Norwegian poet, author of 'A Doll's House'?

J Man's leather jacket?

K District in Yukon where gold was discovered?

L Damage or injury to the body?

Answers **1** Abacus **2** Brimstone **3** Charlock **4** Danzig **5** Epistyle **6** Fuhrer **7** Girtin **8** Hirsel **9** Ibsen **10** Jerkin **11** Klondyke **12** Lesion

Quiz 48 — Alphabet

M Strong Mexican intoxicant?

N Britain's largest bat, wingspan approximately 35cm?

O Mountain in Thessaly Greece?

P Scented ointment for apples?

Q Portable hand mill for grinding corn?

R The killing of a king?

S Cylindrical of conductive wire?

T A tropical revolving storm?

U Having the same mother but different fathers?

V Happening every 20 years?

W The curlew?

Z A corpse reanimated by sorcery?

Answers cont **13** Mescal **14** Noctule **15** Ossa **16** Pommard **17** Quern **18** Regicide **19** Solenoid **20** Typhoon **21** Uterine **22** Vicennial **23** Whaup **24** Zombie

Alphabet — Quiz 49

A Breed of Japanese guard and hunting dog?

B Nun, who became one of the three patron saints of Ireland?

C Mountain lion, also called the puma?

D Reference guide to the titled aristocracy of Great Britain?

E In Greek mythology, a land of perfect peace and happiness?

F Mustaline is an adjective for what creature?

G US baseball player (died 1941) whose nickname was 'Iron horse'

H Evergreen flowing plant such as the Christmas rose?

I Element first isolated from seaweed residues in 1811?

J Religious order founded by Saint Ignatius of Loyala in 1534?

K In biology, what is the highest category into which organisms are classified?.

L Magnetic material used in early compasses?

Answers **1** Akita **2** Brigid **3** Cougar **4** Debrett's **5** Elyeium **6** Ferret **7** Gehrig **8** Hallebore **9** Iodine **10** Jesuits **11** Kingdom **12** Lodestone

Quiz 49

Alphabet

M Which British buccaneer was appointed governor of Jamaica?

N Province in South Africa of which the largest city is Durban?

O Form of government in which the supreme power is vested in a few persons?

P American poet who was married to the British poet Ted Hughes?

Q Another name for the hawthorne?

R Which is the heaviest of the nobel gases?

S The pseudonym of Hector Hugh Munro?

T Who shared the 1964 Nobel Prize for physics for his work on the development of the MASER and later LASER?

U The shortest name in the Bible?

V An instrument for measuring potential difference?

W Island chain which includes Dominica, Martinique and St. Lucia?

Z Which country was formerly the Belgian Congo?

Answers cont **13** Morgan **14** Natal **15** Oligarchy **16** Plath **17** Quickthorn **18** Radon **19** Saki **20** Townes **21** Uz **22** Voltmeter **23** Windward **24** Zaire

Alphabet — Quiz 50

A Small, strong-tasting fish allied to the herring?

B Odd, fantastic, extravagant?

C Evergreen tree from which quinine is made?

D Temper, anger?

E Striking heels together in a dance?

F Gambling card game based on the order of appearance of certain cards?

G Fine grained wood resembling mahogany?

H Hot dusty wind on the Guinea coast?

I What is the correct name for the plant called 'Busy Lizzie'?

J Ancient city in the Dead Sea valley?

K Of motion?

L Strong Indian cheroot?

Answers **1** Anchovy **2** Bizarre **3** Cinchona **4** Dander **5** Entrechat **6** Faro **7** Gaboon **8** Harmattan **9** Impatiens **10** Jericho **11** Kinetic **12** Lunkha

Quiz 50 — Alphabet

M Juicy fruit of the East Indies?

N A new star in the heavens?

O Sound made by town crier to get attention?

P The chief magistrate of a port?

Q Quaking bog?

R Soft sheepskin leather?

S Head of the tribe of North American Indians?

T Body of Jewish civil law?

U Omnipresence?

V Highest part or point?

W Contrivance for hauling?

Y A National Park for public use in California?

Answers cont **13** Mangosteen **14** Nova **15** Oyez **16** Portreeve **17** Quagmire **18** Roan **19** Sagamore **20** Talmud **21** Ubiquity **22** Vertex **23** Windlass **24** Yosemite

Alphabet

Quiz 51

A Portuguese group of nine islands and several islets in the Mid-Atlantic Ocean?

B African language group including most of the languages spoken from the Equator to the Cape of Good Hope?

C Alkaloid found in coffee and most cola beverages?

D Haitian leader known as Papa Doc?

E The wrongful taking, or use of a property, by a person who has been entrusted with it?

F In fencing, a light sword with blunt point?

G Music term meaning light and humorous?

H Composer of 'Saint Louis Blues'?

I Medical condition also known as pruritus?

J Seaport of Mecca province of Saudi Arabia?

K Gold mining town of Western Australia and flying doctor centre?

L The German airforce established in 1935 by Hermann Goring?

Answers **1** Azores **2** Bantu **3** Caffeine **4** Duvalier **5** Emebezzlement **6** Foil **7** Giocoso **8** Handy **9** Itch **10** Jeddah **11** Kalgoorlie **12** Luftwaffe

Quiz 51 — Alphabet

M An early centre of civilisation whose name in Greek means 'between the rivers'?

N Who wrote 'Lolita'?

O Which actor was married to Vivian Leigh?

P Battle of 1757 which led to the British control of Bengal and eventual conquest of India

Q Sport from which horse-shoe pitching developed?

R What was the special-built lunar vehicle called which was used by Apollo astronauts on the moon?

S Group of islands in the Pacific formerly called Navigators Islands

T Former secret organisation of robbers in India who always strangled their victims?

U In the cartoon series and movie, who is the girlfriend of George of the Jungle?

V The scientific study of volcanoes?

W Common name for the trachea?

Y Pseudonym of British novelist Cecil William Mercer?

Answers cont **13** Mesopotamia **14** Nabokov **15** Olivier **16** Plassey **17** Quoits **18** Rover **19** Samoa **20** Thugs **21** Ursula **22** Vulcanology **23** Windpipe **24** Yates

Alphabet — Quiz 52

A King of Spain who abdicated in 1931?

B German musical composer who wrote 'Ein deutsches Requiem'?.

C Russian dramatist who wrote 'The Cherry Orchard'?

D A male duck?

E A pleasing sound?

F Fan-shaped? .

G English novelist who won the Nobel prize in 1932?

H Breed of beef cattle, red and white?

I Egyptian mongoose, 'Pharoah's rat'?

J Tropical American tree?

K Coarse woollen cloth made in Suffolk?

L Ancient kingdom of Western Asia Minor?

Answers **1** Alfonso **2** Brahms **3** Chekov **4** Drake **5** Euphony **6** Flabellate **7** Galsworthy **8** Hereford **9** Ichneumon **10** Jacaranda **11** Kersey **12** Lydia

Quiz 52 — Alphabet

M Lyric ode for single voice?

N Special prayers on successive days?

O A killer-whale?

P A temple dedicated to all the gods?

Q Latin for 'formerly'?

R Small stream?

S Great English cabinet maker 18th century?

T Edinburgh's airport?

U Fabulous mythical animal?

V 18th century British explorer?

W Japanese bamboo?

Y Poet awarded Nobel prize in 1923?

Answers cont **13** Monody **14** Novena **15** Orc **16** Pantheon **17** Quondam **18** Rivulet **19** Sheraton **20** Turnhouse **21** Unicorn **22** Vancouver **23** Whangee **24** Yeats

Alphabet — Quiz 53

A Computer trail to document to path from input to output?

B Science dealing with the motion of bodies projected through space?

C Satellite of Jupiter named after one of the mythological paramours of Jupiter?

D The aborigines of the island of Borneo?

E The largest type of penguin?

F Melancholy type of Portuguese folk song?

G Latin edition of the Bible printed in Germany between 1450a nd 1456 and also known as the 'Mozarin Bible'?

H The first six books of the Bible?

I The most common measure of English verse?

J Spanish poet and winner of the 1956 Nobel Prize for Literature?

K Malay dagger with wavy double-edged blade?

L Town in Africa where Albert Schweitzer established his medical missionary in 1913?

Answers **1** Audit **2** Ballistics **3** Callisto **4** Dayaks **5** Emperor **6** Fado **7** Gutenberg **8** Hexateuch **9** Iamb **10** Jimenez **11** Kris **12** Lambarene

Quiz 53 Alphabet

M The scientific study of the earth's atmosphere?

N Another name for a birthmark?

O Which gulf is linked to the Arabian Gulf by the Strait Hormuz?

P French impressionist painter whose works include 'Brother in the Woods'?

Q Star-like celestial object having great energy and speed?

R Small portable reed organ in use during the 16th-17th centuries powered by two small balloons?

S S – Flat-bottomed Asian houseboat?

T The third longest river in Italy?

U Bone in the arm?

V Lake discovered by John Henning Speke in 1858?

W Who was Queen of the Netherlands from 1890-1948?

Z Who, with his 'Follies of 1907' introduced a new type of revue to the American stage?

Answers cont **13** Meteorology **14** Nevus **15** Oman **16** Pissarro **17** Quasar **18** Regal **19** Sampan **20** Tiber **21** Ulna **22** Victoria **23** Wilhelmina **24** Ziegfeld

Alphabet — Quiz 54

A Fear of pain?

B A jumble of words?

C Dried flower buds from a tree in the Molucca Islands, used as a spice?

D District under care of a Bishop?

E Poem of mourning?

F Adapted for burrowing or digging?

G Breed of cattle. giving rich creamy milk?

H Free-reed keyboard instrument with foot-operated bellows?

I Interior curve of an arch?

J Evil spirits in the 'Arabian Nights'?

K Anglo-Swiss woman painter?

L Side edge of a sail?

Answers **1** Algomania **2** Balderdash **3** Cloves **4** Diocese **5** Elegy **6** Fossorial **7** Guernsey **8** Harmonium **9** Intrados **10** Jinnees **11** Kauffman **12** Leech

Quiz 54 — Alphabet

M Ecclesiastical residence?

N Pertaining to marriage?

O Relating to dancing?

P Study of speech and vocal acoustics? .

Q One who asks questions?

R A cross or crucifix?

S A body-shaking dance?

T Bondage or slavery?

U Coincided in pitch in voices?

V Prophesy, forecast?

W American artist who painted his mother?

Z Warm moist wind in Argentina?

Answers cont **13** Manse **14** Nuptials **15** Orchestic **16** Phonetics **17** Querist **18** Rood **19** Shimmy **20** Thrall **21** Unison **22** Vaticinate **23** Whistler **24** Zonda

Alphabet — Quiz 55

A In the Christian calendar, a season observed in preparation for Christmas?

B Island group which includes Majorca, Minorca and Ibiza?

C American song writer whose works include 'Stardust' and 'Lazy Bones'

D The fourth natural satellite of Saturn?

E Ancient and poetic name for Ireland?

F What is a blacksmith's hammer called?

G Annual herb also called okra?

H The full moon closest to the autumn equinox?

I Oil paint applied with a heavily-loaded brush to make it stand up on the surface of the picture?

J American dance popular in the 1930s and 1940s?

K In Indian tradition, the principle that a person's actions have consequences meriting reward or punishment

L What tennis player was known as the 'Rockhampton Rocket'?

Answers **1** Advent **2** Baleric **3** Carmichael **4** Dione **5** Erin **6** Fuller **7** Gumbo **8** Harvest **9** Impasto **10** Jitterbug **11** Karma **12** Laver

Quiz 55

Alphabet

M Another name for the mythological god Hermes?

N ---------- disease is another name for fowl pest?

O Common name for the plant family oleaceae?

P Screw with a cross-shaped groove n the head?

Q Roman teacher of rhetoric whose chief work was the 'Istitutio Oratoria' (The Training of an Order)?

R Hitler's adviser in foreign affairs who was executed at Nuremberg?

S Who in Japan followed a rigid code of ethics called Bushido?

T What is sometimes referred to as the 'Roof of the World'?

U Russian ballerina who became ballet mistress at the Kirov?

V Russian scientific station in Antarctica and the first generation of Soviet-crewed spacecraft?

W Which cardgame was known as 'triumph' until the late 17th century?

Z The Kariba dam is on which river?

Answers cont **13** Mercury **14** Newcastle **15** Olive **16** Phillips **17** Quintilian **18** Ribbentrop **19** Samurai **20** Tibet **21** Ulanova **22** Vostok **23** Whist **24** Zambezi

Alphabet Quiz 56

A Palace and fortress at Granada, Spain?

B Servant in the army?

C The magic wand of Mercury?

D An Indian tailor?

E Animals with no teeth?

F The nut of the cultivated hazel?

G Silver-grey fresh water fish?

H One who has retired into solitary life?

I Dingy, yellowish grey and drab colour – also a woman's name?

J Slang term for a simpleton?

K Famous violinist born in Vienna 1875?

L Sediment of wine?

Answers **1** Alhambra **2** Batman **3** Caduceus **4** Durzi **5** Edentate **6** Filbert **7** Grayling **8** Hermit **9** Isabel **10** Juggins **11** Kreisler **12** Lees

Quiz 56 Alphabet

M Cornish port once the centre of pilchard fishing?

N Sweetmeat of sugar, honey and almonds?

O Burden on oneself?

P Model of excellence?

Q Type of mineral in prism form?

R Garment with tight sleeves worn by bishops?

S Lizard-like animal supposed to live in fire?

T Form of head dress?

U Servant who acts as a doorkeeper?

V A mass of whirling fluid?

W Capuchin monkey?

Z Small African quadruped, like a skunk?

Answers cont **13** Mousehole **14** Nougat **15** Onus **16** Paragon **17** Quartz **18** Rochet **19** Salamander **20** Tiara **21** Usher **22** Vortex **23** Weeper **24** Zorilla

Alphabet — Quiz 57

A Comic book in which 'Superman' debuted in June 1938?

B Strait which separates Turkey in Asia from Turkey in Europe?

C A mapmaker?

D The capital of Tanzania which replaced Dar Es Salaam in1974?

E Another name for the Lord's supper or Holy Communion?

F Ranine is an adjective for which creature?

G The modern science of hereditry?

H The migration of the prophet Mohammad from Mecca to Medina in 622?

I Island in the Tyrrhenian Sea between the gulfs of Gaeta and Salerno

J Which French film score composer won Oscars for his scores of 'Lawrence of Arabia', 'Dr Zhivago' and 'Passage to India'?

K Japanese martial art of unarmed self-defence?

L The capital of Angola?

Answers **1** Action **2** Bosporus **3** Cartographer **4** Dodoma **5** Eucharist
6 Frog **7** Genetics **8** Hegira **9** Ischia **10** Jarre **11** Karate **12** Luanda

Quiz 57 Alphabet

M Feast day which falls on 29 September?

N The scientific study of the nervous system?

O The Roman goddess of plants?.

P Legendary bird that consumes itself with fire every 500 years and rises from the ashes?

Q Process of sticking together two layers of fabric enclosing a soft substance?

R Infectious disease of cattle, also known as cattle plague?

S The dominant ethnic group of Sri Lanka?

T Saint who was a trusted disciple of St. Paul?

U Milk heated to 132°c for 1 second and packed in an air-tight container to give a long-lasting shelf life?

V What game was invented by William G. Morgan at the Holyoke YMCA Massachussetts in 1895?

W Nocturnal American bird famous for its distinctive call?

Y An often tattooed gangster, who, in Japan, is the equivalent to the Sicilian Mafia?

Answers cont **13** Michaelmas **14** Nurology **15** Ops **16** Phoenix **17** Quilting **18** Rinderpest **19** Sinhalese **20** Timothy **21** UHT **22** Volleyball **23** Whippoorwill **24** Yakuza

Alphabet — Quiz 58

A New Zealand bird with no tail?

B A dark red root vegetable that may be eaten in salads or pickled?

C This peninsula juts into the Black Sea?

D Turf cut out by golf player's club?

E Short musical piece or exercise?

F In music, with loud and forcible expression?

G Triangular piece let into garment?

H Greek physcian, commonly regarded as the father of medicine?

I Word meaning undeveloped?

J One of the large veins on each side of the throat?

K Eskimo canoe of light framework?

L Ritual washing of fingers during a Mass?

Answers **1** Apteryx **2** Beetroot **3** Crimea **4** Divot **5** Etude **6** Forzando **7** Gusset **8** Hippocrates **9** Inchoate **10** Jugular **11** Kayak **12** Lavabo

Quiz 58 — Alphabet

M Tropical tree or shrub, close to shore?

N Outer casing of aeroplane's engine?

O Moulding with a double curve?

P A litter used in Japan?

Q Seasoned ball of fish or meat?

R Receptacle for relics?

S Sickly yellow or yellowish brown colour?

T Shilling of Henry VIII's time?

U Courteous?

V Aboriginal of Sri Lanka?

W Small soft crisp cake?

Y A country bumpkin?

Answers cont **13** Mangrove **14** Narcelle **15** Ogee **16** Palanquin **17** Quenelle **18** Reliquary **19** Sallow **20** Tester **21** Urbane **22** Vedda **23** Waffle **24** Yokel

Alphabet — Quiz 59

A Major seaport of Northern Egypt?

B Large seabird, so named because of the supposed stupidity they show in landing on ships and allowing themselves to be caught?

C Term applied to hereditary classes on the Indian sub-continent ?

D A mobile platform for a film or video camera?

E River which was used in the irrigation projects of ancient Mesopotamia?

F Type of armless chair with high seat and low straight back? . . . .

G English clown (1779-1837) whose nickname Joey came into colloquial use as a synonym for clown?

H What is measured on the 'Mohs' scale?

I A short, simple, descriptive poem idealizing country life?

J A small measure for alcoholic drinks, especially spirits?

K Chess player who, in 1985, became the youngest ever world champion?

L The cross which was the symbol of Joan of Arc?

Answers **1** Alexandria **2** Booby **3** Caste **4** Dolly **5** Euphrates **6** Farthingale **7** Grimaldi **8** Hardness **9** Idyll **10** Jigger **11** Kasparov **12** Lorraine

Quiz 59 Alphabet

M Former popular title of the Emperor of Japan which means literally 'the Gate of the Imperial Palace'?

N What is the name of the notch in an arrow into which the bowstring fits?

O White-flowed species of iris?

P Tree, whose wood is used in the manufacture of golf clubs?

Q A soft dumpling into which meat, fish or poultry has been mixed?

R White full-length linen robe worn by bishops?

S Scottish sailor who was the inspiration for Defoe's 'Robinson Crusoe'?

T Scene of the Gunfight at the OK Corral in 1881?

U Museum in Florence opened to the public by the Medici family in the 17th century?

V ---------- Garavani, Italian fashion designer?

W What is derived from the Irish word 'usquebaugh`' meaning water of life'?

Z 6th century BC Hebrew priest and prophet to whom a book the Old Testament is attributed?

Answers cont **13** Mikado **14** Nock **15** Orris **16** Persimmon **17** Quenelle **18** Rochet **19** Selkirk **20** Tombstone **21** Uffizi **22** Valentino **23** Whisky **24** Zechariah

Alphabet — Quiz 60

A Having a sting?

B Beam across an opening?

C Order of marine mammals, including dolphins?

D Beggar's wench, or in Shakespeare, a mistress?

E Small case for needles?

F Flour or meal of corn, nuts or roots?

G A deep ravine?

H A variety of French bean?

I Adjective meaning beginning?

J Reddish orange gem?

K Japanese silk picture?

L Island in Aegean Sea, also known as Mytilene and home of Sappho?

Answers **1** Aculiate **2** Breastsummer **3** Cetacea **4** Doxy **5** Etui **6** Farina **7** Gorge **8** Haricot **9** Incipient **10** Jacinth **11** Kakemono **12** Lesbos

Quiz 60 — Alphabet

M In Australia, an Aboriginal hut?

N Of the night?

O Volcanic mineral of pale green colour?

P High mountain near Delphi in Greece?

Q Fixed number of members?

R A dwarf in German folklore who requires a maiden to guess his name or give up her first child?

S Hunting expedition, especially in Africa or India (now primarily a tourist activity)?

T Driver of a team?

U The Latin name of two constellations, minor and major?

V Sacred writings of the ancient Hindus?

W Former province of north-west Germany?

Y Bring forth young animals?

Answers cont **13** Miamia **14** Nocturnal **15** Olivine **16** Parnassus **17** Quorum **18** Rumplestiltskin **19** Safari **20** Teamster **21** Ursa **22** Vedas **23** Westphalia **24** Yean

Alphabet — Quiz 61

A Free from blame?

B Canopy over an altar?

C A bevelled edge?

D Block-forming body of pedestal?

E Another name for Irish Gaelic?

F Religious festival in Spain?

G Large sturdy antelope of African Savanna?

H Female deer?

I A twentieth century movement in poetry, aiming at concentration?

J Sideways movement of a balking horse?

K A small kitchen or part of a room equipped as a kitchen?

L Recipient of a legacy?

Answers **1** Absolve **2** Baldachin **3** Chamfer **4** Dado **5** Erse **6** Fiesta **7** Gnu **8** Hind **9** Imagism **10** Jib **11** Kitchenette **12** Legatee

Quiz 61 — Alphabet

M Sound of a cat?

N Mind, intellect or common sense?

O Cast amorous glances?

P Turn aside the course of justice?

Q Hair brushed up above the forehead especially favoured by Teddy Boys?

R Shaky, threatening to collapse?

S City in South West Spain?

T The ship worm?

U Living in a city or town?

V Watching, especially at night, often for religious purposes?

W A human being who changes into a wolf?

Y Piece of enclosed ground, usually attached to a building?

Answers cont **13** Mewl **14** Nous **15** Ogle **16** Pervert **17** Quiff **18** Rickety
19 Seville **20** Teredo **21** Urban **22** Vigil **23** Werewolf **24** Yard

Alphabet — Quiz 62

A A light, malleable ductile silvery-white metallic element?

B Rough prickly shrub?

C The most Northern of the Ionian Islands?

D Annual land tax 10th century?

E A suspension of one liquid in another?

F Voice used by male altos?

G Norwegian composer of 'Peer Gynt'?

H An estate in Spanish speaking countries?

I Large South American lizard?

J Very short time?

K Kind of course narrow cloth?

L An ancient cavalry weapon, with a spearhead at the end of a long shaft?

Answers **1** Aluminium **2** Bramble **3** Corfu **4** Danegold **5** Emulsion **6** Falsetto **7** Greig **8** Hacienda **9** Iguana **10** Jiffy **11** Kersey **12** Lance

Quiz 62 Alphabet

M Small tropical fish with protruding eyes?

N A traditional form of greeting in India?

O Not reflecting light?

P The study of rocks and their composition?

Q Having four parts?

R Revoke?

S Meaning of the Latin phrase compos mentis?

T Repetition of the same word?

U Officer of court to guide people?

V Wart, usually on the foot?

W Threads woven into and crossing the warp?

Y Race of brutes in 'Gulliver's Travels'?

Answers cont **13** Mudskiper **14** Namaste **15** Opaque **16** Petrology **17** Quaternary **18** Rescind **19** Sane **20** Tautology **21** Usher **22** Verruca **23** Weft **24** Yahoo

Alphabet — Quiz 63

A The only US state with the letter 'Z' in its name?

B Joyous, cheerful or gay?

C Capriform antelope found in alps?

D Ten footed crustacean?

E Weaken physically?

F Inconsistent in loyalties or affections?

G Twelve dozen?

H Stained sycamore wood?

I Overflow?

J Shake noisily?

K Capital city of Afghanistan?

L Lustful, wanton – tending to libidinousness?

Answers **1** Arizona **2** Blithe **3** Chamois **4** Decapod **5** Enervate **6** Fickle **7** Gross **8** Harewood **9** Inundate **10** Judder **11** Kabul **12** Lascivious

Quiz 63 — Alphabet

M Pertaining to work of a humiliating or servile nature?

N A tumour consisting of nerve tissue?

O Enclosure with fruit trees?

P Equality in status?

Q Heavy flat ring of iron for throwing in a game?

R One who relapses into crime?

S Staying power?

T Cards used in fortune-telling?

U Large bone in the forearm?

V Variety entertainment, a play with songs and dances?

W Wordy nonsense?

Y Sharp tug or jerk?

Answers cont **13** Menial **14** Neuron **15** Orchard **16** Parity **17** Quoit **18** Recidivist **19** Stamina **20** Tarot **21** Ulna **22** Vaudeville **23** Waffle **24** Yank

Alphabet

Quiz 64

A A plane surface bounded by two circles, example a washer?

B Prayer book used by Roman Catholic clergy?

C Internal diameter of a gun?

D Period of 10 years?

E Blockage of blood vessel?

F Pincer-like medical equipment used for for removing in surgery?

G Fierce brown bear of the Rocky Mountains?

H A Middle Eastern food made from chick peas?

I A word game, where each player guesses objects in view?

J King of Judah?

K A woollen rug from the Middle East?

L That which is left to me by will?

Answers **1** Annulus **2** Breviary **3** Calibre **4** Decade **5** Embolism **6** Forceps
7 Grizzly **8** Hummus **9** I-Spy **10** Josiah **11** Kilim **12** Legacy

Quiz 64

Alphabet

M A song for several voices without music?

N The class of nobles?

O The largest bird in the world?

P Relating to dinner?

Q Odd behaviour?

R A light spar of wood?

S Hot sand-laden wind in North Africa?

T The number four?

U Beyond the visible end of the violet spectrum?

V Substance to kill worms?

W A newly weaned child?

Z Worship of animals?

Answers cont **13** Madrigal **14** Noblesse **15** Ostrich **16** Prandial **17** Quizzical **18** Ribband **19** Simoon **20** Tetrad **21** Ultraviolet **22** Vermicide **23** Weanling **24** Zoolatry

Alphabet

Quiz 65

A Medical condition involving hair loss?

B With two chambers (legislative)?

C The deformed slave in 'The Tempest'?

D Archaic term for handcuffs?

E The sweet-brier; perhaps honeysuckle?

F Long pipe-like ulcer with narrow mouth?

G An old cat?

H Spanish gentleman by birth?

I To dwell in,, to occupy?

J Ancient city in Dead Sea valley?

K A small two-masted vessel?

L Lake or arm of the sea?

Answers **1** Alopecia **2** Bicameral **3** Caliban **4** Darbies **5** Eglantine
6 Fistula **7** Grimalkin **8** Hidalgo **9** Inhabit **10** Jericho **11** Ketch **12** Lough

Quiz 65 Alphabet

M One of the spaces in a net?

N General term for drugs?

O Compound of oxygen with another element?

P Appease?

Q Fundamental essence of a thing?

R The killing of a King?

S Brown colour, of a faded photo for example?

T Bones forming part of the foot, where the leg is articulated?

U Piece of high ground?

V Small rodent?

W Tiny?

Z Fermentation?

Answers cont **13** Mesh **14** Narcotics **15** Oxide **16** Pacify **17** Quiddity **18** Regicide **19** Sepia **20** Tarsus **21** Upland **22** Vole **23** Weeny **24** Zymosis

Alphabet — Quiz 66

A Jewish high priest?

B A mound of earth or stones at a burial place?

C Procession on horseback?

D Small ornamental writing desk?

E Sudden rise of the tide in a river?

F Dumbfound?

G Twilight or dusk?

H A type of pantomime?

I The 'Gem' state is the nickname of which USA state?

J A bringer of bad luck?

K Greek letter?

L One suffering from leprosy?

Answers **1** Ananias **2** Barrow **3** Cavalcade **4** Davenport **5** Eagre **6** Flabbergast **7** Gloaming **8** Harlequinade **9** Idaho **10** Jinx **11** Kappa **12** Leper

Quiz 66 — Alphabet

M The Roman god of war?

N A bit chilly?

O Spoken, not written?

P City standing on river Seine?

Q An expedition in search of something definite?

R An uproar or disturbance?

S Any of the female prophetesses of classical times, each believed to be inspired by an individual deity?

T Author of 'War and Peace' who died in 1910?

U An organisation of independent states with its headquarters in New York City?

V A small document or receipt, often used as substitute for money?

W Small bundle, often of money?

Y Liquid food made from fermented milk?

Answers cont **13** Mars **14** Nippy **15** Oral **16** Paris **17** Quest **18** Rumpus
19 Sibyl **20** Tolstoy **21** United Nations **22** Voucher **23** Wad **24** Yoghurt

Alphabet

Quiz 67

A Roughness, harshness?

B Imaginary terror?

C Mass of material stuck together?

D What is taught?

E The study of insects?

F Bounded, limited?

G Slowly moving mass of ice?

H Bush or small tree bearing nuts?

I Call in question?

J Drug from Mexican climbing plant?

K A ship's inner keel, which binds the floor-timbers to the outer keel?

L Gallery or arcade with open side?

Answers **1** Asperity **2** Bugbear **3** Clot **4** Doctrine **5** Entomology **6** Finite **7** Glacier **8** Hazel **9** Impeach **10** Jalap **11** Keelson **12** Loggia

Quiz 67 Alphabet

M Mohammedan place of worship?

N Tide soon after moon's 1st and 3rd quarters?

O Code name for Allied invasion of France?

P Magnificent, splendid display?

Q A small game bird of the partridge family?

R Monetary unit of Iran?

S Horizontal sheet of cloud?

T Display of temper, especially in a child?

U Ancient ruined city in in Yucatan, Mexico and once capital of the Maya empire?

V Informal, short term for university?

W Childishly sel-willed?

Z African equine with stripes?

Answers cont **13** Mosque **14** Neap **15** Overlord **16** Pomp **17** Quail **18** Rial **19** Stratus **20** Tantrum **21** Uxmal **22** Varsity **23** Wayward **24** Zebra

Alphabet — Quiz 68

A Instrument for taking altitudes? .

B A melee?

C In a running position?

D The smallest and lowest lying of the Scandinavian countries?

E One of the main rivers of Germany?

F One part of a book published by instalments?

G First range of planks laid on ship's bottom?

H Fruit of the hawthorn?

I Arrange like the scales of a fish?

J The policy for separating black people?

K Optical toy invented by Sir David Brewster in 1817?

L Designer of the Suez Canal?

Answers **1** Astrolabe **2** Brouhaha **3** Courante **4** Denmark **5** Elbe **6** Fascicle **7** Gabboard **8** Haw **9** Imbricate **10** Jim Crow **11** Kaleidoscope **12** Lesseps

Quiz 68 — Alphabet

M Middle line of the body?

N Slang term for police spy?

O Drug produced from poppy seeds?

P A shawl made from the soft underfleece of goats?

Q Set of questions designed for entertainment?

R Capital city of Virginia USA?

S Lecturers in ancient Greece?

T Small unimportant details?

U Anointing in oil?

V Resistance to flow?

W Kingdom of west Saxons?

Y Fox hunter's cry?

Answers cont **13** Mesial **14** Nark **15** Opium **16** Pashmina **17** Quiz **18** Richmond **19** Sophists **20** Trivia **21** Unction **22** Viscosity **23** Wessex **24** Yoicks

Alphabet — Quiz 69

A The top or highest point?

B A shady, leafy shelter or recess?

C Medical term for St. Vitus's dance?

D The little grebe?

E Filled-up, like a mosquito, after eating greedily?

F Easily snapped or shattered?

G Sudden rush of wind?

H A dirty, run-down dwelling?

I The Greek rainbow goddess, messenger of the gods?

J Having no flap on a jacket?

K Barrier in a river?

L Reading desk in church?

Answers **1** Acme **2** Bower **3** Chorea **4** Dabchick **5** Engorged **6** Fragile **7** Gust **8** Hovel **9** Iris **10** Jetted **11** Kiddle **12** Lectern

Quiz 69 Alphabet

M Adapted for one eye?

N Large short horned Indian antelope?

O Of an oracle?

P Hawaiian volcano goddess, or Brizilian footballer?

Q One of four offspring?

R Fish or meat coated with breadcrumbs?

S Small mouse-like anima with a long snout?

T Person who has left a will at death?

U Greek letter Y?

V 18th century French author of 'Candide'?

W Twist out of shape?

Y Fishing town in Norfolk England?

Answers cont **13** Monocular **14** Nilgai **15** Oracular **16** Pele **17** Quadruplet **18** Rissole **19** Shrew **20** Testate **21** Upsilon **22** Voltaire **23** Warp **24** Yarmouth

Alphabet

Quiz 70

A French province west of the Rhine?

B Archaic word for a madhouse or lunatic asylum?

C Musical scale proceeded by semi-tomes?

D Type of hat, or horse race?

E King Arthur's magic sword?

F Due from son or daughter?

G Large rich cream cake?

H The mountain home of the snow leopard?

I Wild goat of Europe, North Affrica and Asia, with backward-curving horns?

J Apostle who betrayed Christ?

K Blood relationship?

L Chief opera house in Italy?

Answers **1** Alsace Bedlam **3** Chromatic **4** Derby **5** Excaliber **6** Filial
7 Gateau **8** Himalayas **9** Ibex **10** Judas **11** Kindred **12** La Scala

Quiz 70 Alphabet

M Title of the Emperor of Japan?

N Out of the way corner?

O Edible bivalve?

P Breed of horse from Northern France?

Q Fruit related to the pear?

R Russian monetary unit?

S What has a central pin called a gnomen?

T Bride's outfit?

U City of west central Netherlands?

V German invaders who destroyed works of art in the 14th century

W Old English word meaning 'wooded country'?

Y Mongolian's circular tent?

Answers cont **13** Mikado **14** Nook **15** Oyster **16** Percheron **17** Quince **18** Rouble **19** Sundial **20** Trousseau **21** Utrecht **22** Vandals **23** Weald **24** Yurt

Alphabet — Quiz 71

A In Roman times, the mother of Caligula?

B In the Bible, the youngest son of Jacob and Rachel?

C A state in northern Mexico, which gave its name to a dog?

D Athletic event comprising of 10 disciplines?

E Pertaining to race?

F A railway up the side of a hill?

G The most virtuous knight of the round table?

H Any plant that turns its face to the sun?

I Angry?

J A person who takes on lots of different jobs?

K Crest of a hill?

L Blood-sucking worm?

Answers **1** Agrippina **2** Benjamin **3** Chihuahua **4** Desquanate **5** Ethnic **6** Funicular **7** Galahad **8** Heliotrope **9** Irate **10** Jack of all trades **11** knap **12** Leech

Quiz 71 Alphabet

M Italian composer, whose works include the opera 'Amahl and the night visitors'?

N The world's only Hindu kingdom?

O British author of 'Look Back In Anger'?

P An Indian or far eastern pyramidal temple of many storeys?

Q Attractive virtue, old fashioned?

R A stone slab, discovered in1799 which provided the key to deciphering heiroglyphics?

S English poet drowned in the Ligurian Sea, Italy in 1822?

T Round musical instrument to shake and bang?

U Acronym for the organisation that aids education and child and maternal health in developing countries?

V Study of viruses?

W A wooden panelled lining applied to walls of a room?

X Heavy inert gas?

Answers cont **13** Menotti **14** Nepal **15** Osborne **16** Pagoda **17** Quaint **18** Rosetta stone **19** Shelley **20** Tambourine **21** UNICEF **22** Vitrology **23** Wainscot **24** Xenon

Alphabet — Quiz 72

A Alcoholic drink as appetiser?

B A digit in binary negation 0 or 1?

C Nursery for babies?

D Capacity, 10 litres?

E Speech in praise?

F British comedian who sang to his ukulele?

G Judge of good eating and drinking?

H Language of Northern India?

I Constantinople's modern name?

J English golfer, winner of the 1970 US Open Championship?

K Green parrot?

L The third book of the Old Testament?

Answers **1** Aperitif **2** Bit **3** Creche **4** Decalitre **5** Eulogy **6** Formby
7 Gastronomic **8** Hindi **9** Istanbul **10** Jacklin **11** Kea **12** Leviticus

Quiz 72 — Alphabet

M A horse's bridle?

N 16th century French physician, and author of a book of prophecies?

O A group of eight, especially singers?

P Term applied to the colours red, yellow and blue?

Q Military exercise of tilting at a post?

R The imaginary European country and setting for Anthony Hope's 'Prisoner of Zenda'?

S Largest island of the Inner Hebrides?

T A member of an ancient Germanic people from Jutland?

U Coincidence in pitch?

V Series of short sentences?

W A sorcerer?

Y Another name for green woodpecker?

Answers cont **13** Martingale **14** Nostradamus **15** Octet **16** Primary
17 Quintain **18** Ruritania **19** Skye **20** Teuton **21** Unison **22** Versicle
23 Wizard **24** Yaffle

Alphabet — Quiz 73

A A deep blue, like the colour of a clear blue sky?

B What is the nickname of the USA state of Kentucky?

C A British seaweed?

D Minister of a church?

E Interpretation of scripture?

F Limp or wrinkled?

G What is the nickname of the USA state New Hampshire?

H Greek epic poet, author of the 'Iliad'?

I Image or statue?

J Jawbone or cheek?

K Small hill?

L Allowance of food or clothing for retainers?

Answers **1** Azure **2** Blue Grass **3** Carrageen **4** Deacon **5** Exegesis **6** Flaccid **7** Granite **8** Homer **9** Icon **10** Jowl **11** Knoll **12** Livery

Quiz 73 Alphabet

M Series of private stables?

N Racing tip that professes to being ‘a certainty’?

O Outside the bounds or propriety?

P South African author of ‘Cry, the Beloved Country’?

Q Complaining, peevish?

R Small stream?

S US General, nicknamed ‘Stormin’ Norman’?

T Swing turn in skiing?

U Mountain range in Central Asia?

V Tenor member of violin family?

W A character destined to wander the world eternally as punishment for mocking Christ on the day he was crucified?

Y Herb found on waste ground?

Answers cont **13** Mews **14** Nap **15** Outre **16** Paton **17** Querulous **18** Rill **19** Schwarzkopf **20** Telemark **21** Ural **22** Viola **23** Wandering Jew **24** Yarrow

Alphabet — Quiz 74

A One who has retired from the world?

B The knight who took the dying King Arthur to the ferry for his voyage to Avalon?

C A French town famous for lace and porcelain?

D Species of ephemera used in fly fishing?

E Without accent or stress?

F A religious decree issued by a Muslim leader?

G Picturesque cave?

H Handle of a dagger?

I The study of icons?

J The traditional pirate flag?

K Green insect like a cricket?

L Order of insects such as butterflies?

Answers **1** Anchorite **2** Bedivere **3** Chantilly **4** Drake **5** Enclitic **6** Fatwa **7** Grotto **8** Haft **9** Iconolatry **10** Jolly Roger **11** Katydid **12** Lepidoptera

Quiz 74

Alphabet

M Shakespeare's most celebrated tragedy?

N Inflammation of the kidneys?

O Small bone in the middle ear?

P Russian word meaning destruction?

Q Another name for calcium oxide?

R An ardent male lover?

S Starchy foodstuff from palms?

T Stuffing and mounting animal skins?

U Pendulous organ providing milk?

V Duct-shaped?

W Strip of leather between sole and upper?

Y Large humped animal from Tibet?

Answers cont **13** Macbeth **14** Nephritis **15** Ossicle **16** Pogrom
17 Quicklime **18** Romeo **19** Sago **20** Taxidermy **21** Udder **22** Vasiform
23 Welt **24** Yak

Alphabet — Quiz 75

A Arched or domed roof in church?

B Military rank immediately above a Colonel?

C Pungent condiment of fruit, acid and herbs?

D Body of religious instruction?

E Eskimo found from Greenland to Alaska?

F A swishing sound, as made by a long silk dress?

G Colour between beige and grey?

H Rope with a noose for horses?

I Over-run or to swarm over?

J The Jewish quarter in a town?

K Whip of hide as punishment in Turkey?

L Zinc ornament like jewel used in theatre?

Answers **1** Apse **2** Brigadier **3** Chutney **4** Doctrine **5** Esquimau **6** Froufrou **7** Grege **8** Halter **9** Infest **10** Jewry **11** Kourbash **12** Logie

Quiz 75 — Alphabet

M Custom of being married to only one person?

N Carved piece of ivory worn by Japanese?

O Syrup of honey and vinegar?

P Large thick skinned mammal?.

Q To interrogate?

R Inventor of waterproof watch?

S Large knife?

T Figure with four angles and four sides?

U Salt Lake City is the capital of which US State?

V Wife of a viceroy?

W Good for nothing?

X Fear of strangers?

Answers cont **13** Monogamy **14** Netsuke **15** Oxymel **16** Pachyderm **17** Quiz **18** Rolex **19** Snickersnee **20** Tetragon **21** Utah **22** Vicereine **23** Wasterel **24** Xenophobia

Alphabet — Quiz 76

A One of the brightest stars?

B Elizabethan house in Stamford, Lincs, seat of the Cecil family?

C Cheese originally made in Glamorgan?

D Inventor of the motor cycle?

E Watery tract in Florida?

F Ornamently finishing off apex of roof?

G Summerhouse, usually in the garden with a view?

H British politician, former deputy leader of the Labour party and shadow home secretary?

I Latin for 'by that very fact or act'?

J Youngest son of Jacob and Leah?

K Dull brownish yellow colour often worn by the army?

L Labourer for unloading cargo?

Answers **1** Arcturus **2** Burghley **3** Caerphilly **4** Daimler **5** Everglades **6** Finial **7** Gazebo **8** Hattersley **9** Ipso facto **10** Judah **11** Khaki **12** Lumper

Quiz 76 — Alphabet

M The half sister of King Arthur?

N Province of Northern Spain, whose capital is Pamplona?

O Of the mouth?

P A sea bird with large pouch for catching and storing fish?

Q To make trivial objections?

R The ensign of royalty?

S Jewish sect of unbelievers?

T Large, fast-swimming food fish?

U Being in a definite place?

V Technical name for smallpox?

W A family of small singing birds?

Y Two complementary principles of chinese philosophy?

Answers cont **13** Morgan le Fay **14** Navarre **15** Oscular **16** Pelican
17 Quibble **18** Regalia **19** Sadducees **20** Tuna **21** Ubeity **22** Variola
23 Warblers **24** Yin and Yang

Alphabet — Quiz 77

A System of collodial particles dispersed in air?

B Consisting of two terms?

C Popular sport fish found in rivers?

D Inventor of bicycle tyre?

E Low tree or shrub with black berries?

F Fruitfulness?

G Over shoe of rubber?

H District behind that lying along the coast?

I Saturate with dye?

J Desert rat?

K Hindu god of love?

L Not yet revealed, especially of an infectious disease?

Answers **1** Aerosol **2** Binominal **3** Chub **4** Dunlop **5** Elder **6** Fecundity **7** Galosh **8** Hinterland **9** Imbue **10** Jerboa **11** Kama **12** Latent

Quiz 77

Alphabet

M Fear of mice?

N Small, tailed amphibian?

O Changing of colour, as in an opal?

P Salted biscuit, eaten especially in Germany and US?

Q Shake or tremble?

R Gape of beak?

S Known as the whale-headed stork?

T Of the third order?

U Amount by which a bottle falls short from being full?

V In Hindu religion, supreme cosmic deity?

W Smaller species of kangaroo?

X Stone or rock in a system in which it does not belong?

Answers cont **13** Musomania **14** Newt **15** Opalescence **16** Pretzel
17 Quake **18** Rictus **19** Shoebill **20** Tertiary **21** Ullage **22** Varuna
23 Wallaby **24** Xenolith

Alphabet

Quiz 78

A Mixture of metals?

B Female spirit whose wail portends evil?

C A variety of sprouting broccoli?

D The ten commandments collectively?

E To act on by songs of sorcery?

F King of Egypt in 1936?

G Instrument for measuring electric currents?

H Inventor of the spinning jenny?

I An extinct Mesozoic reptile with a porpoise-like body and limbs like paddles?

J English gold coin?

K Formerly a title bestowed on Chinese Emperors and Mongol and Turk rulers?

L English poet whose works include 'The Whitsun Weddings'?

Answers **1** Alloy **2** Banshee **3** Calabrese **4** Decalogue **5** Enchant **6** Farouk **7** Galvanometer **8** Hargreaves **9** Ichthyosaur **10** Jacobus **11** Khan **12** Larkin

Quiz 78

Alphabet

M Only metal that is liquid at normal temperature?

N The longest river to flow into the Mediterranean?

O Progeny?

P Spread through?

Q Quarter of the circumference of a circle?

R German Nazi politician, foreign minister under Hitler?

S Sacred dung beetle of Egypt?

T Greek philosopher, who believed that water was the origin of all things and predicted a solar eclipse on 28 May 565 BC?

U Term used for criminals and their associates collectively?

V Person acting as a governor of a country?

W A family of insects and grubs that eat leaves of plants?

Y Fibre, cotton, wool or flax?

Answers cont **13** Mercury **14** Nile **15** Offspring **16** Pervade **17** Quadrant **18** Ribbentrop **19** Scarab **20** Thales **21** Underworld **22** Viceroy **23** Weevils **24** Yarn

Alphabet — Quiz 79

A Fear of pain?

B Inventor of ship's propeller?

C Type of pastry to make eclairs?

D Food fish sold as rock salmon?

E Beginning of era in history?

F Created by imagination?

G Prancing about exultantly, yet in a noisy, clumsy way?

H Rope for raising a sail?

I Ungrateful person?

J Mirthful?

K Insect eating bird type of hawk?

L Beetle with long antennae?

Answers **1** Algomania **2** Brunel **3** Choux **4** Dogfish **5** Epoch **6** Fictive **7** Galumph **8** Halyard **9** Ingrate **10** Jocular **11** Kite **12** Longicorn

Quiz 79 Alphabet

M The ancestor of all domestic breeds of duck?

N Absence of knowledge?

O Form of oxygen with three atoms to the molecule?

P Policy of avoiding war?

Q Pack of fox hounds?

R Turned up, especially of the nose?

S Adapted for climbing?

T Relating to having a sense of touch?

U A sub-machine gun of Israeli design?

V Abnormal local dilation?

W Facetious person?

Y Bookbinding in limp leather?

Answers cont **13** Mallard **14** Nescience **15** Ozone **16** Pacifism **17** Quorn **18** Retrousse **19** Scansorial **20** Tactile **21** Uzi **22** Varicose **23** Wag **24** Yapp

Alphabet — Quiz 80

A The most famous of the Greek philosophers?

B The full name for a coot?

C Raised track across marshes and fens?

D Megalithic tomb, flat stone laid upon uprights?

E An abridgement or condensed account?

F Small cask for liquids?

G Fear of women?

H Ugly old woman?

I Laying on colour thickly?

J An adherent of an Indian religion aligned to Brahmanism?

K Overhanging wall of rocks?

L Clothes for a new born baby?

Answers **1** Aristotle **2** Baldicoot **3** Causeway **4** Dolmen **5** Epitome **6** Firkin **7** Gynomania **8** Hag **9** Impasto **10** Jain **11** Krans **12** Layette

Quiz 80 — Alphabet

M Solid part of embattled parapet?

N One of the negroid races in Malaysia?

O Swing like a pendulum?

P Food fish found in Mediterranean?

Q Of the number five?

R Radioactive metallic element discovered in 1898?

S Ocean bird feeds on fish caught by other birds?

T Showy, without taste or worth?

U Working in secret, the police often operate this way?

V Transparent flap for a helmet?

W Roll or wallow?

Z Metallic element?

Answers cont **13** Merlon **14** Negrito **15** Oscillate **16** Pilchard **17** Quinary **18** Radium **19** Skua **20** Tawdry **21** Undercover **22** Visor **23** Welter **24** Zirconium

SECTION 3

Multiple choice

Multiple choice — Quiz 1

1 What was the nickname of Andrew Jackson, the 7th President of the US?
a Old Ironboots **b** Old Hickery **c** Old Glory **d** Old Thunder

2 What type of clouds produce rain or snow?
a Nimbus **b** Cirrus **c** Cumulus **d** Strato

3 What, in Russia, would be contained in Samovar?
a Vodka **b** Coins **c** Tea **d** Ashes

4 How many periods are there in a hockey game?
a 2 **b** 3 **c** 4 **d** 5

5 What was partitioned along the 38th parallel in 1945 after Japan's surrender?
a Korea **b** Tokyo **c** The main Japanese island of Honshu
d The East China Sea

6 What is Bruxomaina?
a Compulsive shouting **b** Excessive impulse to write **c** Compulsive and continual crunching of the teeth **d** A morbid impulse to pull out one's own hair

7 What female christian name means 'little she-bear'?
a Selina **b** Ursula **c** Yvette **d** Bertha

8 Who was the vaudeville star known as the 'Last of the Red-Hot Mamas', whose signature tune was 'Some of the these Days'?
a Fanny Bryce **b** Sophie Tucker **c** Bess Flowers **d** Mae West

9 'Seventy years young' is an example of what figure of speech?
a Haplography **b** Euphemism **c** Hyperbole **d** Antiphrasis

10 What port is at the Atlantic end of the Panama Canal?
a Panama **b** San Jose **c** Colon **d** Limon

Answers **1** b **2** a **3** c **4** b **5** a **6** c **7** b **8** b **9** d **10** c

Quiz 2

Multiple choice

1 What does ternary mean?
a In three parts **b** Monthly **c** Periodically **d** Finished

2 Where do pandas come from?
a Malaysia **b** Tibet **c** China **d** Brazil

3 Nostradamus was born in
a Tobruk **b** Cannes **c** Remy **d** Berlin

4 Which USA state is called the 'Bullion State'?
a Missouri **b** California **c** Alaska **d** Hawaii

5 What is 'Origami'?
a Paper folding **b** A drink **c** A drug **d** A dance

6 What is an 'Ounce'?
a Snow leopard **b** Fish **c** Chaffinch **d** Type of mouse

7 What is a 'Loquat'?
a A lozenge **b** A Japanese tree **c** A drink **d** A dance

8 Who wrote 'White Christmas'?
a Lehar **b** Rodgers **c** Charlie Chester **d** Irving Berlin

9 What is 'brass' made up of?
a Copper and zinc **b** Lead and copper **c** Tin and lead **d** Lead and zinc

10 What type of 'curve' is formed by cutting a cone?
a Hyperbola **b** Circle **c** Redian **d** Diameter

Answers 1a 2c 3c 4a 5a 6a 7b 8d 9a 10a

Multiple choice — Quiz 3

1 Who designed and built the first internal combustion automobile?
a Henry Ford **b** Frank Whittle **c** Karl Benz **d** Rudolf Deisel

2 Brass is an alloy of which two minerals?
a copper and tin **b** copper and zinc **c** lead and tin **d** iron and zinc

3 Who said, "Some weasel took the cork out of my lunch"?
a Dean Martin **b** W C Fields **c** Ernest Hemingway **d** James Thurber

4 What was the name of Kevin Costner's character in the movie JFK?
a Clay Shaw **b** Jim Garrison **c** David Ferrie **d** Dean Andrews

5 Which American President was a former director of the FBI?
a Lyndon B Johnson **b** Gerald Ford **c** George Bush **d** Dwight D. Eisenhower

6 What type of musical composition is a Berceuse?
a Music intended for a morning performance **b** An orchestral piece suggesting a rural scene **c** A cradle song **d** A short simple orchestral piece

7 Which pop singer starred in the 1976 Science Fiction movie 'The Man Who Fell To Earth'?
a David Bowie **b** David Essex **c** Sting **d** Mick Jagger

8 By what name was the American business woman born Florence Nightingale Graham, noted for her beauty salons and cosmetics, better known?
a Helena Rubinstein **b** Mary Quant **c** Elizabeth Arden **d** Coco Chanel

9 Who had his mother poisoned because of her criticism of his mistress Poppaea?
a Claudius **b** Caesar **c** Nero **d** Caligula

10 Which classic novel is narrated by Ismael?
a The Last of the Mohicans **b** Moby Dick **c** The Awakening **d** The Raven

Answers 1c 2b 3b 4b 5c 6c 7a 8c 9c 10b

Quiz 4

Multiple choice

1 What is the meaning of 'slalom'?
a Have a nice day **b** A bend in motor racing **c** A downhill ski race **d** Good morning

2 What is a "jerbon"?
a A swordfish **b** A mammal **c** A bottle **d** A wind

3 Where does the 'Black Petrel' come from?
a New Zealand **b** China **c** Morocco **d** Chile

4 What is 'San Serif'?
a Without honour **b** A plant **c** A greeting **d** A type face

5 Which group did 'Mickey Dolenz' belong to?
a The Monkees **b** The Stagers **c** Chicago **d** New Yorkers

6 Who discovered 'penicillin' in 1928?
a Marie Curie **b** Philip Lazures **c** Alexander Fleming **d** Sir John Daws

7 'Krishna Menan' used to be:
a Steel worker **b** Lawyer **c** Doctor **d** History teacher

8 Where is 'Andalucia'?
a Spain **b** Portugal **c** Cuba **d** Mexico

9 The Black swan is native to which country'?
a Canada **b** China **c** Australia **d** South Africa

10 What is the science of 'genetics'?
a Heart-by-pass **b** Slimming **c** Exercise **d** Heredity

Answers 1c 2b 3a 4d 5a 6c 7d 8a 9c 10d

Multiple choice — Quiz 5

1 Where, in 1886, did the first Modern Olympic Games take place?
a Paris **b** Athens **c** London **d** Stockholm

2 Which name, in Norse, means 'ruler of all'?
a Eric **b** Harold **c** Carl **d** Stephen

3 What day is the first day of Lent?
a Shrove Tuesday **b** Ascension Day **c** Pentecost **d** Ash Wednesday

4 Which gas smells like rotten eggs?
a Hydrogen Sulphide **b** Ammonia **c** Ether **d** Nitrous Oxide

5 What was the name of the papyrus craft in which Thor Heyerdale sailed in 1970 from Morocco to Barbados?
a Kon-Tiki **b** Djibouti **c** Tigris **d** Ra II

6 Which office is third in order of Presidential Succession in the US?
a Speaker of the House **b** President Pro Tempore of the Senate
c Secretary of State **d** Attorney General

7 The musical 'High Society' was a remake of which film?
a The Letter **b** Second Chorus **c** His Girl Friday
d The Philadelphia Story

8 If you ordered 'Adam and Eve on a raft' in a restaurant, what dish would you expect to receive?
a Two eggs on toast **b** Danish open sandwich with cheese
c Marmalade on toast **d** Hot dog with ketchup

9 Which one of these songs was not written by Charlie Chaplin?
a Smile **b** Eternally **c** September Song **d** This is my Song

10 Which of these animals can travel the fastest?
a Coyote **b** Greyhound **c** Whippet **d** Jackal

Answers 1b 2a 3d 4a 5c 6a 7d 8a 9d 10a

Quiz 6

Multiple choice

1 What is a computer's 'central processing unit' called?
a Microprocessor **b** CD ROM **c** Agitator **d** Transducer

2 What is a 'remora'?
a Flower **b** Tree **c** Fish **d** Reptile

3 What is jitney?
a Small bus **b** Bicycle **c** Land Rover **d** Fire engine

4 What is 'dysphazia?
a Difficulty in swallowing **b** Kidney failure **c** Irregular heart beat
d Sleep walking

5 What was the 'Underworld' called in Greek mythology?
a Demon Land **b** Hades **c** Valhalla **d** The dark place

6 What is the capital of Zambia?
a St Leonards **b** Princetown **c** Lusaka **d** Colombo

7 Aristotle was the son of a?
a Physician **b** Lawyer **c** Travelling salesman **d** Shopkeeper

8 Where is 'Bilbao'?
a Portugal **b** Spain **c** Brazil **d** Hungary

9 Who discovered the Philippines?
a Drake **b** Raleigh **c** Vasco de Gama **d** Magellan

10 What is 'fly agaric'?
a Fungus **b** Seaweed **c** Drugs **d** Disinfectant

Answers 1a 2c 3a 4a 5b 6c 7a 8b 9d 10a

Multiple choice — Quiz 7

1 What is the name of the soup or stew thickened with okra?
a Chowder **b** Gumbo **c** Bisque **d** Potage

2 What does a cryometer measure?
a Degrees of transparency **b** Pressure of liquids **c** Extremely low temperatures **d** Small temperature changes

3 Which of the Seven Wonders of the Ancient World was at Ephesus?
a The Tomb of Mausolus **b** The Statue of Zeus **c** The Temple of Artemis **d** The Hanging Gardens

4 What colour is melanite ?
a Orange **b** Brown **c** Purple **d** Black

5 Who said: "There cannot be a crisis next week. My schedule is already full"?
a Henry Kissinger **b** Margaret Thatcher **c** Gerald Ford **d** Ronald Reagan

6 Who sculptured 'Behold The Man' ?
a Rodin **b** Moore **c** Epstein **d** Hepworth

7 In which movie did Humphrey Bogart play Captain Philip Francis Queeg?
a China Clipper **b** The African Queen **c** Action in the North Atlantic **d** The Caine Mutiny

8 At which Olympic Games did Bob Beaman smash the world long-jump record?
a Mexico City **b** Munich **c** Tokyo **d** Rome

9 Of the nine muses, who is the muse of history?
a Clio **b** Urania **c** Terpsichore **d** Erato

10 In what capacity was Gerald Peters connected to both Winston Churchill and Elvis Presley?
a He caddied for them both at golf **b** He wrote both their biographies **c** He was their chauffeur **d** He was their private chef

Answers 1b 2a 3c 4d 5a 6c 7d 8a 9a 10c

Quiz 8 — Multiple choice

1 What is the middle note of a 'piano' called?
a D Flat **b** D **c** Middle C **d** F Sharp

2 What is the capital of 'Mongolia?
a Ulan Bator **b** Lisk **c** Paran **d** Delugi

3 What is a 'praetor'?
a Roman magistrate **b** A soldier **c** A ship **d** A shop keeper

4 What is 'pique'?
a A colour **b** High fashion **c** Irritation **d** Cosmetid

5 What is 'logophobia' the fear of?
a Cats **b** Walking **c** Coal **d** Words

6 What is 'endotherm'?
a Warm stream **b** Warm air **c** Warm blooded **d** Warm clothes

7 What is a 'missal'?
a A cloak **b** A message **c** A weapon **d** A church service book

8 What is the currency of Burma?
a Rupees **b** Soldat **c** Gen **d** Kyat

9 Who discovered X-rays?
a Doyle **b** Celsius **c** Roentgen **d** Fermat

10 What is a 'gerenuk'?
a A mammal **b** A soothing balm **c** An insect **d** A flower

Answers 1c 2a 3a 4c 5d 6c 7d 8d 9c 10a

Multiple choice — Quiz 9

1 In 1970 Mission control received the message, "Houston, we've got a problem here", from which spacecraft?
a Apollo 13 **b** Apollo X **c** Apollo 15 **d** Apollo V

2 Which country's flag consists of six horizontal red and white stripes, and a white star on a dark blue background in the top left-hand corner?
a Indonesia **b** Liberia **c** Cuba **d** Chile

3 Which month is traditionally associated with the gemstones Turquoise and Zircon?
a August **b** February **c** July **d** December

4 What are close encounters of the second kind?
a Personal contact **b** Photographic evidence **c** Physical evidence **d** Sighting of a UFO

5 Native to Australia, what is a 'goanna' a type of?
a Sheep **b** Kangaroo **c** Lizard **d** Snake

6 What are scotophobia, nyctophobia, achluophobia and lygophobia all fear of?
a Darkness **b** Dirt **c** Injustice **d** Poverty

7 What are double loops, radial loops, arches, whorles and ulna loops?
a Movements in aerobatics **b** Types of stitches
c Movements in freeskating **d** Fingerprints

8 How many lines are there in a sonnet?
a 8 **b** 10 **c** 12 **d** 14

9 In 1985, what first was achieved by Senator Jake Garn of Utah?
a The first senator to pilot a plane across the US
b The first senator to have his own art exhibition
c The first senator to fly in space
d The first senator to circumnavigate the globe

10 Who is the patron saint of Bookkeepers, Accountants and Tax Collectors ?
a Matthew **b** Dominic **c** Luke **d** Andrew

Answers 1a 2b 3d 4c 5c 6a 7d 8d 9c 10a

Quiz 10

Multiple choice

1 Where was 'Ezra Pound' the American poet born?
a Washington **b** Utah **c** California **d** Idaho

2 What is 'caldera'?
a Basin shaped crater **b** A mountain pass **c** A lake
d A type of rock

3 Who discovered 'Niagara Falls'?
a Columbus **b** David Livingstone **c** Copernicus **d** Isaac Manifold

4 What is a 'quet'?
a A farmer's shed **b** A silk material **c** A fence **d** A guillemot

5 What is an 'omnivore'?
a Eating only animals **b** Eating plants and animals
c Eating only plants **d** Eating only fruit

6 Which islands did 'Captain Cook' discover?
a Hawaii **b** Solomon **c** Japan **d** Marshal

7 Where was 'Charlie Chaplin' born in 1889?
a London **b** New York **c** Birmingham **d** Scotland

8 What is a 'tarentella'?
a A drink **b** An Italian dance **c** A snake **d** A flower

9 What was the capital of the Byzantine Empire called?
a Constantinople **b** Port Said **c** Cairo **d** Istanbul

10 What is 'coppicing'?
a Digging a trench **b** Pruning trees **c** Repairing nets
d Preparing for sea

Answers 1d 2a 3b 4d 5b 6a 7a 8b 9a 10b

Multiple choice — Quiz 11

1 What is agoraphobia the fear of ?
a Air **b** Heights **c** Cats **d** Open spaces

2 Titan, Mimas, Rhea and Dione are just five of the 20 known moons of which planet ?
a Saturn **b** Venus **c** Neptune **d** Uranus

3 What, in baseball slang, is a Molly Putz ?
a A slowly batted ball **b** A player who performs badly **c** A batter who hits weak balls to the outfield **d** A player who lets his team-mates field balls he should go after

4 It is argued that two of America's five great lakes are in fact just one body of water About which two lakes is this said ?
a Ontario and Huron **b** Michigan and Ontario **c** Erie and Michigan **d** Huron and Michigan

5 What instrument was played by Earl "Fatha" Hines ?
a Trombone **b** Cornet **c** Piano **d** Trumpet

6 Magyar is the official language of which country ?
a Poland **b** Portugal **c** Hungary **d** Romania

7 What name is given to the figure of speech which uses of words ironically in an opposite sense to their generally accepted meaning; for example, 'Eighty years young' ?
a Antiphrasis **b** Euphemism **c** Metonomy **d** Paradox

8 Who said, "I don't know anything about music. In my business you don't have to"?
a Madonna **b** Sid Vicious **c** Michael Jackson **d** Elvis Presley

9 In 1861, which U S newspaper publicised its motto: "It is a newspaper's duty to print the news, and raise hell" ?
a The Wall Street Journal **b** The New York Times **c** The Chicago Times **d** The Washington Post

10 What are Trefly, Potent, Avellane and Patonce types of ?
a Typefaces **b** Heraldic emblems **c** Bridges **d** Crosses

---

Answers **1** d **2** a **3** b **4** d **5** c **6** c **7** a **8** d **9** c **10** d

Quiz 12

Multiple choice

1 What is the official language of Syria?
a Turkish **b** German **c** French **d** Arabic

2 What is 'kendo'?
a Type of coffee **b** Bingo in casino **c** A sword **d** Japanese martial arts

3 Who wrote the 'Blue Danube'?
a Johann Strauss **b** Frederick Boeham **c** Conrad Blom **d** Eric Mauser

4 What is a 'harbinger'?
a A drink **b** A messenger **c** A slave **d** A soldier

5 Where was the source of the 'Inca' Empire?
a Peru **b** Argentina **c** Chile **d** Brazil

6 Who wrote the 'James Bond' books?
a Ian Fleming **b** Arthur Hailey **c** Samuel Parker **d** Charles Dole

7 Who was 'Fides'?
a Roman god of Agriculture **b** Roman god of Faith **c** A war ship
d A barracks

8 What is the capital of Afghanistan?
a Kabul **b** Santiago **c** Montevideo **d** Laska

9 Irregular curvature of the 'cornea' causes?
a Astigmatism **b** Short sightedness **c** A squint **d** Cross eyes

10 What is the science of 'chromatics'?
a Colours **b** Chromosomes **c** Mountains **d** Rivers

Answers **1** d **2** d **3** a **4** b **5** a **6** a **7** b **8** a **9** a **10** b

Multiple choice — Quiz 13

1 A cygnet is the young of which animal?
a Goose **b** Duck **c** Stork **d** Swan

2 Onyx is an appropriate gift to celebrate which wedding anniversary?
a Fifth **b** Seventh **c** Ninth **d** Tenth

3 What is meant by the Latin phrase 'a tergo'?
a Socially correct **b** Seriously **c** From behind **d** Promptly

4 What in carnival slang is a Pink Robber?
a A game for small children **b** A pickpocket **c** Any device to get people to play the game **d** A fashionable or slick dresser

5 Which country had a police force called the tonton-macoutes?
a Cuba **b** Kenya **c** Haiti **d** Korea

6 In the Old Testament, who was the husband of Zipporah ?
a Jonah **b** Moses **c** Jethro **d** Noah

7 Which film was Charlie Chaplin's first full talkie?
a City Lights **b** Limelight **c** The Great Dictator **d** Modern Times

8 What would you find in a formicary?
a Snakes **b** Wasps **c** Lizards **d** Ants

9 Who was Ethel Le Neve the mistress of?
a Al Capone **b** King George V of England **c** English wife murderer Dr Crippen **d** British Prime minister David Lloyd George

10 'Sophie's Choice' (William Styron), 'Humboldt's Gift' (Saul Bellow) and 'Shogun' (James Clavell) were all published in which decade?
a 1950s **b** 1960s **c** 1970s **d** 1980s

Answers 1 d 2 b 3 c 4 a 5 c 6 b 7 c 8 d 9 c 10 c

Quiz 14

Multiple choice

1 What is the currency of Mexico?
a Schilling **b** Peso **c** Franc **d** Dollar

2 What is the currency of France
a Franc **b** Peso **c** Pfennig **d** Dinar

3 What are jodhpurs?
a A hard hat **b** Riding breeches **c** A stirrup **d** A horse box

4 Where did Napoleon die?
a Trinidad **b** St Helena **c** Nova Scotia **d** Paris

5 What is fulgent?
a Shining **b** Restful **c** Energetic **d** Dull

6 What is pasted paper and small objects called?
a Mish-mash **b** Charisma **c** Amalgamation **d** Collage

7 What is 'Mauna Loa'?
a An ancient curse **b** A fish **c** A river bed **d** An island

8 What does the musical direction 'Dulcie' mean?
a Prolonged **b** Sweet **c** Loud **d** Soft

9 What is the 'Eisteddford' in Wales?
a Festival of music **b** Banquet **c** A church **d** A cemetery

10 How did 'Robespierre' die?
a Poisoned **b** Guillotined **c** Gassed **d** Hanged

Answers **1** b **2** a **3** b **4** b **5** a **6** d **7** b **8** b **9** a **10** b

Multiple choice — Quiz 15

1 Who said: "Quitting smoking is easy, I've done it hundreds of times"?
a Bette Davis **b** Mark Twain **c** Humphrey Bogart **d** Tallulah Bankhead

2 Who said: "The man who views the world at 50 the same as he did at 20 has wasted 30 years of his life"?
a Albert Einstein **b** Aristotle **c** Sigmund Freud **d** Muhammed Ali

3 Who said: "The surest way to make a monkey out of a man is to quote him"?
a Newt Gingrich **b** Will Rogers **c** Robert Benchley **d** George Bernard Shaw

4 Who said: "The person who knows how to laugh at himself will never cease to be amused"?
a Andy Warhol **b** Al Capp **c** Shirley Maclaine **d** Nancy Astor

5 Who said: "I was married by a judge I should have asked for a jury"?
a Mickey Rooney **b** Groucho Marx **c** Arthur Miller **d** W C Fields

6 Who said: "I've been in more laps than a napkin"?
a Zsa Zsa Gabor **b** Brigitte Bardot **c** Gypsy Rose Lee **d** Mae West

7 Who said: "If the aborigine drafted an IQ test, all of Western civilization would presumably flunk it"?
a George Orwell **b** Mao Tse-tung **c** Joseph Stalin **d** Ghandi

8 Who said: "I have left orders to be awakened at any time in case of national emergency, even if I am in a cabinet meeting?
a Gerald Ford **b** Lyndon Baines Johnson **c** Ronald Reagan **d** Dan Quayle

9 Who said: "I never put on a pair of shoes until I've worn them at least five years"?
a Liberace **b** Samuel Goldwyn **c** Imelda Marcos **d** Woody Allen

10 Who said: "I'm not a real movie star I've still got the same wife I started out with 28 years ago"?
a Will Rogers **b** Bob Hope **c** Gregory Peck **d** John Wayne

Answers 1b 2d 3c 4c 5b 6d 7d 8c 9b 10a

Quiz 16 — Multiple choice

1 Which group of people originated the flamenco dance?
a Aborigines **b** Inuits **c** Gypsies **d** Slaves

2 Which USA state is called the 'Old line state'?
a Washington **b** Ohio **c** Utah **d** Maryland

3 What is a 'jitney'?
a A five cent coin **b** A tavern **c** A village **d** A fair ground

4 What is the capital of Kenya?
a Belize **b** Nairobi **c** Colombo **d** George Town

5 What is a 'coati'?
a A crocodile **b** A racoon **c** A monkey **d** A tiger

6 What is a 'brindise'?
a A drinking song **b** A drink of gin **c** An omelette **d** A fish

7 What does 'doppio' mean?
a Double the preceeding speed **b** Faster **c** Slower **d** Half the proceeding speed

8 What does 'flebile' mean?
a Lissom **b** Happy **c** Tearful **d** Ugly

9 Where was Martin Luther King assassinated?
a Tennessee **b** Washington **c** New York State **d** Alabama

10 Who rejected the love of the nymph 'Echo'?
a Hercules **b** Narcissus **c** Amayou **d** Roland

Answers 1c 2d 3a 4b 5b 6a 7a 8c 9a 10b

Multiple choice — Quiz 17

1 Whose book, 'Profiles of Courage' (1956), won a Pulitzer Prize in 1957?
a Earnest Hemingway **b** Douglas MacArthur **c** John F Kennedy
d Arthur Miller

2 What action by the British in 1930 caused Mahatma Gandhi to lead thousands of his followers on a march to the sea?
a They had threatened to deport several of his relatives **b** They had put a tax on salt **c** They had imposed a severe curfew throughout parts of India **d** They had refused to enter talks on independence

3 Who paid his 'first ever visit' to Paris on 20 May 1927?
a Adolf Hitler **b** Winston Churchill **c** Charles De Gaulle
d Charles Lindbergh

4 Which composer wrote 'Just One of Those Things' and 'Begin the Beguine'?
a Irving Berlin **b** George Gershwin **c** Jerome Kern **d** Cole Porter

5 Who is Agnes Gonxha Bojaxhiu better known as?
a Carman Miranda **b** Mother Teresa of Calcutta **c** Madonna
d Eva Peron

6 Who did Muhammed Ali defeat in Kinshasa, Zaire on 30 October 1974 to regain his World Heavyweight boxing title?
a George Foreman **b** Joe Frazier **c** Leon Spinks **d** Larry Holmes

7 Who said "Anyone seeing a psychiatrist should have his head examined?
a Howard Hughes **b** Sam Goldwyn **c** Bugs Bunny **d** Salvador Dali

8 Who, in 1962, was given the biggest ticker-tape parade in history when New York showered 3,474 tons of paper on him?
a John Glenn **b** John F Kennedy **c** Pope John XXIII
d Alan B Shepard Jr

9 Who won a Golden Globe Award in 1960 for her role in 'Suddenly Last Summer' ?
a Grace Kelly **b** Ingrid Bergman **c** Elizabeth Taylor
d Audrey Hepburn

10 Where did Martin Luther King Jr deliver his "I Have a Dream"speech ?
a Montgomery, Alabama **b** Birmingham, Alabama **c** Washington D C
d Atlanta, Georgia

Answers **1** c **2** b **3** d **4** d **5** b **6** a **7** b **8** a **9** c **10** c

Quiz 18

Multiple choice

1 What is 'lichen'?
a Blueberries **b** A stream **c** A vegetable **d** Tree moss

2 'Claudette Colbert's'real name was?
a Carasbrook **b** Chendell **c** Charlotte **d** Chauchoin

3 What is 'loa'?
a A garland **b** A greeting **c** An island **d** A river

4 What is the currency of Saudi Arabia?
a Shekel **b** Franc **c** Guilder **d** Riyal

5 Where was Bob Hope born?
a England **b** USA **c** Australia **d** France

6 Who wrote the opera 'Cosi Fan Tutte'?
a Cromer **b** Bizet **c** Chopin **d** Mozart

7 What is the capital of Sri Lanka?
a Jackson **b** George Town **c** Colombo **d** Palermo

8 What is a 'Queue'?
a A church ritual **b** A tapestry **c** A plait of hair **d** A loose cloak

9 Who wrote 'Airport'?
a Arthur Hailey **b** William Stuart **c** John Le Carre **d** Barry Fitzgerald

10 What is the unit of 'acceleration' used in geographical survey?
a Fermats **b** Euclids **c** Hertz **d** Galileos

Answers **1** d **2** d **3** b **4** d **5** a **6** d **7** c **8** c **9** a **10** d

Multiple choice — Quiz 19

1 In 'The Magnificent Seven Ride!' (1972), who took over the role made famous by Yul Brynner?
a Lee Marvin **b** Charles Bronson **c** Lee Van Cleef **d** Steve McQueen

2 In the film 'Batman Forever', who plays Batman?
a Michael Keaton **b** Val Kilmer **c** Adam West **d** Adam Sandler

3 In which movie did James Cagney utter the immortal last words: "Look Ma! Top of the World!"?
a Torrid Zone **b** Each Dawn I Die **c** White Heat **d** The Roaring Twenties

4 Which veteran comedy actor played the pink-clad uncle in the 1995 movie 'Arizona Dream'?
a Walter Matthau **b** Sid Caesar **c** Jack Lemmon **d** Jerry Lewis

5 In 'The Brady Bunch Movie' (1995), who played the mother Carol?
a Bet Midler **b** Diane Keaton **c** Shelly Long **d** Michelle Pfeiffer

6 The actress Carol Kane played Woody Allen's first wife in which movie?
a Annie Hall **b** Manhattan **c** A Midsummer Night's Sex Comedy **d** Stardust Memories

7 In the 1958 movie 'Cat on a Hot Tin Roof', what is Elizabeth Taylor's response to Paul Newman's question: "What is the victory of a cat on a hot tin roof?"?
a "I guess I don't know, is it really a victory?" **b** "Its her choice to be there" **c** "Just staying on it, I guess. Long as she can" **d** "She can jump off, anytime she wants"

8 Who directed 'Halloween'(1978), 'The Thing'(1982) and 'Prince of Darkness'(1978)?
a Steven Spielberg **b** Joe Dante **c** Wes Craven **d** John Carpenter

9 In the 1950 movie 'Born Yesterday', Judy Holliday won the Oscar for best-actress. Who recreated her role of Ellie Dawn in the film's 1993 remake?
a Melanie Griffith **b** Greta Scacchi **c** Madeline Kahn **d** Kim Basinger

10 Near the end of the film 'Waterworld' the Smokers pirate ship is sunk and we get a glimpse of the ships name for the first time as it slides beneath the water Is it:
a Titanic **b** Nosmo King **c** Exxon Valdez **d** Mary Celeste

Answers 1 c 2 b 3 c 4 d 5 c 6 a 7 c 8 d 9 a 10 c

Quiz 20

Multiple choice

1 What is lasagna?
a Vinegar **b** A pie **c** A pasta dish **d** Herrings

2 Where will you find the 'koa' tree?
a Kenya **b** Japan **c** China **d** Hawaii

3 What is a 'goy' in Hebrew?
a A Palestinian **b** A gentile **c** King **d** A Jew

4 What is a macaco?
a An insect **b** A rum punch **c** A sweet meat **d** A lemur

5 Who wrote 'Brigadoon'?
a Alan Lerner **b** Rodgers **c** Hammerstein **d** Earl Hines

6 What is a 'sackbut'?
a Clarinet **b** Trombone **c** Trumpet **d** Saxophone

7 'Buffalo Bill's' real name was?
a Frederick Farnsworth **b** Bill Brady **c** George Ramsey **d** William Cody

8 Who wrote the 'Minute Waltz'?
a Mozart **b** Strauss **a** Chopin **a** Debussy

9 What was Nikita Kruschov employed as?
a A shepherd boy **b** A painter **c** A coal miner **d** A bus driver

10 Who wrote 'Brave New World'?
a George Fitzwilliam **b** Aldous Huxley **c** Kevin Starr
d Robert Fleming

Answers **1** c **2** d **3** b **4** d **5** a **6** b **7** d **8** c **9** a **10** b

Multiple choice — Quiz 21

1 Who was Clara Petacci the mistress of?
a Mussolini **b** J Edger Hoover **c** Hitler **d** Idi Amin

2 Apart from Anne Boleyn, which other of his wives did Henry VIII of England have executed?
a Jane Seymour **b** Catherine Parr **c** Catherine Howard **d** Catherine of Aragon

3 Mamie Geneva Doud was the wife of which US President?
a Coolidge **b** Hoover **c** Taft **d** Eisenhower

4 What first was achieved by Dr Kathryn D Sullivan in 1984?
a To carry out a heart-transplant operation **b** To walk in space **c** To go over Niagara Falls in a barrel **d** To abseil down the Empire State Building

5 Who, in 1907, was the first woman to receive the Order of Merit?
a Florence Nightingale **b** Marie Curie **c** Jenny Lind **d** Emmeline Pankhurst

6 Who, in Greek mythology has a name meaning 'all gifts'?
a Ariadne **b** Eurydice **c** Pandora **d** Electra

7 The record breaking stunt woman and U S racing car driver Kitty O'Neil once said "A handicap is not a defeat, but a challenge to conquer". To what handicap was she referring?
a She was deaf **b** She had only partial vision **c** She was a polio sufferer **d** She was paralysed

8 Janet Reno was the first woman to be appointed to what position in U S Government?
a Secretary of state **b** Postmaster-General **c** Attorney General **d** Secretary of Defence

9 Which woman is the subject of an opera by Richard Strauss?
a Helen of Troy **b** Salome **c** Jezebel **d** Aphrodite

10 In which field did Maria Montessori gain eminence?
a Physics **b** Aviation **c** Writing **d** Education

Answers **1** a **2** c **3** d **4** b **5** a **6** c **7** a **8** c **9** b **10** d

Quiz 22 — Multiple choice

1 Who is the Greek god who holds up the Earth?
a Atlas **b** Hercules **c** Thor **d** Pegasus

2 Where was 'Fibonacci' born?
a Egypt **b** Austria **c** Spain **d** Italy

3 Where was the 'ukele' developed?
a China **b** Hawaii **c** France **d** West Indies

4 Where did the word 'vaudeville' originate?
a England **b** France **c** USA **d** Spain

5 Who wrote 'Tinker, Soldier, Sailor, Spy'?
a Dorothy L Sayers **b** John Le Care **c** William Goldsmith
d Michael Foot

6 What distinction has 'Scalar Quantitus'?
a Direction **b** Magnitude **c** Direction but no magnitude
d Magnitude but no direction

7 What is the distance from the Earth to the Sun?
a 76 million miles **b** 83 million miles **c** 86 million miles
d 93 million miles

8 Why was 'Goebbels' banned from joining the army?
a Deformed foot **b** Bad eyesight **c** Kidney problems **d** Bad hearing

9 What is 'orphrey'?
a Looking glass **b** Gold embroidery **c** Seaweed **d** Scallops

10 What was 'George Gershwin's' brother's Christian name?
a Ira **b** Jim **c** Charles **d** Percy

Answers **1**a **2**d **3**b **4**b **5**b **6**d **7**d **8**a **9**b **10**a

Multiple choice — Quiz 23

1 Which novel contains the simple dedication, 'To J R M'?
a Moby Dick b Tobacco Road c Gone With the Wind
d Finnegan's Wake

2 Sidney Carton is the hero of which Dicken's novel ?
a Great Expectations b Bleak House c A Tale of Two Cities
d Pickwick Papers

3 Who wrote 'As You Like It'?
a Francis Bacon b Jerome K Jerome c Ben Jonson
d William Shakespeare

4 Which novel by Robert James Waller was made into a film starring Clint Eastwood and Meryl Streep?
a The Alienist b The Bridges of Madison County c Debt of Honor
d The Celestine Prophesy

5 'The Shape of Things to Come' (H G Wells), 'Tender is the Night'(F Scott Fitzgerald) and 'Grand Hotel'(Vicki Baum) were all first published during which decade?
a Twenties b Thirties c Forties d Fifties

6 Which of Edgar Allan Poe's works begins, 'Once upon a midnight dreary, while I pondered weak and weary'?
a The Haunted Palace b Spirits of the Dead c A Dream Within a Dream d The Raven

7 What is the name of the major poetry collection by Walt Whitman which he continually revised and added to during his lifetime?
a Leaves of Grass b Out of the Cradle Endlessly Rocking
c Speciman Days d Drum Taps

8 Which poet, physician and writer, and member of the American Hall of Fame, wrote 'Old Ironsides', 'Elsie Vanner' and 'The Poet at the Breakfast Table'?
a Edward Taylor b Oliver Wendell Holmes c Henry W Longfellow
d Washington Irving

9 What nationality was George Bernard Shaw?
a Irish b English c American d Welsh

10 Whose works include 'Black Spring' (1938) and 'Tropic of Capricorn' (1939)?
a Nathanael West b Erskine Caldwell c John Steinbeck
d Henry Miller

Answers 1 c 2 c 3 d 4 b 5 b 6 d 7 a 8 b 9 a 10 d

Quiz 24 — Multiple choice

1. What is a ‘hautboy’?
   a Violin **b** Oboe **c** Harp **d** Double Bass

2. What is a ‘canticle’?
   a A quadrille **b** A dance step **c** A biblical hymn **d** A poem

3. Henry Ford was a devout?
   a Conservatist **b** Moslem **c** Pacifist **d** Catholic

4. What is the musical sign for ‘crescendo’?
   a > **b** < **c** ± **d** ≠

5. What is ‘hodophobia’ fear of?
   a Snakes **b** Travel **c** Dogs **d** Rabbits

6. ‘Ho Chi Mihn’ was political leader of which country?
   a Vietnam **b** Japan **c** Tibet **d** Korea

7. What is ‘lassa’ fever spread by?
   a Flies **b** Food **c** Caterpillars **d** Urine

8. Where do ‘okapi’ come from?
   a Morocco **b** Zaire **c** Ethiopia **d** Brazil

9. What is a ‘lamprey’?
   a Fish **b** Bird **c** Turtle **d** Penguin

10. Who wrote ‘Les Miserables’?
    a Philip Louis **b** Roger de Courtney **c** Frederick Lotch
    d Victor Hugo

Answers 1b 2c 3c 4b 5b 6a 7d 8b 9a 10d

Multiple choice — Quiz 25

1 What term was derived from the title of a painting by Monet?
a Expressionism **b** Naturalism **c** Imagism **d** Impressionism

2 In which country did George Bizet set his opera 'The Pearl Fishers'?
a Cyprus **b** Ceylon **c** Jamaica **d** Portugal

3 With 6,137 performance from 1975 to 1990 what musical holds the record for the longest Broadway run ?
a Oh, Calcutta **b** 42nd Street **c** A Chorus Line **d** Grease

4 What 20th-century art movement stresses the fantastic dreamworld of the subconscious?
a Surrealism **b** Op Art **c** Futurism **d** Fauvism

5 What was Adolf Hitler originally employed as?
a A head of a library **b** A chemist **c** A taxi driver **d** A draughtsman

6 Which lyricist was portrayed in the 1948 movie 'Words and Music' by Mickey Rooney?
a Richard Rogers **b** Johnny Mercer **c** Lorenz Hart **d** Ira Gershwin

7 Which French painter left Paris to live and work in Tahiti, where he produced many of his most famous paintings?
a Degas **b** Gauguin **c** Renoir **d** Cezanne

8 What was the American Charles Eames (1907-1978) famous for designing?
a Stage scenery **b** Long-playing record sleeves **c** Shopping malls
d Plywood furniture

9 What did Dr Johnson describe as "The power of doing something not taught by nature and instinct"?
a Skill **b** Creativity **c** Art **d** Passion

10 The musicologist Ludwig Ritter von Kochel is best known for his catalogue of the works (Kochel numbers) of which composer?
a Beethoven **b** Mozart **c** Haydn **d** Handel

Answers **1** d **2** b **3** c **4** a **5** d **6** c **7** b **8** d **9** c **10** b

Quiz 26 — Multiple choice

1 What is an 'hombre' in Spanish?
a A hat **b** A garden **c** A man **d** A servant

2 Where was 'Alan Pinkerton' born?
a Glasgow **b** Edinburgh **c** London **d** New York

3 Who built the 'Suez Canal'?
a Samuel Colleridge **b** Henry Ford **c** Ferdinand Lessops **d** Frank Wright

4 Who wrote 'The Naked and the Dead'?
a William Forester **b** Norman Mailer **c** Richard Bruce **d** Benjamn Tooley

5 Who was 'Haile Selassi'?
a Emperor of Ethiopia **b** King of Indonesia **c** King of Borneo **d** Emperor of Tibet

6 What is the common name of the tree 'Populus Tremula'?
a Cherry **b** Horsebeam **c** Oak **d** Weeping Willow

7 What did Elmer Sperry invent?
a Gyro b **b** Parachute **c** Aldis lamp **d** Beacons

8 What did Elisha Otis invent?
a Elevators **b** High rise skyscrapers **c** Ice cream **d** Crisps

9 What is the name of the 'unit of heat'?
a Coulomb **b** Watts **c** Joule **d** Ohms

10 What is the study of the nervous system?
a Biopsy **b** Neurology **c** Lucositis **d** Priasma

Answers **1** c **2** b **3** c **4** b **5** a **6** d **7** a **8** a **9** c **10** b

Multiple choice — Quiz 27

1 What element, atomic number 74, has the symbol W?
a Antimony **b** Silicon **c** Tungsten **d** Cobalt

2 Why are helicopters fitted with tail propellers?
a So that they will not twist with the rotor blades **b** So that they can have forward motion **c** So that they are able to hover **d** So that the flying speed of the helicopter can be varied

3 What was invented by Dr Lee De Forest in 1923?
a Sound film **b** Neon lamp **c** Parking meter **d** Combine harvester

4 What is measured on the Mohs' scale?
a The electronic reproduction of transmitted images **b** The brightness of stellar objects **c** The hardness of minerals **d** The density of liquids

5 For what purpose did J P Ekert and J W Mauchly design the first electronic digital computer?
a To play chess **b** To store student data at the University of Pennsylvania **c** To calculate pi to an indefinite number of places **d** To calculate ballistic trajectories

6 Why does an eclipse of the moon occur?
a The moon passes directly between the earth and the sun **b** The moon waxes **c** The moon passes into the shadow of the earth **d** The moon wanes

7 What alloy contains 65% iron and 35% nickel?
a Invar **b** Bronze **c** Brass **d** Pewter

8 Which inventor was born at Milan Ohio?
a King Camp Gillette **b** Thomas Edison **c** George Eastman **d** George Westinghouse

9 What, in 1989, was developed by Tim Berners-Lee, a British computer specialist?
a The World Wide Web **b** Spreadsheets **c** Notebook computers **d** Clipboard computers

10 What is measured in poundals ?
a Mass **b** Force **c** Volume **d** Weight

Answers **1** c **2** a **3** a **4** c **5** d **6** c **7** a **8** b **9** a **10** b

Quiz 28 — Multiple choice

1. Who wrote the 'Story of Esther Costello'?
   a Walt Mason **b** Daniel Frost **c** Nicholas Montsarrat **d** Samuel Seed
2. What was the earlier occupation of Beethoven?
   a Harpsichordist **b** Conductor **c** Violinist **d** Double bass player
3. Who painted the 'Water Lilies'?
   a William Morris **b** Goldworthy **c** Claude Monet **d** Charles Lamb
4. 'Alexander the Great' was King of which country?
   a Macedonia **b** Greece **c** Italy **d** Somaliland
5. Who wrote the 'Grapes of Wrath'?
   a Truman Capote **b** John Steinbeck **c** Stephen King **d** Hunter S Thompson
6. Who wrote the 'Elements of Geometry'?
   a Gregory **b** Einstein **c** Fermat **d** Euclid
7. What is 'Yosemite'?
   a A rift **b** A plain **c** Israeli citizen **d** A National Park
8. What is 'wampun'?
   a Quicksilver **b** Roasted ox **c** Beads used as money **d** A tent
9. What is a 'nematode'?
   a A gnat **b** A worm **c** A frog **d** A butterfly
10. What is 'magma'?
    a Ravins **b** Quick sands **c** Molten rock **d** Split rocks

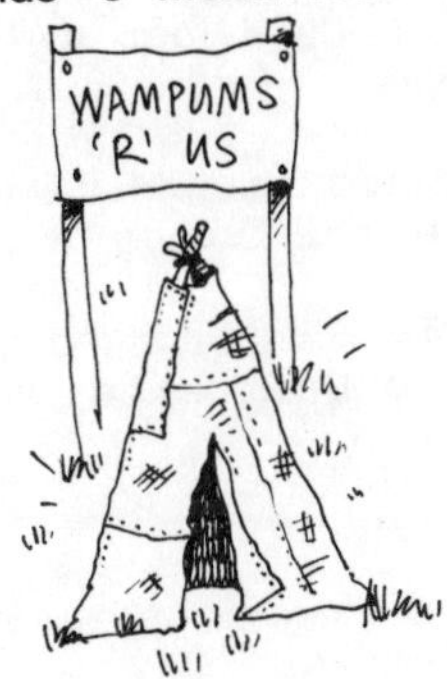

Answers 1c 2a 3c 4a 5b 6d 7d 8c 9b 10c

Multiple choice

Quiz 29

1. Who is said to have dived off Brooklyn Bridge on 23 July 1886?
   a Paul Bunyan **b** Steve Brodie **c** Mike Fink **d** Clementine

2. What was Johnny Appleseed's real name?
   a John Emmett **b** John Colton **c** John Deere **d** John Chapman

3. Which writer created the 'Uncle Remus' tales?
   a Zora Neale Hurston **b** Edward Taylor
   c Ann Bradstreet **d** Joel Chandler Harris

4. In the Arabian Nights, why does Schcherazarde relate one of the tales each night to her husband, Schariar?
   a To divert his mind from amorous intentions **b** To stop him banishing her from the kingdom **c** As a punishment for being unfaithful **d** To stop him killing her

5. Whose Almanacs, published between 1835 and 1856, contain tall tales based on oral legends about frontier heroes such as Daniel Boone and Kit Carson?
   a James Fenimore Cooper **b** Davy Crockett **c** Jim Bowie **d** Benjamin Franklin

6. Who wrote the opera 'Don Giovanni', which was inspired by the legend of Don Juan?
   a Puccini **b** Donizetti **c** Strauss **d** Mozart

7. Who was the wife of Leofric, Earl of Mercia?
   a Boudicca **b** Godiva **c** Nell Gwynn **d** Guinevere

8. The Flying Dutchman is a Dutch mariner doomed to sail eternally around which part of the world?
   a The Rock of Gibraltar **b** Cape Horn **c** The Arctic Circle
   d The Cape of Good Hope

9. What name in Spanish, means 'The Gilded One'?
   a El Cid **b** Don Quixote **c** El Dorado **d** Don Juan

10. Hiawatha was the chief of which tribe of Indians ?
    a Choctaw **b** Iroquois **c** Cherokee **d** Blackfoot

Answers 1 b 2 d 3 d 4 d 5 b 6 d 7 b 8 d 9 c 10 b

Quiz 30

Multiple choice

1 Herod the Great was ruler of which country?
a Mesopotamia **b** Persia **c** Palestine **d** Arabia

2 What is a 'Fandango'?
a A crowd **b** A hat **c** A gala **d** A dance

3 What is 'shogi'?
a A board game **b** A Japanese garden **c** A gin drink **d** A gun

4 What are the 'fauteuils' in a theatre?
a Stage **b** Stalls **c** Props **d** Circle

5 What was the name of the clown in 'Loves Labour Lost'?
a Costard **b** Bluebill **c** Francis **d** Romeo

6 What did 'Clive of India' become?
a An MP **b** A doctor **c** A lawyer **d** A governor

7 Who wrote "Any man who goes to a psychiatrist should have his head examined"?
a Stan Laurel **b** Sam Goldwyn **c** James Cagney **d** Groucho Marx

8 What does 'diurnal' mean?
a Dawn **b** During the day **c** Twice a day **d** Three times a day

9 What is the point above an observer's head called?
a Zenith **b** Horizon **c** Alteria **d** Nader

10 What is a full set of chromosomes called?
a Dianthus **b** Ginome **c** Pyranth **d** Prolapse

Answers **1** c **2** d **3** a **4** b **5** a **6** a **7** b **8** b **9** a **10** b

Multiple choice — Quiz 31

1 Ladybirds, glow-worms and Whirligigs are types of which order of insects?
a Orthoptera **b** Fly **c** Beetle **d** Ichneumon

2 Why is the raft-spider so called?
a It can walk on water **b** It can swim **c** It can build a raft-like construction **d** One bit George Raft during filming the movie 'Some Like it Hot'

3 Which is the largest type of bear?
a Polar **b** Black **c** Brown **d** Grizzly

4 'Panthera uncia' is the scientific name for which animal?
a Cheetah **b** Prairie Dog **c** Snow Leopard **d** Florida Cougar

5 What kind of creature is a loach?
a A seabird **b** A freshwater fish **c** A small lizard **d** A sheep native to Asia

6 Of the creatures below, which can travel the fastest?
a Squirrel **b** Black Mamba snake **c** Domestic pig **d** Elephant

7 Which bird, during courtship, inflates its throat pouch like a large red balloon?
a Dottrel **b** Frigate Bird **c** Quail **d** Flamingo

8 Anguine is the related adjective for which creature?
a Snake **b** Ape **c** Ferret **d** Seal

9 Apart from the freshwater swamps, lakes and bayous of the southeastern US which is the only other country in the world where alligators exist?
a Brazil **b** China **c** Australia **d** Congo

10 What is the maximum charge that a large electric eel is capable of emitting ?
a 600 volts **b** 200 volts **c** 1000 volts **d** 450 volts

Answers **1** c **2** a **3** a **4** c **5** b **6** d **7** b **8** a **9** b **10** a

Quiz 32

Multiple choice

1 What is 'Parthenophobia' the fear of?
a Girls **b** Monkeys **c** Tigers **d** Spiders

2 What is 'ikebana'?
a Flower arranging **b** Printing on linen **c** A Japanese shrine
d Moslem Prince

3 What is 'henbane'?
a A disease of chickens **b** A wild plant **c** A plant with fruit
d A breed of chickens

4 What is 'potophobia'?
a Fear of windows **b** Fear of cards **c** Fear of photographs
d Fear of drinks

5 What is 'orogenesis'?
a Formation of estuaries **b** Formation of mountains **c** Formation of rivers **d** Formation of plains

6 What is 'betelgeuse'?
a A chewing drug **b** A market **c** A native dwelling **d** A star

7 What type of musical instrument is 'cimbalom'?
a Trumpet **b** Clarinet **c** Dulcimer **d** Piano

8 Who wrote "I think therefore I am"?
a Augustus **b** Euclid **c** Newton **d** Descartes

9 Walt Disney was born in?
a Chicago **b** Buffalo **c** Las Vegas **d** Canada

10 Who said: "I want to be a white man's brother, not his brother-in-law?
a Walt Whitman **b** Gandhi **c** Martin Luther King **d** Haile Selassi

Answers 1 a 2 a 3 b 4 d 5 b 6 d 7 c 8 d 9 a 10 c

Multiple choice

Quiz 33

1 Where would you find the 'Mount of Jupiter', the 'Mount of Saturn', the 'Mount of Apollo' and the 'Mount of Venus'?
a On the dark side of the moon **b** On your hand **c** On the sun
d On the human skull

2 What first was achieved by Fran Phipps on 5 April 1971?
a First woman to reach the summit of Everest **b** First woman to reach the North Pole **c** First woman astronaut to take a space walk
d First woman to climb the North face of the Eiger

3 Who was born Jeanne Antoinette Poisson who lived in France from 1721-64?
a Saint Theresa of Lisieux **b** Comtesse Du Barry **c** Marquise de Montespun **d** Madame Pompadour

4 What is meant by the musical term 'Andante'?
a Gradually quickening **b** Briskly **c** At a moderate tempo
d With passion

5 What did Max Baer say to Primo Carnera when they both fell to the canvas in the first round of their World Heavyweight Championship fight in June 1934?
a Stay there I'll help you up **b** Let's call it a draw **c** It's hardly worth you getting up **d** Last one up's a sissy

6 What type of furniture are Davenports and Escritoires?
a Wooden chairs **b** Low cabinets **c** Writing desks **d** Tables

7 What star sign would you be if you were born on 30 August?
a Taurus **b** Leo **c** Virgo **d** Gemini

8 What was the first word conveyed to her blind and deaf pupil, Helen Keller, by her teacher Anne Sullivan?
a Love **b** Helen **c** Water **d** Hope

9 What people were ruled by the Mameluke dynasty in the 13-16th centuries?
a Turkish **b** Persian **c** German **d** Egyptian

10 In what is an oenologist an expert?
a Wine **b** Ghosts **c** Whales and dolphins **d** Music

Answers **1** b **2** b **3** d **4** c **5** d **6** c **7** c **8** c **9** d **10** a

Quiz 34 — Multiple choice

1 Who said: "Literature is news that stays news"?
a Roosevelt **b** Bob Hope **c** Isaac Newton **d** Ezra Pound

2 Who said "You are not drunk if you can lie on the floor without holding on"?
a Ralph Richardson **b** Danny Kaye **c** Dean Martin **d** Ezra Pound

3 What is 'corryrium'?
a Flea powder **b** Eye salve **c** Cooking oil **d** Hot drink

4 What is 'epis taxis'?
a Bleeding from the nose **b** Pins and needles **c** Floribunda
d Low blood pressure

5 What is 'fluxion'?
a Flexibility **b** Flowing **c** Coarse linen **d** Paper tearing

6 What is 'gusto'?
a Furniture polish **b** Weariness **c** Folly **d** Zest

7 What is a 'fardel'?
a A litter of pigs **b** A bundle **c** A musical instrument **d** An Austrian farm

8 What is a 'frump'?
a A type of fruit **b** A trampoline **c** A stream **d** A dowdy person

9 What is 'hoosh'?
a A thick soup **b** A warning cry **c** An illegal drink of whisky
d A plant

10 What is a 'janissary'?
a A soldier **b** An insect **c** A fruit **d** A storehouse

Answers 1d 2c 3b 4a 5a 6d 7b 8d 9a 10a

Multiple choice

Quiz 35

1 From what is the Japanese drink Saki made?
a Bird's nests **b** Egg **c** Rice **d** Honey

2 What is olfactophobia a fear of?
a Teeth **b** Dreams **c** Smell **d** Vehicles

3 During the golden age of the cinema of what was a Mitchell a famous brand?
a Microphone **b** Sound boom **c** Arc light **d** Camera

4 Which US President became the first to die in office just one month after his inauguration?
a James Knox Palk **b** William Henry Harrison **c** Franklin Delano Roosevelt **d** Andrew Johnson

5 The faranole is a national dance of which country?
a France **b** Spain **c** Brazil **d** Hungary

6 What was Elvis Presley's first record?
a Jailhouse Rock **b** Are You Lonesome Tonight? **c** That's All Right (Mama) **d** Blue Suede Shoes

7 Who said, "Never eat more than you can lift"?
a Mohammed Ali **b** Oliver Hardy **c** Miss Piggy **d** Roscoe "Fatty" Arbuckle

8 Which river runs 512 miles from Hemphill County in Ohio to the Ohio River between Illinois and Indiana?
a Wabash **b** Trinity **c** Green **d** Washita

9 Which of the following was the only one not guillotined during the French Revolution?
a Comtesse Du Barry **b** Antoine Lavoisier **c** Madame Pompadour **d** Georges Danton

10 Which Biblical King of Judah was the son of Asa and father of Jehoram?
a Rehaboam **b** Jehoshaphat **c** Amazia **d** Josiah

Answers 1c 2c 3d 4b 5a 6c 7d 8a 9c 10b

Quiz 36

Multiple choice

1 Who said: "In the future everybody will be world famous for 15 minutes"?
a President Clinton **b** Charles de Gaulle **c** Will Hay **d** Andy Warhol

2 Who said "It has got to be proven that intelligence has any survival value"?
a Neil Armstrong **b** Disraeli **c** Arthur C Clarke **d** Churchill

3 What is a 'dunock'?
a A fool **b** A hedge sparrow **c** A daisy **d** A fish

4 What is 'mesial'?
a A middle line **b** A painting **c** A torture weapon **d** A poem

5 What is a monody?
a A speech **b** A step **c** A pillar **d** A lyric poem

6 What is a 'misericord'?
a A dagger **b** A psalm **c** A church door **d** A church bell

7 What is a 'neap'?
a A small hill **b** A tide **c** A river estuary **d** A pathway

8 Who was 'Nimrod'?
a A castle **b** A ship **c** A great hunter **d** A clockwork idol

9 What is an 'oast'?
a A wheat dish **b** A field **c** A tree **d** A hop drying kiln

10 What is an 'oppidan'?
a A type of quartz **b** A scholar **c** A lava flow **d** A planet's ring

Answers 1d 2c 3b 4a 5d 6a 7b 8c 9d 10b

Multiple choice

Quiz 37

1 What is the other name for Cupid, in mythology the son of Aphrodite?
a Apollo **b** Hector **c** Eros **d** Hyacinthus

2 What is the sixth letter of the Greek alphabet?
a Zeta **b** Iota **c** Eta **d** Epsilon

3 Major Major Major is a character in which novel?
a Catch **22** **b** A Clockwork Orange **c** Foucault's Pendulum
d Portnoy's Complaint

4 How tall was King Charles I of England before he was beheaded?
a 4 foot 9 inches **b** 5 foot 1 inch **c** 5 foot 3 inches **d** 5 foot 5 inches

5 'Dancer' was the secret service code name for which US first lady?
a Barbara Bush **b** Eleanor Roosevelt **c** Rosalyn Carter **d** Nancy Reagan

6 Prospero, Miranda, Ferdinand, Ariel and Caliban are characters in which Shakespeare play?
a The Tempest **b** Twelfth Night **c** Love's Labor's Lost
d The Winter's Tale

7 In computer technology, what do the initials VGA stand for?
a Virtual Graphics Array **b** Virus Glitch Alert **c** Video Graphics Array
d Visual Graphics Array

8 Which golfing legend won three US Open titles in 1948, 1950 and 1951, and was called 'The Iceman' and 'The Killer'?
a Walter Hagan **b** Gene Sarazen **c** Ben Hogan **d** Bobby Jones

9 Who wrote the 'Sabre Dance'?
a Rimsky-Korsakov **b** Khachaturian **c** Stravinsky **d** Tchaikovsky

10 What are trefoil, ogee, lancet and parabolic types of?
a Arches **b** Bridges **c** Towers **d** Pottery

Answers **1** c **2** a **3** a **4** a **5** c **6** a **7** c **8** c **9** b **10** a

Quiz 38

Multiple choice

1 What does 'pane' mean?
a To trim **b** To compare **c** To undress **d** To scarify

2 What does 'parlous' mean?
a Ridiculous **b** Perilous **c** Mean **d** Talkative

3 Who wrote "The lunatics have taken over the asylum"?
a Richard Rowland **b** George II **c** Clement Atlee **d** Dorothy L Sayers

4 What is 'oscular'?
a Of the mouth **b** Riding habit **c** A type of shoe **d** A drink

5 What is a 'paramo'?
a A suitor **b** A plateau **c** A sword **d** A dish

6 What does 'parky' mean?
a Mendacious **b** Pale **c** Flushed **d** Chilly

7 What does 'pastoral' mean?
a Of shepherds **b** Of sheep **c** Of fields **d** Of rivers

8 What is a 'pawnee'?
a A pawnbroker **b** A jewel **c** A dragon **d** An Indian

9 What is a 'pennon'?
a A cornice **b** A dog **c** A flag **d** A kerb

10 What is a 'petrel'?
a A beacon **b** A bird **c** A steeple **d** An insect

Answers 1a 2b 3a 4a 5b 6d 7a 8d 9c 10b

Multiple choice — Quiz 39

1 What colour is produced by adding together the primary colours of yellow and cyan?
a Green **b** Blue **c** Red **d** Magenta

2 What triviality was introduced by Louie Marx in 1929?
a The Hula Hoop **b** Musical Birthday Cards **c** The Yo-Yo
d Water Pistols

3 Dactyology is a means of communication better known by what other name ?
a Semaphore **b** Finger-spelling **c** Morse code **d** Sign language

4 What musical sign lowers a pitch by a semitone?
a Clef **b** Flat **c** Rest **d** Sharp

5 In the Olympic Games the distance over which the marathon is run is 26 miles and how many yards?
a 325 **b** 345 **c** 385 **d** 415

6 In March 1997 which famous person made a parachute jump "just for fun"?
a Billy Graham **b** Jimmy Carter **c** George Bush **d** Clint Eastwood

7 Denmark's flag consists of a white cross on what colour background?
a Blue **b** Green **c** Gold **d** Red

8 In 1882 a weird and wonderful new type of alarm was invented. How did it work?
a It sprayed the sleeper with a fine jet of water **b** It tipped 20 wooden blocks onto the sleeper **c** It stuck a fine needle into a sleeping dog so that the resultant barking woke up the sleeper **d** The bed tilted sideways and slid the sleeper gently out of bed

9 Where do the native speak English and spend Shillings?
a Tanzania **b** Somalia **c** Senegal **d** Malawi

10 Who in the Bible destroyed the golden calf?
a Jesus **b** Aaron **c** David **d** Moses

Answers **1** a **2** c **3** b **4** b **5** c **6** c **7** d **8** b **9** a **10** d

Quiz 40 — Multiple choice

1 What is the meaning of 'crass'?
a Coarse b Thick c Hairy d Warm

2 Who said "Any man that hates dogs and babies can't be all bad"?
a Leonard Rossiter b Bette Davis c Charlie Chaplin d W C Fields

3 What is the meaning of 'crore'?
a Earl's cloak b 10 millions c Church staff d Sunken ditch

4 What is a 'cruse'?
a A medallion b A weapon c A pot d A coat

5 What is a 'crypt'?
a Ghostly figure b Underground cell c Mauseleum d Church vestry

6 What is a 'cruzeiro'?
a Ocean liner b Monetary unit of Brazil c Brigand d Soothsayer

7 What is a 'denizen'?
a Dark object b An inhabitant c Ghost d A miller

8 Who was 'Edgar'?
a A poet b A clergyman c A Prince's valet d A King of England

9 What is a 'fanfare'?
a A moat b Flourish of trumpet c A flower garden d A barricade

10 What is a 'fedora'?
a A dance b A wine bar c A felt hat d A shop

Answers 1b 2d 3b 4c 5b 6b 7b 8d 9b 10c

Multiple choice — Quiz 41

1 Who said: "You can build a throne with bayonets, but you can't sit on it for very long"?
a Mahatma Ghandi **b** Henry Kissinger **c** Boris Yeltsin **d** Leo Tolstoy

2 Who said: "The length of a film should be directly related to the endurance of the human bladder"?
a Alfred Hitchcock **b** Cecil B de Mille **c** Walter Winchell **d** Jack Warner

3 Who said: "Things should be made as simple as possible, but not any simpler"?
a Aristotle **b** Albert Einstein **c** Woodrow Wilson **d** Bertrand Russell

4 Who said, "My problem lies in reconciling my gross habits with my nett income"?
a Ernest Hemingway **b** Howard Hughes **c** Errol Flynn **d** John D Rockefeller

5 Who said: "I'm going to stay in show business until I'm the last one left"?
a Bob Hope **b** Jack Benny **c** George Burns **d** Milton Berle

6 Who said: "An intellectual snob is someone who can listen to the 'William Tell Overture' and not think of 'The Lone Ranger'?
a David Letterman **b** Jay Leno **c** Johnny Carson **d** Dan Rather

7 Who said: "Everything you can imagine is real"?
a Isaac Asimov **b** Thomas Edison **c** Madame Curie **d** Pablo Picasso

8 Who said: "I'd marry again if I found a man who had 15 million dollars, would sign over half to me, and guarantee that he'd be dead within a year"?
a Mae West **b** Bette Davis **c** Gipsy Rose Lee **d** Xavier Holland

9 Who said: " I feel sure that no girl would go to the altar if she knew all"?
a Queen Victoria **b** Elizabeth Taylor **c** Princess Diana **d** Bette Davis

10 Who said: "It is better to be looked over than overlooked"?
a Rosalind Russell **b** Mae West **c** Katherine Hepburn **d** Joan Rivers

---

Answers 1 c 2 a 3 b 4 c 5 c 6 d 7 d 8 b 9 a 10 b

Quiz 42 Multiple choice

1 Who wrote: "I know two things about a horse and one of them is rather coarse"?
a Gracie Fields **b** Queen Elizabeth **c** Gordon Richard
d Naomi Royde-Smith

2 What does 'burlesque' mean?
a Chaos **b** Comely **c** Caricaturing **d** Romanesque

3 What is a 'conger'?
a A line of people **b** Consistency **c** An eel **d** Comfortable

4 What is a 'divot'?
To deck out **b** Part of an animal's tail **c** A draught horse
d A piece of turf

5 Who said "I want to be alone"?
a Margaret Powell **b** Greta Garbo **c** Doctor Johnson **d** Gypsy Rose Lee

6 What is 'embonpoint'?
a Draw forth **b** Make bitter **c** Ornamental **d** Plumpness

7 What is a 'fatling'?
a A suburb **b** Young fatted animal **c** The pharynx **d** A young buck

8 What is a 'goon'?
A thorn **b** A tree **c** A fool **d** A colony of ants

9 What is 'homing'?
a A globule **b** Coarse maize **c** A whetstone **d** Wild goose's cry

10 What is 'invective'?
a Abusive oratory **b** Invincible **c** Inverted **d** Examination

Answers 1d 2c 3c 4d 5b 6d 7b 8c 9b 10a

Multiple choice — Quiz 43

1 Which element, number 79, has the symbol Au?
a Silver **b** Copper **c** Gold **d** Iron

2 Which country's flag has a white bordered blue cross on a red background?
a Norway **b** Iceland **c** Sweden **d** Greece

3 What was invented by a French doctor, Rene Theophile Hyacinthe?
a Forceps **b** The Scalpel **c** The Lancet **d** The Stethoscope

4 Which US city is served by Hartsfield airport?
a Dallas **b** Chicago **c** Pheonix **d** Atlanta

5 Where, in the human body, are the parietal and occipital bones?
a Hand **b** Back **c** Skull **d** Foot

6 In the game of chess, what is the name of the piece that can move two squares straightforward, then one square to the side in any direction?
a Castle **b** Queen **c** King **d** Knight

7 Which golfing legend suffered with putting problems (the 'yips'), throughout his career and once said, "You know those two-foot downhill putts with a break? I'd rather see a rattlesnake"?
a Sam Snead **b** Gary Player **c** Tom Watson **d** Ben Hogan

8 What is Kakorraphiaphobia the fear of?
a Failure **b** Flogging **c** Volcanic eruptions **d** Responsibility

9 Deimos and Phobos are moons of which planet?
a Mercury **b** Saturn **c** Mars **d** Uranus

10 Which television personality was a former mayor of Cincinnati?
a Bill Mahar **b** Jerry Springer **c** Kelsey Grammer **d** Jay Leno

Answers **1** c **2** a **3** d **4** d **5** c **6** d **7** a **8** a **9** c **10** b

Quiz 44

Multiple choice

1 What does 'propitiate' mean?
a Encourage **b** Scander **c** Appease **d** Form

2 Who wrote "For a salesman there is no rock bottom to life"?
a George Orwell **b** Arthur Miller **c** Monica Dickens **d** D H Lawrence

3 What is a 'riddel'?
a Two horse carriage **b** Curtain at side of an altar **c** A promisary note **d** A beading around a door

4 Who wrote "The United States are essentially the greatest poem"?
a Walter Lipman **b** Walt Witman **c** Art Linklater **d** Billy Graham

5 What is a 'shebang'?
a School **b** Card game **c** Party **d** Saloon

6 What is 'Alumnus'?
a A former pupil **b** A meeting **c** An illuminated script **d** A cinema

7 What is an 'ampersand'?
a Electrical current **b** Coarse grit **c** Trickery **d** The sign for the word 'and'

8 What is an 'archipelago'?
a Group of islands **b** A creek **c** An inlet **d** A strip of land

9 What is 'batik'?
a Designs on textiles **b** Native of Java **c** Eastern wind **d** Mountan

10 What is a 'biffin'?
a A small meal **b** A variety of apple **c** A fight **d** A cold luncheon

Answers 1c 2b 3b 4b 5d 6a 7d 8a 9a 10b

Multiple choice

Quiz 45

1 Who, in Egyptian mythology, is the goddess of motherhood and fertility?
a Hephthys **b** Nut **c** Hathor **d** Isis

2 Where was the Russian revolutionary Trotsky assassinated?
a Mexico **b** Paris **c** London **d** Bolivia

3 What is Ereuthrophobia the fear of?
a Solitude **b** Blushing **c** Narrowness **d** Clouds

4 How many years marriage are celebrated at a sapphire wedding anniversary?
a 45 **b** 35 **c** 40 **d** 55

5 What sport did US President Teddy Roosevelt once try to outlaw because too many people were getting killed?
a Boxing **b** Harness Racing **c** Football **d** Auto Racing

6 What colour is formed by mixing blue, green and red?
a Yellow **b** White **c** Cyan **d** Black

7 Which country's flag has a blue cross on a white background?
a Iceland **b** Argentina **c** Dominican Republic **d** Finland

8 How long would it take the world's fastest snail, moving continuously flat out, to slither a mile?
a 24 hors **b** 6 days **c** 10 days **d** One month

9 Which is the largest island of Japan?
a Shikoku **b** Kyushu **c** Honshu **d** Hokkaido

10 Pardine is the related adjective for which animal?
a Kangaroo **b** Hare **c** Leopard **d** Pig

Answers **1** d **2** a **3** b **4** a **5** c **6** b **7** d **8** b **9** c **10** c

Quiz 46 — Multiple choice

1 Who wrote "The King asked the Queen, the Queen asked the Dairy Maid, could we have some butter?"
a T S Elliot **b** Mae West **c** A A Milne **d** Lewis Carroll

2 What is 'dowlas'?
a Calico **b** Dockside dwellings **c** Welsh sheep **d** Distillery

3 What is 'dudgeon'?
a Fish **b** Resentment **c** Jail **d** Temper

4 What is 'wansook'?
a Fabric **b** Chinese labourer **c** Card game **d** Counterfeit money

5 What is an 'oratory'?
a Painting **b** Small chapel **c** Statue **d** Feeling of despair

6 Who wrote "It's best not to change horses, when crossing streams"?
a Arthur C Clarke **b** The Marx brothers **c** Sam Goldwyn
d Abraham Lincoln

7 What is a 'pikelet'?
a Small pig **b** Muffin **c** Weapon **d** Armour

8 What is a satyr
a A fruit **b** A musical instrument **c** A monkey **d** A woodland god

9 What is a 'shoveler'?
a A duck **b** Excavating machine **c** A narrow boat **d** Post man

10 What is a 'spinet'?
a Medical instrument **b** Keyboard instrument **c** Knitting machine
d Sailor's compass

Answers 1c 2a 3b 4a 5b 6d 7b 8d 9a 10b

Multiple choice — Quiz 47

1 Which psychologist differentiated people according to types, extroverted and introverted?
a Edward Lee Thorndike **b** Hermann Rorschach **c** Carl Jung **d** Sigmund Freud

2 Which Hungarian-born American physicist is known as the "father of the H-bomb"?
a Edward Teller **b** Erwin Muller **c** Otto Hahn **d** Dennis Gabor

3 What was invented in 1930 by Sir Frank Whittle?
a Latex foam rubber **b** Transistors **c** The Hovercraft **d** The jet engine

4 What was innovative about a pencil patented in 1858 by Hyman L Lipman?
a It was a propelling pencil **b** It never wore out
c It had an attached eraser **d** It wrote in several different colours

5 Which is the heaviest of the noble gases?
a Krypton **b** Radon **c** Neon **d** Xenon

6 How is deoxyribonucleic acid better known?
a DDT **b** RNA **c** DNA **d** Insulin

7 What first was achieved by Major Henry O de Hane in 1927?
a First person to drive a motor vehicle over 200 mph
b First person to carry out an aerial crop-dusting operation
c First person to make a successful flight over the North Pole
d First person to drive a motor vehicle in reverse from New York City to Los Angeles

8 What is measured in dynes?
a Power **b** Force **c** Temperature **d** Velocity

9 On what area of the moon did Armstrong, Aldrin and Collins make their landing on 20 July 1969?
a The Lake of Dreams **b** The Sea of Serenity **c** The Sea of Tranquility **d** The Sea of Vapors

10 How many bytes can a computer with a 64K memory handle?
a 64768 **b** 64000 **c** 79360 **d** 65536

Answers 1c 2a 3d 4c 5b 6c 7a 8b 9c 10d

Quiz 48 — Multiple choice

1 Who said "Wooing, so tiring"?
a Greta Garbo **b** Gypsy Rose Lee **c** Za Za Gabor **d** Nancy Mitford

2 Who said "No, I shall have mistresses"?
a Henry VII **b** William II **c** George II **d** Henry VIII

3 Who wrote "The great nations have always acted like gangsters"?
a Laurie Lee **b** Stanley Kubrik **c** Sean Olasy **d** Ronald Reagan

4 Who wrote "Dear pig, are you willing to sell for one shilling your ring?"
a Lewis Carroll **b** Charlie Knox **c** Mickey Mouse **d** Edward Lear

5 What is a 'sparoid'?
a Insect **b** Tree **c** Fish **d** Vegetable

6 What is a 'fluke'?
a Flat fish **b** Insect **c** Bird **d** Vase

7 What is a 'mutch'?
a A sign **b** Garden rake **c** Beaker **d** Linen cap

8 What is a 'randen'?
a A winding path **b** A stagnant pond **c** An outpost **d** A spree

9 What is a 'rocquet'?
a A croquet stroke **b** A French sailor **c** A monastery walkway
d A dagger

10 What is 'rapini'?
a Plundering **b** Oil seed **c** Brusque manner **d** Type of lock

Answers 1d 2c 3b 4d 5c 6a 7d 8a 9a 10a

Multiple choice — Quiz 49

1 Who starred with Tom Cruise and Jack Nicolson in the 1992 movie 'A Few Good Men'?
a Jodi Foster **b** Demi Moore **c** Sharon Stone **d** Bridget Fonda

2 Which singer provides one of the voices in the animated 1997 movie 'Cats Don't Dance'?
a Natalie Cole **b** Celine Dion **c** Reba McEntire **d** Mariah Carey

3 Who wrote the music for 'Gone With the Wind'?
a Dimitri Tiomkin **b** Herbert Stothart **c** Max Steiner **d** Victor Young

4 Which 1997 film tells the true story of David Helfgott, a gifted pianist who suffers a nervous breakdown?
a Tree Lounge **b** The Piano **c** Grace of My Heart **d** Shine

5 Apart from compilation films, what was the last movie that Laurel and Hardy made together?
a Jitterbugs **b** Utopia **c** The Big Noise **d** Nothing But Trouble

6 Who, in the 1992 movie, was 'The Lawnmower Man'?
a Pierce Brosnan **b** Liam Neeson **c** Jeff Fahey **d** Lukas Haas

7 Which was the first film to win all five major Oscars: Picture, Actor, Actress, Director and Screenplay?
a It Happened One Night **b** Gone With The Wind **c** Schindler's List
d Inherit the Wind

8 In the 1992 movie, 'A League of Their Own', Tom Hanks is the manager of a team of women in what sport?
a Tennis **b** Basketball **c** Football **d** Baseball

9 Who played Marlon Brando's son, Michael Corleone, in 'The Godfather'?
a Al Pacino **b** James Caan **c** Robert Duvall **d** John Cazale

10 The team of Robert Redford and Paul Newman (Butch Cassidy and the Sundance Kid, 1969) were reunited for which 1973 movie?
a The Towering Inferno **b** The Great Gatsby **c** The Sting
d The Mackintosh Man

Answers 1 b 2 a 3 c 4 d 5 b 6 c 7 a 8 d 9 a 10 c

Quiz 50

Multiple choice

1 What is a 'mendicant'?
a A teacher **b** A beggar **c** A doctor **d** A pharmacist

2 What is the meaning of 'regimen'?
a Soldiers on parade **b** A badge **c** Sympathy **d** Rule

3 What is a 'stemma'?
a A sluice gate **b** A loose robe **c** A family tree **d** A stutter

4 Who said "A man who carries a cat by its tail, learns something in no other way"?
a Mark Twain **b** David Copperfield **c** Mae West **d** Winston Churchill

5 What colour is 'verdant'?
a Blue **b** Green **c** Yellow **d** Red

6 What is 'gabelle'?
a A Marine **b** A revolving dias **c** A tax **d** A water bus

7 What is 'emery'
a A type of plaster **b** Foot stool **c** Coarse carborundum
d Piano lid

8 What does 'ductile' mean?
a Flexible **b** Channel **c** Settled **d** Abrupt

9 What does 'desultory' mean?
a Maudlin **b** Disconnected **c** Effervescent **d** Likeable

10 What does 'compile' mean?
a Collect **b** Attack **c** Retreat **d** Liken

Answers 1 b 2 d 3 c 4 c 5 b 6 c 7 c 8 a 9 b 10 a

SECTION 4

Almanac

This section contains 366 questions, one for every day of the year, including leap years.

There are twelve quizzes, one for each month of the year, and the number of each question coincides with the date in that month on which the event occurred.

For example, question number 12 in the January Quiz refers to an event which occurred on 12 January in a particular year

Almanac — January

1 Who announced his discovery of X-rays in 1896?

2 Who went on trial in Flemington New Jersey on charges of the kidnapping and murder of the infant son of Charles A. Lindberg?

3 Who was the Beatles' music producer born in 1922?

4 Which American president delivered the first State of the Union speech in 1790?

5 How was Peter Sutcliffe, arrested in England in 1981, better known?

6 Who was the fourth wife of King Henry VIII, whom he married in 1540?

7 Galileo discovered Io, Europa and Ganymede, the satellites of which planet, in 1610?

8 On making his first professional appearance in 1962 at the age of 21, which golfer was placed 50th in the Los Angeles open, winning $33.33?

9 Who was the future 37th President of the United States born at Yorba Linda, California in 1913?

10 Which US crime writer, author of 'The Maltese Falcon' died in 1961?

11 In 1946, which Eastern European country became a peoples republic after the overthrow of its ruler King Zog?

12 Who was the creator of detectives Miss Marple and Hercule Poirot who died in 1976?

13 In 1967 which British pop group appeared on The Ed Sullivan Show, but were forced to change the lyrics of 'Let's Spend the Night Together' to 'Let's Spend Some Time Together'?

Answers **1** William Rontgen **2** Bruno Richard Hauptmann **3** Sir George Martin **4** George Washington **5** The Yorkshire Ripper **6** Anne of Cleves **7** Jupiter **8** Jack Nicklaus **9** Richard Nixon **10** Samuel Dashiell Hammett **11** Albania **12** Dame Agatha Christie **13** The Rolling Stones

January

Almanac

14 Who was the N Y Yankee baseball player who married Marilyn Monroe in 1954?

15 In 1919 which famous pianist became the first premier of Poland?

16 Which British explorer found the magnetic south pole in 1909?

17 Which US Statesman, who was th first to suggest that buildings be given lightning conductors, was born in Boston on 17th January 1706?

18 Which future Hollywood heartthrob was born Archibald Alexander Leach in England in 1904?

19 Who was the daughter of Nehru, who was elected India's third prime minister in 1966?

20 President Jimmy Carter announced the U S boycott of which Olympic Games in 1980?

21 Which Beatle married model/actress Patti "Layla" Boyd in 1966?

22 In which year did Queen Victoria die, at the age of 82?

23 Which TV mini-series based on an Alex Haley novel began airing on ABC television in America in 1977?

24 What was discovered at Sutten's Mill, California on 24thJanuary 1848?

25 In 1915, which inventor inaugurated the U S transcontinental 'phone service with a call made between New York and San Francisco?

26 The name of the French film director who discovered Brigette Bardot who was born in 1929?

27 Which composer was born in Salzburg, Austria in 1756?

28 What was the name of the space shuttle which exploded in 1986, 73 seconds after take-off, killing all seven crew members?

29 Whose poem 'The Raven' was published in 1845?

30 Which German president appointed Adolf Hitler chancellor in 1933?

31 Passed in the U S in 1865, what was abolished by the 13th Amendment?

Answers cont **14** Joe de Maggio **15** Ignace Jan Paderewski **16** Ernest Shackleton **17** Benjamin Franklin **18** Cary Grant **19** Indira Ghandi **20** Moscow **21** George Harrison **22** 1901 **23** Roots **24** Gold **25** Alexander Graham Bell **26** Roger Vadim **27** Wolfgang Amadeus Mozart **28** Challenger **29** Edgar Allen Poe **30** Hindenburg **31** Slavery

Almanac February

1 What is the name of the daughter of Elvis Presley, born in 1968?

2 Who was the song and dance legend of such films as 'An American In Paris' who died in 1996?

3 Which rock and roll star died with Buddy Holly and JP 'the Big Bopper' in a plane crash in 1959?

4 Who was the newspaper heiress captured by the Symbionese Liberation Army in 1974?

5 What was the first Charlie Chaplin movie to have sound effects, which opened in 1937?

6 Which English King died in 1952?

7 What game was invented in 1935 by Charles Darrow?

8 Born this day in 1925, who won the 1973 Best Actor Oscar for his performance in 'Save the Tiger'?

9 What life saving device was patented in 1863 by Alanson Crane?

10 Which country did France cede to England under the Treaty of Paris in 1763?

11 Which Saint first saw a vision of the Virgin Mary at Lourdes, France in 1858?

12 Which queen of England was beheaded in 1554, aged 17, after a 13 day reign?

13 Which talk show host, and former mayor of Cincinnati, was born in 1944?

14 Which German city was almost totally destroyed by allied bombers, under the command of 'Bomber Harris', on 14 February 1945?

Answers **1** Lisa Marie Presley **2** Gene Kelly **3** Richie Valens **4** Patricia Hearst **5** Modern Times **6** George VI **7** Monopoly **8** Jack Lemmon **9** The fire extinguisher **10** Canada **11** Saint Bernadette **12** Lady Jane Grey **13** Jerry Springer **14** Dresden

February

Almanac

15 Renee O'Conner, born in 1971, is a star of which TV series?

16 What, in 1937, was first developed by a U S research team led by Dr Wallace Carothers?

17 Who was the last Apache chief to surrender to the American government, who died in 1909?

18 Who was the Austrain physicist and philosopher, born 18th February 1838, who gave his name to the unit of velocity of sound in air?

19 Who patented the phonograph in 1878?

20 Who became the first astronaut to orbit the earth in 1962?

21 What type of camera was first demonstrated by its inventor, Edwin H Land in 1947?

22 Which actress, star of the movie 'Educating Rita', was born in 1950?

23 What was the name of the sheep cloned in Scotland in 1997?

24 In 1903, the United States signed an agreement acquiring a naval station at Guantanamo Bay in which country?

25 Who was the Philippine president who fled the country in 1986 after 20 years of rule?

26 Whose recording, 'What's Love Got To Do with It', won a Grammy in 1985?

27 At the age of 16, who became the youngest PGA golfer in 35 years when he teed off at the Los Angeles Open in 1992?

28 Olaf Palme, assassinated in 1986, was Prime Minister of which country?

29 Who was the Prime Minister of Canada who resigned in 1984?

Answers cont **15** Xena, Warrior Princess **16** Nylon **17** Geronimo **18** Ernst MAch **19** Thomas Alva Edison **20** John Glenn **21** Polaroid **22** Julie Walters **23** Dolly **24** Cuba **25** Ferdinand Marcos **26** Tina Turner 27 Tiger Woods **28** Sweden **29** Pierre Trudeau

Almanac — March

1 Who was the lead singer of the pop group 'The Who' born in 1944?

2 What was the name of the Beatles first movie, on which filming began on 2nd March 1964?

3 Who composed the opera 'Carmen' which premiered in 1875 at the Opera Comique, Paris?

4 Who, in 1801, was sworn in as the third US President?

5 Who, in 1946, in a speech at Westminster College in Fulton, Missouri first used the phrase 'Iron Curtain'?

6 What was captured by General Antonio Lopez de Santa Anna in 1836?

7 Who defeated James Smith to become boxing's youngest heavyweight title holder in 1987?

8 Micky Dolenz, born in 1945, was a member of which pop group?

9 Which famous comedian died in 1996 shortly after his 100th birthday?

10 Who became dictator of Cuba in 1952?

11 Who, on this day in 1942 left the Philippines vowing 'I shall return'?

12 Which skaters in 1984 became the first to receive nine perfect 6s in a World Championship?

13 In 1868 the impeachment trial of which US president began in the US senate?

14 Who was found guilty in 1964 of murdering Lee Harvey Oswald?

Answers **1** Roger Daltrey **2** A Hard Day's Night **3** George Bizet **4** Thomas Jefferson **5** Winston Churchill **6** The Alamo **7** Mike Tyson **8** The Monkees **9** George Burns **10** Fulgencio Batista **11** General Douglas MacArthur **12** Torvill & Dean **13** Andrew Johnson **14** Jack Ruby

March

Almanac

15 Who composed 'My Fair Lady' which opened on Broadway in 1956?

16 Which Portuguese navigator reached the Philippines in 1521?

17 Who became prime minister of Israel in 1969?

18 What 'first' was achieved by Soviet cosmonaut Aleksei A. Leonov in 1965?

19 Which 'Die Hard' and 'Pulp Fiction' actor was born in 1945?

20 Whose anti-slavery novel 'Uncle Tom's Cabin' was first published in book form in 1852?

21 Which island prison was emptied of its last prisoner in 1963?

22 Which actor, born in 1931, was Captain James T Kirk of the Star Ship Enterprise?

23 Who composed the 'Messiah' oratorio which had its London premier in 1743?

24 Which vessel ran aground in Prince William Sound, Alaska in 1989 causing America's largest oil spill?

25 The European Economic Community was established by what treaty in 1957?

26 Which two middle east leaders signed the Camp David peace treaty at the White House in 1979?

27 In 1996 Yigal Amir received a life sentence for assassinating which Israeli Prime Minister in November 1995?

28 In 1930, to what was the Turkish city of Angora renamed?

29 Who won the best actress Oscar in 1993 for her role in 'Howard's End'?

30 What was special about a pencil patented by Hyman L. Lipman in 1858?

31 Which Mexican-American singer was shot to death in Corpus Christie by the founder of her fan club in 1995?

Answers cont **15** Lerner and Loewe **16** Ferdinand Magellan **17** Golda Meir **18** The First Spacewalk **19** Bruce Willis **20** Harriet Beecher Stowe **21** Alcatraz **22** William Shatner **23** Handel **24** Exxon Valdez **25** The Treaty of Rome **26** Menachem Begin and Anwar Sadat **27** Yitzhat Rabin **28** Ankara **29** Emma Thompson **30** It had an attached eraser **31** Selena

Almanac — April

1 Why, in 1985, did George Plimpton introduce the readers of 'Sports Illustrated' to Sidd Finch a 28 year old aspiring monk who could throw a 168 mph baseball?

2 Who was the mob boss, known as Telfton Don, convicted of murder and racketeering in 1992?

3 Who did Bob Ford shoot in 1882?

4 Which treaty was established by the signature of its original 12 nations on 4 April 1949?

5 On which mountain, according to tradition did Noah's Ark land in 2348 BC?

6 Which Mormon leader married his 27th, and last, wife in 1868?

7 For which movie did John Wayne win his only Oscar in 1970?

8 Kurt Cobain, found dead with self-inflicted gunshot wounds in Seattle in 1994, was singer-musician with which rock band?

9 Which former Panamanian dictator was found guilty of drug trafficking and money-laundering in 1992?

10 From which port did the 'Titanic' set sail on its ill-fated maiden voyage in 1912?

11 Who won best actress Oscar for Moonstruck in 1988?

12 Who, in 1961, became the first man to fly in space?

13 Which spaceship was crippled four-fifths of the way to the moon in 1970 when a tank containing liquid oxygen burst?

14 In 1985 President Lincoln was assassinated at Ford's Theatre while watching a performance of which play?

15 Which notorious leader of the Khmer Rouge died in 1998?

Answers **1** It was an April Fool **2** John Gotti **3** Jesse James **4** North Atlantic Treaty Organisation (NATO) **5** Mt Ararat **6** Brigham Young **7** True Grit **8** Nirvana **9** Manuel Noriega **10** Southampton **11** Cher **12** Yuri Gagarin **13** Apollo 13 **14** Our American Cousin **15** Pol Pot

April Almanac

16 Which aviation first was achieved by Harriet Quimby in 1912?

17 Who was convicted of assassinating Robert F. Kennedy in 1969?

18 Who began a ride from Charlestown to Lexington in 1775?

19 In 1951 which soldier bid farewell to Congress, quoting a line from a ballad, "Old soldiers never die; they just fade away"?

20 Who was born this day in 1889 at Braunau in Austria?

21 Who was the author of 'Jane Eyre', born in 1816?

22 Who was the 37th US President who died in 1994?

23 Who was the alleged assassin of Martin Luther King who died in 1998?

24 How was Wallis Warfield, who died in 1986, better known?

25 For which unfortunate first did highwayman, Nicolas Jacques Pelletier, achieve notoriety in France in 1792?

26 In 1964, which two African nations merged to become Tanzania?

27 Who, in 1956, retired as the undefeated World Heavyweight Boxing Champion?

28 Fletcher Christian led the mutiny on the Bounty against which sea captain in 1789?

29 Which actor, star of 'My Left Foot' and 'In the Name of the Father' was born in 1957?

30 Who died saving passengers when the Cannonball Express crashed in 1900?

Answers cont **16** First woman to fly across the English Channel **17** Sirhan Sirhan **18** Paul Revere **19** General Douglas MacArthur **20** Adolf Hitler **21** Charlotte Bronte **22** Richard M Nixon **23** James Earl Ray **24** The Duchess of Windsor **25** The first person to be guillotined **26** Tanganyika and Zanzibar **27** Rocky Marciano **28** William Bligh **29** Daniel Day-Lewis **30** Casey Jones

Almanac — May

1 Which motor racing champion was killed in the San Marino Grand Prix of 1994?

2 How old was Tony Blair when be became Britain's youngest Prime Minister for 185 years in 1997?

3 Born in 1933, who is known as the 'Godfather of Soul'?

4 Who was the inspiration for the character 'Alice in Wonderland', born this day in 1852?

5 On which island did Napoleon Bonaparte die in 1821?

6 Who on 6 May 1957, won the Pullitzer Prize for 'Profiles in Courage'?

7 Which actress, in 1987, made her last appearance as Diane in the TV show 'Cheers'?

8 Which French chemist, who identified oxygen, was guillotined during the French Revolution?

9 Which country was annexed by Italy in 1936?

10 Who was named FBI director in 1924?

11 What was the name of the supercomputer that defeated world champion Gary Kasparov at chess in 1997?

12 Which 'Spice Girl' is Melanie Chisholm, born in 1976?

13 Which South American republic was founded in 1830 under the presidency of Juan Jose Flores?

14 Who became King of France aged 4 in 1643?

15 In 1988 Russia began withdrawing its 115,000 troops from which country?

16 How old was Marie Antoinette when she married the future King of France in 1770?

17 Maureen O'Sullivan, born in 1917, starred in the early series of which movies?

Answers **1** Ayrton Senna **2** 44 **3** James Brown **4** Alice Liddell **5** St Helena **6** John F. Kennedy **7** Shelley Long **8** Antoine-Laurent Lavoisier **9** Ethiopia (then Abbysinia) **10** J Edgar Hoover **11** Deep Blue **12** Sporty Spice **13** Ecuador **14** Louis XIV **15** Afghanistan **16** 14 **17** Tarzan (she was Jane)

May

Almanac

18 Which volcano in Washington State exploded in 1980 resulting in the deaths of 57 people?

19 How did T. E. Lawrence (Lawrence of Arabia) die in 1935?

20 What was patented by H D Hyde in 1930?

21 Who married Humphrey Bogart in 1945?

22 Who, in 1992, signed off as host of 'The Tonight Show' in the US after 30 years?

23 Who was the Nazi Chief of Police who committed suicide the day after being captured in 1945?

24 Who transmitted the first telegraph message, 'What hath God wrought', in 1844?

25 Miles Davis, born in 1926, is a jazz virtuoso on what instrument?

26 Which Germman religious reformer was outlawed by 'The Edict of Worms' on 26th May 1521?

27 In 1936, which liner sailed on its maiden voyage from Southampton to New York, carrying more than 1,800 passengers?

28 Who was James Bond's creator, born 1908?

29 Which Spice Girl is Melanie Brown, born 1975?

30 Who was the voice of Bugs Bunny, born in 1908?

31 Israel signed an agreement with which country on the Golan Heights in 1974?

Answers cont **18** Mount St Helens **19** From injuries received in a motorcycle crash **20** The fountain pen **21** Lauren Bacall **22** Johnny Carson **23** Heinrich Himmler **24** Samuel Morse **25** Trumpet **26** Martin Luther **27** Queen Mary **28** Ian Fleming **29** Scary Spice **30** Mel Blanc **31** Syria

Almanac — June

1 Who was the 15th President of the US who died this day in 1868?

2 Who, in 1897, said: "the report of my death was an exaggeration"?

3 Who, in the US, did an actress and feminist, Valerie Solanas, shoot and critically wound in 1968?

4 What sport was played professionally by Andrea Jaeger, born in 1965?

5 Which screen cowboy was played by William Boyd, born 1898?

6 Which character has been portrayed several times on screen by Robert England, born 1949?

7 Which sovereign state came into being in 1929 as copies of the Lateran Treaty were exchanged in Rome?

8 In 1994, President Clinton received an honorary doctorate from which British University where he was a Rhodes scholar?

9 How did the Emperor Nero die in 68 AD?

10 Who was born Frances Gumm in 1922?

11 Who was the first wife of Henry VIII, who he married in 1509?

12 Sentenced to life imprisonment in 1978, by what name was serial killer David Berkowitz better known?

13 What was the name of the 1900 Rebellion in China against foreigners and Chinese Christians?

14 Which country surrendered to Nazi Germany in 1940?

15 Who performed a kite-flying experiment in 1752, to demonstrate that electricity and lightning were related?

Answers **1** James Buchanan **2** Mark Twain **3** Andy Warhol **4** Tennis **5** Hopalong Cassidy **6** Freddy, in the 'Nightmare on Elm Street' series **7** The Vatican City **8** Oxford **9** He committed suicide **10** Judy Garland **11** Catherine of Aragon **12** Son of Sam **13** The Boxer Rebellion **14** France **15** Benjamin Franklin

June Almanac

16 Which half of the Laurel and Hardy duo was born in England in 1890?

17 Who was accused of murdering Ronald Goldman in 1994?

18 Who, in 1928, became the first woman to fly across the Atlantic Ocean?

19 Who was the 19th-century Philadelphia bishop who Pope Paul VI proclaimed the first US male saint in 1977?

20 In which US state was Lizzie Borden found innocent of the axe murders of her father and stepmother in 1893?

21 Who opened his first '5 & 10 cent' store in 1899?

22 Who was 'The Bionic Woman' born in 1949?

23 The world's oldest parliament was established in which country in 930 AD?

24 Where did Robert the Bruce of Scotland defeat the English in 1314?

25 Which Indian chief routed Custor's 7th Cavalry at 'The Battle of the Little Big Horn' in 1876?

26 The charter for which organisation was signed by 50 countries in San Francisco in 1945?

27 Which founder of the Mormon Church was killed by a mob in 1844?

28 Which actress, star of 'Misery' and 'Fried Green Tomatos' was born in 1948?

29 Actor Bob Crane, found murdered in a hotel in Scottsdale, Arizona in 1978 starred in which TV comedy series?

30 Who was the last Aztec emperor, killed during the Spanish conquest of Mexico in 1520?

Answers cont **16** Stan Laurel **17** O J Simpson **18** Amelia Earhart **19** John Neumann **20** Massachusets **21** F W Woolworth **22** Lindsay Wagner **23** Iceland **24** Bannockburn **25** Crazy Horse **26** The United Nations **27** Joseph Smith **28** Kathy Bates **29** Hogan's Heroes **30** Montezuma II

Almanac July

1 Which annual sporting event was first held in London in 1877?

2 Who founded the Salvation Army in 1865?

3 Who, in Germany, drove the first automobile in 1886?

4 What did France present to the US in 1884?

5 What was innovative about the swimsuit unveiled by Louis Reard at a fashion show in Paris in 1946?

6 Which black tennis player won Wimbledon in 1957 by defeating fellow American Darlene Hard?

7 What was the original name of the Hoover Dam on which construction started in 1930?

8 Carlos Saul Menem was inaugurated as President of which country in 1989?

9 Born in 1954, how is rhythm-and-blues singer Debbie Sledge better known?

10 What is the name of the offiicial news agency of the Soviet Union, established in 1925?

11 Which pope excommunicated King Henry VIII in 1533?

12 At which battle in Ireland in 1690 did William of Orange defeat the army of James II?

13 Which French revolutionary writer was stabbed to death in his bath in 1793 by Charlotte Corday?

14 What was the real name of outlaw Billy the Kid, killed this day in 1881 by Sherriff Pat Garrett?

15 Who was the fashion designer shot dead outside his Miami home in 1997?

16 Which novelist published 'The Catcher in the Rye' in 1951?

17 What did the British royal family change their name to Windsor from in 1917?

Answers **1** The Wimbledon Tennis Championships **2** William Booth **3** Karl Benz **4** The Statue of Liberty **5** It was the first bikini **6** Althea Gibson **7** Boulder Dam **8** Argentina **9** Sister Sledge **10** Tass **11** Clement VII **12** The Battle of the Boyne **13** Jean Paul Marat **14** William H Bonney **15** Gianni Versace **16** J D Salinger **17** Saxe-Coberg Gotha

July **Almanac**

18 Where did a great fire begin this day in AD 64?

19 Sandinista guerillas gained control over which Central American capital city in 1979?

20 Who became the second man to walk on the moon after Neil Armstrong in 1969?

21 Born in 1948, by what name in his singing career was Yusuf Islam better known?

22 Which notorious bank robber was killed by Federal agents outside Chicago's Biograph Theatre in 1934?

23 Which Egyptian king was overthrown by General Abdel Nasser in 1952?

24 Who was 'Wonder Woman' born in 1951?

25 Who introduced the first steam locomotive in 1814?

26 The Potsdam Declaration, signed by the US, Britain and China on 26 July 1945, demanded the unconditional surrender of which nation?

27 From which US State did Sir Walter Raleigh bring tobacco to England in 1566?

28 Jim Davis, born in 1945, created which cartoon character?

29 Who was the cousin of Mary Queen of Scots who she married in 1565?

30 Ed Byrnes, born 1933, played the character of Cookie in which vintage TV series?

31 Who, in 1498, discovered Trinidad?

Answers cont **18** Rome **19** Managua (Nicaragua) **20** Edwin 'Buzz' Aldrin **21** Cat Stevens **22** John Dillinger **23** King Farouk I **24** Lynda Carter **25** George Stephenson **26** Japan **27** Virginia **28** Garfield **29** Henry Stuart, Lord Darnley **30** *77 Sunset Strip* **31** Christopher Columbus

Almanac — August

1 What form of transportation, invented by Andrew S. Hallidie for the City of San Francisco, was successfully tested in 1873?

2 Which country was invaded by Iraq in 1990?

3 Calais, France surrendered to which English King in the Hundred Years War?

4 Who invented champagne in 1693?

5 Who founded the first English colony in North America at St John's, Newfoundland in 1583?

6 Which comedienne who was married to Desi Arnez was born in 1911?

7 In 1974 French stuntman Philippe Petit walked a tightrope strung between the twin towers of which New York building?

8 Which actor, star of 'The Graduate' and 'Rain Man' was born in 1937?

9 On which Japanese city did the United States drop their second atomic bomb in 1945?

10 Who was the 31st President of the United States born in 1874?

11 Who became King of Jordan in 1952?

12 Who patented a sewing machine with rocking treadle in 1851?

13 Who created the comic strip 'Li'l Abner' which made its debut in 1934?

14 Which actor, star of 'Father of the Bride' and 'Roxanne' was born in 1945?

15 Which King of Scotland was slain by King Durean's son in 1057?

16 How is the singer Louise Ciccone, born 1958, better known?

Answers **1** The Cable Car **2** Kuwait **3** Edward III **4** Dom Perignon **5** Sir Humphry Gilbert **6** Lucille Ball **7** The World Trade Center **8** Dustin Hoffman **9** Nagasaki **10** Herbert Hoover **11** King Hussain **12** Isaac Singer **13** Al Capp **14** Steve Martin **15** Macbeth **16** Madonna

August | Almanac

17 Which country was divided on the 38th parallel in 1945?

18 Which Mongol conqueror died this day in 1227?

19 Gene Roddenberry, born 1921, was the creative force behind which cult TV and movie series?

20 Which Russian revolutionary was fatally wounded by a Spanish communist in Mexico City in 1940?

21 Which work of art was stolen from the Louvre in 1911?

22 Which science fiction writer, whose works include 'Fahreneit 451' and 'The Martian Chronicles' was born in 1920?

23 Who is 'The Six Million Dollar Man', born in 1940?

24 Who applied for a patent for his motion picture camera in 1891?

25 What first was achieved by Captain Matthew Webb in 1875?

26 Who published 'Animal Farm' in 1946?

27 What disaster resulted in the deaths of 36,000 people in Java and Sumatra in 1883?

28 Who pleaded innocent in 1981 to charges of attempting to kill President Reagan?

29 In 1742 Edmund Hoyle published his 'Short Treatise' on which card game?

30 Jean-Claude Killy, born 1943, was a world champion at which sport?

31 Which former Teamsters president went missing, never to be seen again in 1975?

Answers cont **17** Korea **18** Genghis Khan **19** Star Trek **20** Leon Trotsky **21** The Mona Lisa **22** Ray Bradbury **23** Lee Majors **24** Thomas Alva Edison **25** First person to swim the English Channel **26** George Orwell **27** The eruption of Krakatoa **28** John W Hinckley **29** Whist **30** Skiing **31** Jimmy Hoffa

Almanac

September

1 For what did Russia begin taxing males in 1689?

2 Which calendar did the Gregorian calendar replace in 1752?

3 The coronation of which King of England took place in Westminster Abbey in 1189?

4 In 1972 which US swimmer won a record seventh Olympic gold medal, in the 400-meter relay at the Munich Summer Olympics?

5 Who was the Albanian-born 1979 Nobel Peace Prize winner who died in 1997?

6 The coronation of which queen took place in the Netherlands in 1948?

7 Keith Moon, who died of an overdose of pills in 1978 was the drummer with which rock group?

8 The German blockade of which Russian city, which lasted until January 1944, began in 1941?

9 What was founded by Colonel Harland Sanders, born this day in 1890?

10 In an act that was to lead to the toppling of the Berlin Wall, which country opened its borders to the West in 1989?

11 Who first performed his song 'Oh! Susanna' in 1847?

12 Which obelisk, originally cut from the quarries of Aswan in about 1475, was erected in London on 12 September 1878?

13 Who was the 'Willy Wonka and the Chocolate Factory' author born in 1916?

14 Which US President died of wounding in 1901 following an assassination attempt on 6 September?

15 Who discovered penicillin in 1928?

16 Who discovered Lake Nyasa in Africa in 1859?

17 Which actress, star of 'The Graduate' and 'Miracle Worker' was born in 1931?

Answers **1** Beards **2** The Julian Calendar **3** Richard I (The Lionheart) **4** Mark Spitz **5** Mother Theresa **6** Queen Juliana **7** The Who **8** Leningrad **9** Kentucky Fried Chicken **10** Hungary **11** Stephen Foster **12** Cleopatra's Needle **13** Roald Dahl **14** William McKinley **15** Alexander Fleming **16** David Livingstone

September **Almanac**

18 In which capital city was Greta Garbo born in 1905?

19 Elizabeth Barrett eloped with which other poet in 1846?

20 Who helped Bonnie Prince Charlie flee to France from Scotland in 1746?

21 What was the name of the first nuclear submarine commissioned in 1954?

22 Catherine Oxenberg, born in 1961, played Amanda Carrington in which TV series?

23 Who in 1952 went on television to deliver what came to be known as the 'Checkers' speech as he refuted allegations of improper campaign financing?

24 Who was the Muppet creator, born in 1936?

25 Born in 1951, which character was played by Mark Hamill in the movie 'Star Wars'?

26 Who, in 1960, made the longest speech in United Nations history at 4 hours 29 minutes?

27 The singer Marvin Lee Aday, born in 1951, is better known by what name?

28 Who was elected Prime Minister of South Africa in 1978?

29 Which rock star, nickname 'The Killer' was born in 1935?

30 Whose publication of the Bible became the first book ever published in 1452?

Answers cont **17** Anne Bancroft **18** Stockholm **19** Robert Browning **20** Flora McDonald **21** USS Nautilus **22** Dynasty **23** Richard M. Nixon **24** Jim Henson **25** Luke Skywalker **26** Fidel Casto **27** Meat Loaf **28** P W Botha **29** Jerry Lee Lewis **30** Johann Guttenberg

Almanac — October

1 Who became President of the Soviet Union in 1988?

2 Which Sultan of Syria captured Jerusalem from the Christians in 1187?

3 To what did the Kingdom of Serbs, Croats and Slovenes change its name in 1929?

4 Which silent film comedian and star of 'The General' was born in Piqua, Kansas in 1895?

5 What natural disaster destroyed most of Calcutta in 1864 killing 70,000 people?

6 The Reno Brothers committed which crime in the US in 1866, the first ever of its kind?

7 Which writer of mysterious and macabre stories, himself died mysteriously aged 40 in 1849?

8 Which composer, in 1892, first performed his 'Prelude in C-sharp-Minor' in Moscow?

9 What was salvaged from the frigate HMS Lutine when she sank off the Dutch coast in 1799?

10 Which Vice-President of the US resigned in 1973 after being charged with tax evasion?

11 On who did Pope Leo X bestow the title of 'Defender of the Faith' in 1492?

12 What in 1901 did President Theodore Roosevelt rename his 'Executive Mansion'?

13 Which Roman emperor died after eating poisoned mushrooms given to him by his wife Agrippina in 54 AD?

14 How did Erwin Rommel die in 1944?

15 Which Soviet leader was removed from office in 1964?

16 Which Chinese leader began his 6,000 mile 'Long March' with 25,000 troops in 1934?

Answers **1** Mikhail Gorbachev **2** Saladin **3** Yugoslavia **4** Buster Keaton **5** A cyclone **6** Train robbery **7** Edgar Allan Poe **8** Sergei Rachmaninoff **9** The ship's bell now mounted in Lloyd's of London **10** Spiro Agnew **11** King Henry VIII **12** The White House **13** Claudius **14** By committing suicide **15** Nikita Krushchev **16** Mao Tse-Tung

October Almanac

17 At which athletics event did Bob Seagren break the world record five times in one day in 1968?

18 In the US which boundary between North and South was established in 1767?

19 Which author of spy novels, including 'The Tailor of Panama' and 'Russia House' was born in 1931?

20 Who was the star of 'Elmar Gantry' who died aged 80 in 1994?

21 At which battle was Lord Nelson killed in 1805?

22 What was the nickname of bank robber Charles Floyd, shot and killed by Federal Agents this day in 1934?

23 Who did the Soviet authorities pressurise into relinquishing the Nobel Prize for Literature which he won today in 1958?

24 Which trade union was granted recognition by Poland's communist authorities in 1980?

25 Who, in 1854, led the 'Charge of the Light Brigade' at Balaclava?

26 Hanged in 1440, what tale was inspired by Gilles de Rais, a French marshall who fought for Joan of Arc and was convicted of Satanism and the murder of 140 children?

27 What did Du Pont name its new synthetic fibre in 1938?

28 What is the popular name given to Tchaikovsky's 'Symphony Number Six in B minor', which he first conducted in 1893?

29 For what was Sir Walter Raleigh beheaded in 1618?

30 In which year on 30th October did engineers digging the Chunnel, to connect Britain and France under the English Channel, first achieve a link-up?

31 Who was 'Miss Ellie' of Dallas born in 1922?

Answers cont **17** Pole vault **18** The Mason-Dixon Line **19** John Le Carre **20** Burt Lancaster **21** Trafalgar **22** Pretty Boy **23** Boris Pasternak **24** Solidarity **25** Lord Cardigan **26** Bluebeard **27** Nylon **28** Pashetique **29** Treason **30** 1990 **31** Barbara Bel Geddes

Almanac November

1 Whose painting on the Sistine Chapel went on display in 1572?

2 Who was re-elected US President in 1948?

3 What was patented by Dr Richard Gatling in 1862?

4 Into which capital city did the Soviet Union send the tanks to crush a rebellion in 1956?

5 Who is the ‘Paper Moon’ actress and Oscar winner born in 1963?

6 The Bolshevik revolution began in Russia in 1917 with the capture of which palace?

7 Which cargo ship, later to be found mysteriously abandoned, set sail from New York in 1872?

8 What first was achieved in New York by David Dinkins in 1989?

9 Who was ‘The Incredible Hulk’ born in 1951?

10 Who, in 1871, said "Dr Livingstone I presume"?

11 Angola became independent from which country in 1975 after 500 years of colonial rule?

12 Who, in body-hugging costume, performed the first flying trapeze act without a safety net in 1859?

13 Which Walt Disney film depicting pieces of music set to cartoons opened in 1940?

14 Who first published his novel ‘Moby Dick’ in 1851?

15 Who patented the razor with disposable blades in 1904?

Answers **1** Michelangelo **2** Harry S. Truman **3** The machine gun **4** Budapest (Hungary) **5** Tatum O'Neill **6** The Winter Palace **7** Mary Celeste **8** He was elected the city's first black mayor **9** Lou Ferringo **10** Henry Morton Stanley **11** Portugal **12** Jules Leotard **13** Fantasia **14** Herman Melville **15** King Camp Gillette

November Almanac

16 Who succeeded his father Henry III to the throne of England in 1272?

17 Which two seas are linked by the Suez Canal which opened in 1869?

18 What did a Brooklyn toymaker Morris Michton name after President Theodore Roosevelt in 1902?

19 Who is the 'Sleepless in Seattle' actress born 1961?

20 Patented by Pierre Lallemont in Paris in 1866, what was 'the bone shaker' a type of?

21 Why in America in 1980 did an estimated 83 million viewers tune into an episode of Dallas?

22 Killed this day in 1718, who was Edward teach better known as?

23 Whose double-album 'The Wall' was released in 1979?

24 What is 'Air Force One', which was christened on 24th November 1954?

25 Which rock group made its farewell appearance in 1976, an event filmed and made into a movie by Martin Scorsese called 'The Last Waltz'?

26 Which country launched its first satellite, Astrix 1, in 1965 to become the third country in space?

27 What did John Walker invent in England in 1826?

28 What first was achieved in Britain in 1919 by Lady Nancy Astor?

29 Who was the Chief Justice appointed in 1963 to head the commission on investigating the assassination of President Kennedy?

30 Which former British colony in the West Indies became independent in 1966?

Answers cont **16** Edward I **17** Mediterranean and Red **18** The teddy bear **19** Meg Ryan **20** Bicycle **21** It was the 'Who Shot JR?' episode **22** Blackbeard **23** Pink Floyd **24** The US Presidential airplane **25** The Band **26** France **27** Matchsticks **28** First woman elected to sit in the House of Commons **29** Earl Warren **30** Barbados

Almanac — December

1 In which book, in 1887, did Sherlock Holmes make his first appearance in print?

2 Who starred opposite Joan Crawford in his first film 'Dancing Lady' in 1933?

3 Who wrote 'A Streetcar Named Desire' which opened on Broadway in 1947?

4 What, in India, was the practice of 'suttee' which was abolished by the British in 1829?

5 What is the former name of the island now contaning Haiti and the Dominican Republic which Colombus discovered in 1492?

6 Who, in 1821, finished his piano sonata, Opus 109?

7 Which US space probe began orbiting Jupiter in 1995?

8 Who murdered John Lennon in 1980?

9 Whose poem, 'The Charge of the Light Brigade' was published in 1854?

10 Who died in a plane crash in 1967 shortly after recording his biggest hit 'Sittin' on the Dock of the Bay'?

11 Who was 'Little Miss Dynamite' born in 1944?

12 Who patented the first hovercraft prototype in 1955?

13 Which Dutch explorer discovered New Zealand in 1642?

14 Who in 1969 made their first appearance on 'The Ed Sullivan Show' singing their first hit "I Want You Back'?

15 What was the name of the group led by John Lennon and Yoko Ono which played their first and only concert at London's Lyceum Ballroom on 15th December 1969?

16 In which city was Ludwig van Beethoven born in 1770?

Answers **1** A Study in Scarlett **2** Fred Astaire **3** Tennessee Williams **4** The widow burning herself to death on her husband's funeral pyre **5** Hispaniola **6** Beethoven **7** Galileo **8** Mark David Chapman **9** Alfred Lord Tennyson **10** Otis Redding **11** Brenda Lee **12** Christopher Cockerell **13** Abel Tasman **14** The Jackson Five **15** The Plastic ONo Band **16** Bonn

December

Almanac

17 From where did Wilber and Orville Wright make their first successful flight in 1903?

18 Born 1943, Keith Richards plays guitar with which rock group?

19 Who, under the name Richard Saunders began publishing 'Poor Richard's Almanac' in 1732?

20 What name was first given to New York's Broadway when it was lit up by electricity in 1880?

21 What was the former name of the state of Eire which declared its independence in 1948?

22 Who directed 'Dr Zhivago' which premiered in 1965?

23 Who in 1888 cut off his ear in a fit of depression?

24 Which reclusive US millionaire industrialist and film producer was born in 1905?

25 Who devised the centigrade temperature scale in 1741?

26 Who was the future Tarzan film actor who retired from amateur swimming in 1928 after never losing a freestyle race?

27 Aboard which vessel did Charles Darwin set sail in 1831?

28 Who in Paris, in 1895, held their first commercial exhibition of projected motion pictures?

29 Which Archbishop of Canterbury was murdered in 1170 by the supporters of Henry II?

30 Who proclaimed the establishment of the Union of Soviet Socialist Republics in 1922?

31 What game was patented by Charles Darrow in 1935?

Answers cont **17** Kittyhawk **18** The Rolling Stones **19** Benjamin Franklin **20** Great White Way **21** Irish Free State **22** David Lean **23** Vincent van Gogh **24** Howard Hughes **25** Andreas Celsius **26** Johnny Weissmuller **27** HMS Beagle **28** The Lumiere Brothers **29** Thomas A Becket **30** Lenin **31** Monopoly

SECTION 5

Miscellaneous

Miscellaneous Quiz 1

1 Republic of south-eastern Europe whose name means ‘Eagles Country’.

2 What are ‘oriflamme’ and ‘burgee’ types of?

3 Where in the US were the 1904 Olympic Games held?

4 Guillotined in the French Revolution, who was the mistress of King Louis XV?

5 Which champagne bottle size is equal to a double magnum?

6 What in 1939, did Winston Churchill describe as a riddle, wrapped in a mystery inside an enigma?

7 Who in the House of Lords sits on the Woolsack?

8 Which game of ancient Chinese origin is played with a full set of 152 tiles divided into seven suits?

9 Which famous composer was born in Salzburg, Austria?

10 What is the more common name of the pelargonium?

11 What was the by name of James Buchanan Brady (1856-1917), an American financier and philanthropist, who had a predilection for expensive jewellery?

12 What was invented by Bartolommico Christopheri in 1709?

13 Who was the second wife of Henry VIII?

14 What is the American equivalent of Sandhurst?

15 Of where is Mogadishu the capital?

Answers **1** Albania **2** Flags **3** St.Louis **4** Madame Du Barry **5** Jeroboam **6** Russia **7** The Lord Chancellor **8** Mah Jongg **9** Mozart **10** Geranium **11** He was known as Diamond Jim **12** The piano **13** Anne Boleyn **14** West Point **15** Somalia

Quiz 2 — Miscellaneous

1 A variety of sheep with fine silky wool?

2 Monetary unit of Chile?

3 A sweetmeat made at Pontefract, Yorkshire?

4 What is the science of bodily structure?

5 An isolated flat-top hill?

6 An enchantress who kept Odysseus on her island and turned his men into swine?

7 A length of one-tenth of a metre?

8 To whip, scourge or flog?

9 What type of English architecture has ‘zigzag’ or ‘chevron’ mouldings?

10 A short handled whip with a leather thong at one end?

11 An ancient Roman coin, worth a quarter of a denarius?

12 A small seal, often fixed to a ring

13 What is a trigram?

14 What does dirigible mean?

15 A fine whetstone, especially for sharpening razors?

Answers **1** Merino **2** Peso **3** Pomfret cake **4** Anatomy **5** Butte **6** Circe **7** A decimetre **8** Flagellate **9** Norman **10** A quirt **11** Sesterce **12** Signet **13** A figure of three lines **14** Capable of being steered **15** Hone

Miscellaneous — Quiz 3

1 Which queen journeyed to Jerusalem to test the wisdom of Solomon?

2 Where in Kansas in the late 19th century did the outlaw Dalton Gang lose several of his members in a failed bank robbery?

3 What is the Russian word for citadel?

4 Where would you find people wearing a dress called a Muu-muu?

5 Who originated the phrase "there's a sucker born every minute"?

6 Which Muslim leader captured Jerusalem from the Crusaders?

7 In the Chinese calendar which year follows the Tiger?

8 What was the name of the dog launched into space by Russia in 1957?

9 Rubella is another name for which disease?

10 Which Roman epic poet said 'They can because they think they can'?

11 Which element was discovered in 1789 by Martin Heinrich Klaproth?

12 What is the name of the towered temple in the shape of a steep pyramid constructed by the ancient Babylonians?

13 Who succeeded Dag Hammarskjoeld as Secretary General of the UN?

14 What is the commonest molecular compound on earth?

15 Who was elected US President in 1968?

Answers **1** The Queen of Sheba **2** Coffeeville **3** Kremlin **4** Hawaii **5** P.T. Barnum **6** Saladin **7** Rabbit **8** Laika **9** German measles **10** Virgil **11** Uranium **12** Ziggurat **13** U. Thant **14** Water **15** Richard Nixon

Quiz 4 — Miscellaneous

1 A faint luminous ring which can sometimes be seen projecting on to a cloud?

2 In Christianity, the gold or silver cup containing the wine at mass?

3 To pour liquid, especially wine, from one container to another without disturbing any sediment?

4 An archaic term for old age?

5 From 17th century French meaning 'false step', used to describe a social blunder or indiscretion?

6 A free, but not noble landowner of 14th and 15th Century England?

7 A rope for lowering a sail?

8 Congenital, existing in a person from birth?

9 Jokey and good humoured?

10 Which Saint's day falls on 17 March?

11 Which sport features a movement called a Veronica?

12 Of or relating to the palate?

13 A short post, used as a upright strut?

14 Former Parliament of Denmark?

15 A large group of fish?

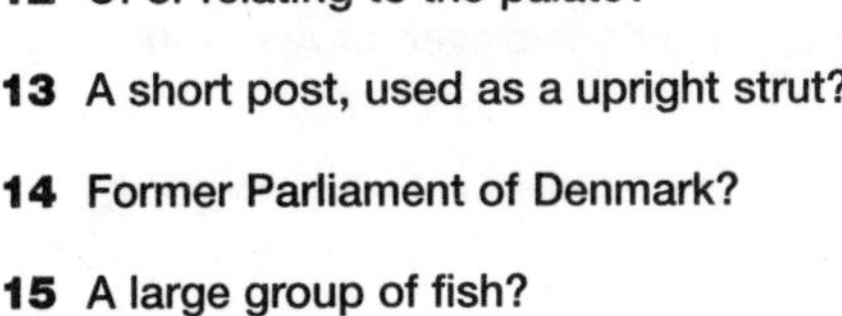

Answers **1** Anthelion **2** Chalice **3** Decant Eld **5** Faux pas **6** Franklin **7** Halyard **8** Innate **9** Jocular **10** St Patrick **11** Bullfighting **12** Palatine **13** Puncheon **14** Rigsdag **15** Shoal

Miscellaneous — Quiz 5

1 Of where is Port-au-Prince the capital?

2 What is Greco-Roman a style of?

3 Singultus is the technical term for which condition?

4 Which singer, known as the 'Sweetheart of Colombia Records', was portrayed in the 1955 movie 'Love Me or Leave Me' by Doris Day?

5 Mary Jane Kelly was the last known victim of which serial killer?

6 Which Dutch scholar (1466-1536) said 'When I get a little money I buy books. And if there is any left over I buy food'?

7 What is the former name of Ethiopia?

8 Against which country did Saddam Hussein declare a holy war in 1980?

9 Who lost his right arm at the Battle of Cape Vincent?

10 At the Royal Variety Show John Lennon invited those in the cheap seats to clap. What did he invite those in the expensive seats to do?

11 In the Bible who is the elder brother of Moses and founder of the Hebrew priesthood?

12 What is the name of the line from which a darts player throws at the board?

13 What is the popular name for the General Purpose vehicle unveiled by Willys in 1940?

14 What is the Arabic word for 'submission' to the will of Allah?

15 Which film actress was born Betty Joan Perske?

Answers **1** Haiti **2** Wrestling **3** Hiccups **4** Ruth Etting **5** Jack the Ripper **6** Erasmus **7** Abyssinia **8** Iran **9** Horatio Nelson **10** Rattle their jewellery **11** Aaron **12** Oche **13** Jeep **14** Islam **15** Lauren Bacall

Quiz 6 — Miscellaneous

1 Equal to or having three times as many or as much?

2 A South African gazelle, also the name of the South African rugby team?

3 In feudal times, a fee sometimes taken by a lord from his vassall in lieu of military service?

4 Flour cooked in melted fat and used as the basis for sauces?

5 Formerly a minor official of a town or district in england or USA. Still used in parts of rural Canada to describe the President of a local council?

6 Easily appeased?

7 Who was the slave in 'The Tempest?

8 Any small, silvery European fish?

9 A small can, especially when used as a drinking vessel?

10 A West African country, a province of Portugal until 1975?

11 Very great, but also extremely bad?

12 Froth from fermenting malt liquor?

13 A bundle of twigs used as a brush?

14 A card game for two to four players, played with two packs, using only cards above seven?

15 Plump and comely, especially of a woman?

Answers **1** Threefold **2** Springbok **3** Scutage **4** Roux **5** Reeve **6** Placable **7** Caliban **8** Bleak **9** Cannikin **10** Angola **11** Abysmal **12** Barm **13** Besom **14** Bezique **15** Buxom

Miscellaneous — Quiz 7

1 A mild tropical fever, with similar symptoms to sunstroke?

2 A Highland fighting man

3 A person who relies to much on learning and is concerned with unimportant detail?

4 Someone, like a pirate who lives off plundered goods?

5 Acid fruit for making jelly

6 A US slang word for jail, from the Mexican Spanish jusgado, meaning prison?

7 A simpleton?

8 The nest in which insects deposit eggs?

9 Fur of the coypu?

10 A poisonous evergreen shrub, with pink, white or purple flowers. Also known as rosebay??

11 Pig-like mammals of Northern USA and Central and South America?

12 A square dance for couples, also the piece of music for such a dance?

13 A necklace of diamonds

14 A porcelain manufactured with the addition of bone-ash, by English potter, Josiah ...... (1754-1827)?

15 Short musical composition for solo instruments?

Answers **1** Calenture **2** Catcran **3** Pedant **4** Freebooter **5** Guava **6** Hoosegow **7** Juggins **8** Nidus **9** Nutria **10** Oleander **11** Peccary **12** Quadrille **13** Rivi're **14** Spode **15** ...tude

Quiz 8 — Miscellaneous

1 From which plant is hashish obtained?

2 Female fox?

3 Native tropical and sub-tropical American plant, having saw-like leaves and white flowers?

4 A double-reeded woodwind musical instrument?

5 Treeless plain of South America?

6 The person making a will?

7 A table with three legs, often used to hold cameras?

8 To take the place of something old fashioned?

9 The period for hatching out eggs?

10 Who discovered the island of Cuba?

11 Mischievous, roguish child?

12 The abominable snowman?

13 A state of perplexity?

14 A small piece of live coal?

15 White of an egg?

Answers **1** Cannabis **2** Vixen **3** Yucca **4** Oboe **5** Pampas **6** Testator **7** Tripod **8** Supersede **9** Incubation **10** Columbus **11** Urchin **12** Yeti **13** Quandary **14** Ember **15** Albumen

Miscellaneous — Quiz 9

1 Who is Snoopy's sister in the comic strip 'Peanuts'?

2 In computer science what is a measurement of 1,024 bytes?

3 Who in early 20th century Russia was the Mad Monk?

4 Which actor has starred in 'Romeo and Juliet', 'Growing Pains' and 'What's Eating Gilbert Grape'?

5 Ant-eating mammal whose name in Afrikaans means 'earth pig'

6 Who wrote 'Candide'?

7 A line on a weather map linking places of equal barometric pressure?

8 The Irrawaddy is the principle river of which country?

9 Which singer had a 'Pretty Good Year' in the charts in 1994?

10 Who, in 1927, succeeded Leon Trotsky as leader of the Communist Party in Russia?

11 What is the group of 600 small islands and islets in the Windward Islands which include Carriacou, Union and Mustique?

12 Which Turkish empire was dominant from the 16-19th centuries?

13 Who did Michael Moorer defeat to win the World Heavyweight boxing title in 1994?

14 Who is the King of the Fairies in Shakespeare's 'A Midsummer Night's Dream'?

15 Which musical term means increasing degrees of loudness?

Answers **1** Belle **2** Kilobyte **3** Rasputin **4** Leonardo Di Caprio **5** Aardvark **6** Voltaire **7** Isobar **8** Burma (Republic of Myanmar) **9** Tori Amos **10** Joseph Stalin **11** Grenadines **12** Ottoman **13** Evander Holyfield **14** Oberon **15** Fortissimo

Quiz 10 — Miscellaneous

1 Mainly US or Canadian slang for a crazy person. Often used to describe a type of comedy film?

2 To make a grating or creaking sound?

3 Wife of a Sultan

4 Any of various small ducks, that are related to a mallard?

5 An edible sea cucumber, eaten by the Chinese and Japanese?

6 A nut or fruit sweet covered in hard sugar icing?

7 A high voice in men?

8 Of or relating to public revenue?

9 Everlasting?

10 An informal term for a brawl or commotion?

11 An unlicensed house selling drink, especially in South Africa and Ireland?

12 A historical Japanese ruler?

13 Aromatic substance in ointments obtained from a native Indian plant, with rose-purple flowers?

14 A small dagger wuith a slender tapered blade, also a very pointed heel on a shoe?

15 A particle of dust?

Answers **1** Screwball **2** Scroop **3** Sultana **4** Teal **5** Trepang **6** Dragee
7 Falsetto **8** Fiscal **9** Sempiternal **10** Shindy **11** Shebeen **12** Shogun
13 Spikenard **14** Stiletto **15** Mote

Miscellaneous — Quiz 11

1 What abbreviation in computer language means Formula Translation?

2 What is another name for pyrite?

3 Alan Price played keyboard and sang with which pop group in the 1960s?

4 At which Olympic sport do the competitors never cross the finishing line?

5 Who wrote 'Moby Dick'?

6 Who in mythology was the eldest of the Titans and god of waters?

7 Who, in 1881, did Charles J. Guiteau assassinate?

8 Which seabirds are nicknamed 'goonies' because of their fearlessness around humans?

9 Which poet wrote: 'I wandered lonely as a cloud'?

10 Who, in 1908, presented the quantum theory of light?

11 Which female monsters in mythology had snakes for hair and glances that turned mortals to stone?

12 City of Northern Syria, also known as Halab

13 What in Hawaii is Kilauea?

14 Pseudonym of French writer Francois Marie Arouet?

15 What do the initials OPEC stand for?

Answers **1** Fortran **2** Fool's Gold **3** The Animals **4** Swimming **5** Herman Melville **6** Oceanus **7** President James Garfield **8** The albatross **9** Wordsworth **10** Albert Einstein **11** Gorgons **12** Aleppo **13** A volcano **14** Voltaire Organisation of Petroleum Exporting Countries

Quiz 12 — Miscellaneous

		Answer starts with
1	Another name for a pineapple?	A
2	What is collusion?	C
3	Words inscribed on a tomb?	E
4	A word which means 'of iron'?	F
5	What in Italy is 'La Stampa'?	N
6	Vacuum flask?	T
7	A small stream or rivulet?	R
8	Capital of Liberia?	M
9	Plants that flower every year?	P
10	What does the term 'wagon-lit', usually applied to European trains, mean?	S
11	Brass musical instrument formerly called a sackbut?	T
12	Setting to music of a religious theme?	O
13	Helps a priest at mass?	A
14	The longest river in China?	Y
15	Covered with a sticky substance?	V

Answers **1** Ananas **2** Cahoots **3** Epitaph **4** Ferric **5** Newspaper **6** Thermos **7** Rill **8** Monrovia **9** Perennials **10** Sleeping car **11** Trombone **12** Oratorio **13** Acolyte **14** Yangtze **15** Viscid

Miscellaneous — Quiz 13

1 Who plays Scully in The X-Files?

2 Mac Maurice Wilkins was the first man ever to break the 70-metre barrier at which sport?

3 Which film star was born Rodolpho Guglielmi?

4 What caused the Mississippi River to flow backwards in 1811?

5 Whose last major work as 'Rhapsody on a Theme of Paganini' (1934)?

6 What, in mythology, were Aeolus, Boreas and Zephyrus?

7 Who, on television, plays 'Frasier'?

8 Who was King of the Huns from 406 to 453?

9 What is the capital of Brazil?

10 Who succeeded Queen Mary to the throne of England?

11 Which two seas are linked by the Suez Canal?

12 Who was the thief released by Pontius Pilate instead of Jesus?

13 What material was invented around 1910 by a Swiss chemist Jacques Brandenburger?

14 In military science, what is the name given to operations carried out in support of combat units?

15 Who plays Captain Picard in 'Star Trek'?

Answers **1** Gillian Anderson **2** Discus **3** Rudolf Valentino **4** An earthquake **5** Rachmaninov **6** Winds **7** Kelsey Grammer **8** Attila **9** Brasilia **10** Elizabeth I **11** Mediterranean and Red **12** Barabbas **13** Cellophane **14** Logistics **15** Patrick Stewart

Quiz 14 Miscellaneous

		Answer starts with
1	Open carriage?	B
2	Winged staff of Mercury?	C
3	What is the name given to a person born or living in the Orkneys?	O
4	Sea ducks with fine down?	E
5	Money pool in card games?	J
6	Stage name for Frances Gumm?	G
7	The tinkling sound of bells?	T
8	Largest island in the West Indies?	C
9	A sea fish of the cod family?	H
10	Herbaceous plant having red, blue, white or yellow five-lobed flowers, the lower three forming a lip?	L
11	Large flightless bird?	C
12	Bird's second stomach for grinding food?	G
13	Black and white in patches?	P
14	Rate of change of position?	V
15	Paste of meat?	P

Answers **1** Britzka **2** Caduceous **3** Orcadian **4** Eider **5** Jackpot **6** Garland **7** Tintinnabulation **8** Cuba **9** Haddock **10** Lobelia **11** Cassowary **12** Gizzard **13** Piebald **14** Velocity **15** Pate

Miscellaneous — Quiz 15

1 Who plays TV's Ally McBeal?

2 What is the more common name of the giant tree 'sequoia sempervirens'?

3 Which tiny shrimp-like sea creatures are eaten by whales?

4 Which US city, known as the 'Mile High City', is served by Stapleton International Airport?

5 Another name for tetanus?

6 Which classic Spielberg movie features a chase between a tank truck and a car driven by Dennis Weaver?

7 Who made his first screen appearance in a 1928 film 'Steamboat Willie'?

8 Which book of the Bible features the stories of Shadrack, Meshach and Abednego?

9 Of where is Dakar the capital?

10 Which is the second highest mountain in North America?

11 What word meaning 'rebirth' referred to the 'discovery of the world and of man' in the 16th century?

12 Which school did Billy Bunter go to?

13 Another name for the god Poseidon?

14 If someone is lentigineous, what distinctive feature would they display?

15 River in the Irish Republic which flows into Limerick Bay?

Answers **1** Calista Flockhart **2** Redwood **3** Krill **4** Denver **5** Lockjaw
6 Duel **7** Mickey Mouse **8** Daniel **9** Senegal **10** Mount Logan
11 Renaissance **12** Greyfriars **13** Neptune **14** Freckles **15** Shannon

Quiz 16 — Miscellaneous

		Answer starts with
1	Small yellowish brown deer?	F
2	Not liable to sin?	I
3	Smooth variety of peach?	N
4	Fit or worthy to be chosen?	E
5	Circular violent storm?	C
6	Former name of Iraq?	M
7	Small mug or wooden cup?	N
8	Former royal family of Austria?	H
9	To flow out of a body?	E
10	The science of light and vision?	O
11	A trembling in the voice?	Q
12	Capital of Malta?	V
13	Island where Jakarta is situated?	J
14	Ash obtained from seaweed?	K
15	Order of butterflies?	L

Answers **1** Fallow **2** Impeccable **3** Nectarine **4** Eligible **5** Cyclone **6** Mesopotamia **7** Noggin **8** Hapsburgs **9** Exude **10** Optics **11** Quaver **12** Valletta **13** Java **14** Kelp **15** Lepidoptera

Miscellaneous — Quiz 17

1 What kind of car is driven by 'Mr. Bean'?

2 Who said 'Genius is eternal patience'?

3 Which actress drowned in 1981 while filming the movie 'Brainstorm'?

4 Who did Claus Schenk Graf von Stauffenberg attempt to assassinate in 1944?

5 Which country gave Guam to the US in 1898?

6 Who was the former US Senator of Kansas and a 1996 US presidential candidate?

7 Who starred in 'Cheers' and the movie 'The People vs Larry Flint'?

8 Who did Satwat Singh, executed in 1989, assassinate in 1988?

9 Paul-Henri Spaak who became Secretary-General of NATO, was a former Prime Minister of which country?

10 What do the letters PS stand for at the end of a letter?

11 Where were the first winter Olympics held in 1924?

12 How old was James VI when be became King of Scotland in 1567 on the abdication of Mary Queen of Scots?

13 Where did Matthew Webb, the first man to swim the English Channel, drown in 1883?

14 From which prison did Ronald Biggs escape in 1974?

15 Who in 1814 introduced the first steam locomotive?

Answers **1** Mini **2** Michelangelo **3** Natalie Wood **4** Adolf Hitler **5** Spain **6** Bob Dole **7** Woody Harrelson **8** Indira Gandhi **9** Belgium **10** Postscript **11** Chamonix **12** 1 year old **13** At Niagara Falls trying to swim the rapids **14** Wandsworth **15** George Stephenson

Quiz 18 — Miscellaneous

		Answers starts with
1	Sweet minty drink?	J
2	Gruesome?	M
3	Hanging plaited hair, or standing in line?	Q
4	Group of three?	T
5	Short wooden wax match?	V
6	A group of states?	E
7	Genus of cone bearing trees?	C
8	The central wedge of an arch?	K
9	A proportionate share?	Q
10	Underground burial place?	C
11	Convert into glass?	V
12	Guardian's care?	W
13	Fine sword blade?	T
14	Small high pitched flute?	P
15	Bordering on the improper?	R

Answers **1** Julep **2** Macabre **3** Queue **4** Triad **5** Vesta **6** Empire **7** Cedars **8** Keystone **9** Quota **10** Catacombs **11** Vitrify **12** Wardship **13** Toledo **14** Piccolo **15** Risque

Miscellaneous — Quiz 19

1 Who was the first test tube baby, born 1978?

2 Who was the Duke of Lancaster and third son of Edward III of England?

3 Who was the Nobel prize-winning author deported from the USSR and deprived of Soviet citizenship in 1974?

4 What first was achieved in 1969 by Sharon Adams?

5 Which actress starred in 'Speed' and 'The Net'?

6 At which sport was Dorothy Hamill an Olympic Champion in the 1970s?

7 Which actress was born Ilynea Lydia Mironoff?

8 What is the nickname of snooker player Alex Higgins?

9 Which king was known as 'Coeur de Lion'?

10 The Duke of Monmouth who led an unsuccessful rebellion against James II was the illegitimate son of Lucy Walter and which English king?

11 What useful little device was first patented by Walter Hunt in 1849?

12 What name is given to the first five books of the Old Testament?

13 Which classic novel features an asylum called Lowood?

14 Who directed 'Four Weddings and a Funeral'?

15 What in 1924 was the name of the first pictorial postage stamp issued in Britain?

Answers **1** Louise Jay Brown **2** John of Gaunt **3** Alexander Solzhenitzy **4** First woman to sail alone across the Pacific Ocean **5** Sandra Bullock **6** Figure skating **7** Helen Mirren **8** Hurricane **9** Richard I **10** Charles II **11** The safety pin **12** The Pentateuch **13** Jane Eyre **14** Mike Newell **15** The Wembley Commemorative

Quiz 20 Miscellaneous

		Answers starts with
1	What was the language of Jesus?	A
2	Greenish yellow suffocating gas?	C
3	Small cucumber used for pickling?	G
4	Who is the creator of Harry Potter?	R
5	A word meaning snake-like?	A
6	Short light capricious composition?	F
7	Rich embroidered silk fabric?	K
8	A stupid person?	D
9	What is hyssop a type of?	H
10	An archaic or dialect word for ant?	E
11	A metric foot of three syllables?	I
12	What does legato mean?	S
13	Piece of furniture with shelves?	W
14	Ornamental loop in yarn?	K
15	Who wrote the novel 'Ulysses'?	J

Answers **1** Aramaic **2** Chlorine **3** Gherkin **4** Rowling **5** Anguine **6** Fianchetto **7** Kincob **8** Dunderhead **9** Herb **10** Emmet **11** Iambus **12** Smooth **13** Whatnot **14** Knop **15** Joyce

Miscellaneous **Quiz 21**

1 Who was the fifth wife of Henry VIII?

2 Guillotined in 1794, who was the revolutionary who in France launched the reign of terror and was known as 'The Incorruptible'?

3 In 1821 Peru declared itself independent of which country?

4 Rick White was keyboardist with which rock group?

5 Against who did Paula Jones launch a legal action in 1994?

6 Which cricketer scored 501 in one innings against England in 1994?

7 Who is Patrick Tambay?

8 What was the name of the mother of the late Martin Luther King, who was herself assassinated during a church service in 1974?

9 Which two German tennis players won the Men's and Women's Wimbledon Tennis Championships respectively in 1989?

10 Who married Michael Jackson in 1994?

11 What was invented by Wiel Kellogg in 1898?

12 Who, in 1774, discovered oxygen?

13 How was the terrorist Slich Rameriz Sanchez better known?

14 What was the name of Edward Heath's yacht, wrecked in a storm off Shoreham in 1974

15 Which was the first country to use the metric system?

Answers **1** Catherine Howard **2** Robespierre **3** Spain **4** Pink Floyd **5** President Clinton **6** Brian Lara **7** A French Grand Prix racing driver **8** Alberta King **9** Boris Becker and Steffi Graf **10** Lisa Marie Presley **11** Cornflakes **12** Joseph Priestly **13** Carlos the Jackal **14** Morning Cloud **15** France

Quiz 22 Miscellaneous

		Answers starts with
1	An archaic word for sulphur?	B
2	The word for killing hares?	L
3	Opera is the plural of which word?	O
4	A blue clay lying close to a vein of coal?	U
5	Cuttle bones come from?	S
6	The word meaning hook-shaped?	U
7	Which architect designed the Marble Arch?	N
8	A mainly British slang term for a prison?	Q
9	French 18th century novelist who wrote a best seller in prison?	V
10	Large white North American owl?	W
11	A stockade?	Z
12	White marble-like stone?	A
13	Who killed the minotaur in the Cretian labyrinth?	T
14	What is a blacksmith's hammer called?	F
15	The quantity that a cask wants of being full?	U

Answers **1** Brimstone **2** Leporicide **3** Opus **4** Urry **5** Squid **6** Unciform **7** Nash **8** Quod **9** Voltaire **10** Wapacut **11** Zareba **12** Alabaster **13** Theseus **14** Fuller **15** Ullage

Miscellaneous **Quiz 23**

1 Francis Rossi is associated with which rock group?

2 What was the name of the Hashemite kingdom of Jordan prior to 1940?

3 By what name is Lesley Hornby better known?

4 In which century was the composer Frederic Chopin born?

5 Who directed 'Nightmare on Elm Street' and 'Scream'?

6 What was invented by Dom Perignon in 1693?

7 What first was achieved by Ffyona Campbell in 1994?

8 Which new market opened at Nine Elms, Battersea London in 1974?

9 Who was the little known 'stalking horse' who challenged Margaret Thatcher for leadership of the Conservative Party in 1989?

10 Michael Manley was Prime Minister of which country from 1972-80?

11 What did Agatha Christie describe as the best husband a woman could have, because the older she gets, the more interested he becomes in her?

12 Who wrote 'The Little Mermaid'?

13 What fate befell Andrew and Abby Borden on 8 April 1892 at Fall River, Massachusetts?

14 Prior to 1916 the US Virgin Islands was an overseas territory of which country?

15 What first was achieved by Gertrude Ederle in 1926?

Answers **1** Status Quo **2** Transjordan **3** Twiggy **4** The 19th century (1849) **5** Wes Craven **6** Champagne **7** She was the first woman to walk round the world **8** Covent Garden (the new venue) **9** Sir Anthony Meyer **10** Jamaica **11** An archaeologist **12** Hans Christian Anderson **13** They were axed to death by their daughter Lizzie **14** Denmark **15** The first woman to swim the English Channel

Quiz 24

Miscellaneous

		Answer starts with
1	A person in fear of bees?	A
2	Having a prickly skin?	E
3	West Indian dance, which involves leaning backwards under a bar?	L
4	What is the nickname for a 'fox'?	R
5	Having five angles?	Q
6	Flat river vessel?	G
7	Resembling a grape?	U
8	Turkish heel-less shoe?	B
9	A small fort?	F
10	Tax on salt in France?	G
11	Sweating?	H
12	Having no trace of life?	A
13	Currency of Panama?	B
14	A graceful solo Spanish dance and the music composed of it?	C
15	Study of trees?	D

Answers Apiphobe **2** Echinoderm **3** Limbo **4** Reynard **5** Quinquangular **6** Gabbart **7** Uveous **8** Babouche **9** Fortalice **10** Gabelle **11** Hidrosis **12** Azoic **13** Balbao **14** Cachucha **15** Dendrology

Miscellaneous — Quiz 25

1 By what name was the circus clown Nikolai Poliakov better known?

2 Who, in mythology, slew Achilles at Troy?

3 Which is the largest island in Denmark?

4 The Latin version of the Bible, dating from the 4th century AD

5 Anserine is resembling or characteristic of which creature?

6 Who was the Iroquois chieftain who inspired a poem by Longfellow?

7 Of where is Hobart the capital?

8 What name connects a conspicuous constellation in the northern hemisphere and an aquatic songbird?

9 Who composed 'The Barber of Seville'?

10 Another name for the European viper?

11 Former city in Iraq that was the capital of the Assyrian empire at its height

12 Who in World War II was known as the Desert Fox?

13 Common name for various nocturnal insects constituting the order Dermaptera?

14 From where in Durham did unemployed workers march to London in 1936?

15 Who, in 1835, invented the revolver?

Answers **1** Coco the clown **2** Paris **3** Zealand **4** Vulgate **5** Goose **6** Haiwatha **7** Tasmania **8** Dipper **9** Rossini **10** Adder **11** Nineveh **12** Rommel **13** Earwig **14** Jarrow **15** Samuel Colt

Quiz 26 — Miscellaneous

		Answer starts with
1	Ideal rustic paradise?	A
2	Temporary encampment without tents?	B
3	A knowledgeable person who guides tourists?	C
4	Lozenge of gelatine?	J
5	Building with circular ground plan?	R
6	Old name for chemist?	A
7	Crustacean with ten feet?	D
8	Dam across a river?	W
9	A repartee?	Q
10	Jumping movement in skating?	A
11	A medical term for sunstroke?	H
12	Right handed?	D
13	Yielding honey?	M
14	Wedge-shaped writing?	C
15	A famous lighthouse, destroyed by an earthquake in the 14th century?	P

Answers **1** Arcady **2** Bivouac **3** Cicerone **4** Jujube **5** Rotunda **6** Apothecary **7** Decapod **8** Weir **9** Quip **10** Axel **11** Heliosis **12** Dextral **13** Melliferious **14** Cuneiform **15** Pharos

Miscellaneous — Quiz 27

1 What is the better known name of Yangon City?

2 Who was the popular Czech long distance runner who won the 10,000 metres at the 1948 London Olympics?

3 Who plays agent Fox 'Spooky' Mulder in The X-Files?

4 Uppsala is a University city in which country?

5 In which ancient country was the Biblical city of Ur situated?

6 Freshwater lake near Salt Lake City?

7 The Battle of Amiens was fought in which conflict?

8 What are International Star and Finn classes of?

9 An excess of which acid in the body causes gout?

10 Who said, 'You can tell a lot about a fellow's character by his way of eating jelly beans'?

11 Which actress and singer played Crickett Blake in the vintage TV series 'Hawaiian Eye'?

12 What is the capital of Paraguay?

13 What personality test is based on the subject's interpretations of ink blots?

14 Confederate American soldier whose troops stood against the Union forces 'like a stone wall'?

15 Who was the female lead opposite Mel Gibson in 'Conspiracy Theory'?

Answers **1** Rangoon **2** Emil Zatopak **3** David Duchovny **4** Sweden **5** Mesopotamia **6** Utah **7** World War I **8** Yachts **9** Uric **10** Ronald Reagan **11** Connie Stevens **12** Asuncian **13** Rorschach **14** Andrew Jackson **15** Julia Roberts

Quiz 28 — Miscellaneous

		Answer starts with
1	Study of shells?	C
2	To what do piscary laws apply?	F
3	A soft-toned organ stop?	S
4	Pertaining to the cheek?	M
5	Genus of yellow waterlily?	N
6	Ancient gun?	A
7	Deep volcanic crater?	C
8	The sweet-brier?	E
9	Currency of Argentina?	A
10	Group of boys?	B
11	An intelligent, long-haired breed of sheep dog?	C
12	What is a Portuguese man-o-war?	J
13	Another name for paraffin?	K
14	What is vespertialian an adjective for?	B
15	What is a group of ferrets called?	B

Answers **1** Conchology **2** Fishing **3** Salicet **4** Malar **5** Nuphar **6** Arquebus **7** Caldera **8** Eglantine **9** Austral **10** Blush **11** Collie **12** Jellyfish **13** Kerosene **14** Bat **15** Business

Miscellaneous — Quiz 29

1. Oasis town in Jerusalem and scene of a famous siege during the Israelite conquest of Canaan?
2. What are letters of the earliest Teutonic alphabet known as?
3. Which disease struck down Franklin D. Roosevelt in 1921?
4. Who composed the 'Maple Leaf Rag' and 'The Entertainer'?
5. Where in Germany do Passion plays take place every ten years?
6. Oberon is the outermost satellite of which planet?
7. What name is applied to a member of a camera crew in films or TV who moves equipment and mountings?
8. Who was the Carthaginian general who crossed the Alps in 218-217 BC?
9. Which US actress, born in 1911, became known as the 'Blonde Bombshell'?
10. What is the capital of Vietnam?
11. Who said: "The pendulum of the mind alternates between sense and nonsense, not between right and wrong"?
12. Who wrote 'The Tales of Hoffman'?
13. The liner Arupahoe became, in 1909, the first to use which life-saving device?
14. What was the name of the US schooner which became the first vessel to win the America's Cup?
15. Pyrosis is a name for which medical condition?

Answers **1** Jericho **2** Runes **3** Polio **4** Scott Joplin **5** Oberammergau **6** Uranus **7** Grip **8** Hannibal **9** Jean Harlow **10** Hanoi **11** Carl Jung **12** Offenbach **13** The SOS distress call **14** America **15** Heartburn

Quiz 30 — Miscellaneous

		Answer starts with
1	Which mathematician invented logarithms?	N
2	Creature produced by mating a mule with a female donkey?	H
4	Type of chicory from Italy?	R
4	What shape is allantold?	S-S
5	Having pairs of feet equal?	E
6	Judo suit worn during contests?	J
7	Who in AD62 did the Emperor Nero marry?	P
8	Of what is the study called bryology?	M
9	Bridge of stringed instrument?	P
10	The word used to describe wing-shaped?	A
11	The back side of the head?	O
12	What does a pluviometer measure?	R
13	A spot on the skin?	M
14	Wing-footed creature?	A
15	A vivid red colour?	V

Answers **1** Napier **2** Hinny **3** Radicchio **4** Sausage-shaped **5** Equipedal **6** Judogi **7** Poppaea **8** Mosses **9** Ponticello **10** Aliform **11** Occiput **12** Rainfall **13** Macula **14** Aliped **15** Vermilion

Miscellaneous — Quiz 31

1 Island in the North Sea which served as a major German submarine base during World War II?

2 The principle formulated in 1927 by Werner Heisenberg?

3 In Norse mythology, the Great Hall of Asgard where Odin received souls of heroes killed in battle?

4 Musical instrument whose name in Hawaiian means 'flea'?

5 The volcano Etna lies on the Eastern coast of which island?

6 Boadicea was a member of which tribe?

7 Which composer was the son-in-law of Franz Liszt?

8 What type of telephone was patented in 1889 by William Gray?

9 Who said that in the future everyone would be world-famous for fifteen minutes?

10 What is the 'Queen of the Adriatic'?

11 Which constellation was known in ancient times as a fertility or harvest symbol?

12 Bashar Assad aceded to the presidency of which country in 2000?

13 Who said, in reply to comments about General Grant's drinking problems "Find out what whiskey he drinks and send all my generals a case, if it will get the same results"?

14 Mountain pass through the Alps which connects Innsbruck, Austria and Bolzano, Italy

15 Who was portrayed in the TV series 'The Untouchables' by Robert Stack?

Answers **1** Heligoland **2** Uncertainty **3** Valhalla **4** Ukulele **5** Sicily **6** Iceni **7** Wagner **8** The coin-operated telephone **9** Andy Warhol **10** Venice **11** Virgo **12** Syria **13** Abraham Lincoln **14** Brenner **15** Elliot Ness

Quiz 32 — Miscellaneous

1 A Parisian seamstress or sales girl in a clothes shop girl?

2 A member of a North American native people of Arizona, New Mexico and Utah?

3 A flat-headed, freshwater fish with barbels around its mouth?

4 A colourless, odourless gas, used in illuminations and signs?

5 A tool for engraving on copper?

6 Defamatory statements about another person?

7 Lodging assigned to a campaigning army, especially in the winter?

8 Eve of 1 May, believed in German folklore to be the night of a witches' sabbath?

9 One of the second order of angels, whose special gift is knowledge?

10 Figure of speech in writing?

11 A full length mirror, mounted to swing in a frame?

12 Confused alarm?

13 Disease of the liver, often caused by excess alcohol?

14 Admirals, tortoiseshells and the Camberwell beauty, belong to this group of butterflies?

15 The male head of a tribe or family?

Answers **1** Midinette **2** Navajo **3** Burbot **4** Neon **5** Burin **6** Obloquy **7** Cantonment **8** Walpurgis night **9** Cherub **10** Topology **11** Cheval-glass **12** Trepidation **13** Cirrhosis **14** Vanessids **15** Patriarch

Miscellaneous — Quiz 33

1 Who said: “an army marches on its stomach”?

2 In mythology, who was the Gorgon killed by Perseus?

3 Which rock and roll icon wrote ‘Roll over Beethoven’ and ‘Johnny B. Goode’?

4 Which violin playing American comedian was born Benjamin Kubelsky in Chicago in 1894?

5 Island group in French Polynesia known in French as Iles Sous le Vent

6 The drink of the gods in classical mythology

7 What was divided in 1945 by the 38th parallel?

8 Which actress played neighbour Ethel Mertz in ‘I Love Lucy’?

9 City of Sri Lanka famous for producing tea and known as the ‘City of Five Hills’

10 Which actor starred in the films ‘Taxi Driver’ and ‘Cape Fear’?

11 Which US President issued his ‘Proclamation of Neutrality in 1914 to keep the US out of World War I?

12 What is the most common plant of the genus digitalis?

13 Which two countries are connected by the Khyber Pass?

14 What nationality was Jim Morrison who made the first westbound transatlantic solo flight in 1932?

15 Bay in Northern Egypt where Nelson fought the Battle of the Nile in 1798

Answers **1** Napoleon **2** Medusa **3** Chuck Berry **4** Jack Benny **5** Leeward **6** Nectar **7** Korea **8** Vivian Vance **9** Kandy **10** Robert de Niro **11** Woodrow Wilson **12** Foxglove **13** Afghanistan and Pakistan **14** Scottish **15** Abukir

Quiz 34 — Miscellaneous

1 Resembling a lynx, having keen-eye sight?

2 The time from one new moon to the next?

3 A small two-masted coasting vessel?

4 In the philosophy of the Stoics a space filled with matter, but more commonly an enclosed area containing gas at a higher pressure than the surrounding environment?

5 Area of dead tissue, resulting from an obstruction of blood to that area?

6 A small hammer with a rubber head, used in testing reflexes?

7 A cannon with a short or medium barrel with a low muzzle velocity and a steep angle of fire?

8 Having a loud deep sound, like the moaning of animals?

9 A resin obtained from several species of pine?

10 A woman's loose dressing gown, which was originally worn while the hair was combed?

11 A band worn on the forehead, projecting from a woman's headdress?

12 Gout of the foot or big toe?

13 The expanse of the sky; heavens?

14 Pasture of swine, especially in a forest?

15 A Scottish word for a person who undertook military service in order to defend his homeland only?

Answers **1** Lyncean **2** Lunation? **3** Ketch **4** Plenum **5** Infarct **6** Plexor **7** Howitzer **8** Plangent **9** Gallipot **10** Peignoir **11** Frontlet **12** Podagra **13** Firmament **14** Pannage **15** Fencible

Miscellaneous **Quiz 35**

1 Of where is Accra the capital?

2 What is the name of the US former president Jimmy Carter's wife?

3 Who composed 'On Hearing the First Cuckoo in Spring'?

4 Who directed the films 'Rosemary's Baby' and 'Chinatown'?

5 For which German record label did the Beatles record?

6 Small type of kangaroo about the size of a rabbit?

7 Sir Philip Carter is the Chairman of which soccer team?

8 Ken Russell directed which film starring Glenda Jackson based on a 1921 D.H. Lawrence novel?

9 In the 'Muppet Show' who is the companion of Statler?

10 In which century did the Salem witchcraft trials and executions take place?

11 Wild or domesticated Tibetian ox?

12 What is the annual award for outstanding work in the US theatre called?

13 Born in Budapest in 1874, by what name is Erich Weiss better known?

14 Paul Muni won an Oscar in 1936 for his portrayal of which French chemist?

15 A town in North Holland which gives its name to the sweet-milked cheese produced there?

Answers Ghana **2** Rosalynn Smith Carter **3** Delius **4** Roman Polanski **5** Polydor **6** Wallaby **7** Everton **8** Women in Love **9** Waldorf **10** 17th (1692) **11** Yak **12** Tony **13** Harry Houdini **14** Louis Pasteur **15** Edam

Quiz 36 — Miscellaneous

1 A rock intermediate between clay-slate and mica-schist?

2 What is the world's largest palace?

3 On which of the four main Channel Islands are cars prohibited?

4 What is a rapscallion?

5 What is the meaning of apterous?

6 What is the scientific term for 'resembling a root'?

7 Of what was Artemis the goddess?

8 What is the name given to a quick return thrust in fencing?

9 Where was Attica?

10 What is a rulley?

11 What does avouch mean?

12 Which type of flower does saffron come from?

13 What is a billet-doux?

14 What is sectile?

15 What and where is the Bowery?

Answers **1** Phyllite **2** Versailles **3** Sark **4** A rogue **5** Wingless **6** Rhizoid **7** Chastity **8** Riposte **9** District of ancient Greece **10** A four wheeled dray **11** Guarantee **12** Crocus **13** A love letter **14** That which can be cut **15** A street in New York

Miscellaneous — Quiz 37

1 Who opened the box containing all human ills?

2 Who was the hero of the German version of Arthurian legend and subject of a Wagner opera?

3 Which German philosopher said 'There are no facts, only interpretations'?

4 Who was the US spy-plane pilot shot down by the Russians over Soviet territory in 1960?

5 What does a numismatist collect?

6 Which river does Quebec stand on?

7 Who in 1990 said, "For NASA, space is still a high priority"?

8 About which event in 1940 did Winston Churchill say "Never in the field of human conflict was so much owed by so many to so few"?

9 What name connects a crossbow bolt and a diamond-shaped window pane?

10 What is something if it is described as oleaginous?

11 What is quicksilver?

12 What is the name of the bulldog in the Tom and Jerry cartoons?

13 Who in Greek mythology was the mother of Oedipus?

14 Which large English town is located on the Wirrel Peninsular across the Mersey River from Liverpool?

15 Type of sharp tooth at the front of the mouth?

Answers **1** Pandora **2** Lohengrin **3** Nietzsche **4** Gary Powers **5** Coins **6** St. Lawrence **7** Dan Quayle **8** The Battle of Britain **9** Quarrel **10** Oily **11** Mercury **12** Butch **13** Jocasta **14** Birkenhead **15** Incisor

Quiz 38

Miscellaneous

1 What is a milliard?

2 What does anent mean?

3 What does recalcitrant mean?

4 What colour is aquamarine?

5 A rough-leaved cabbage or a luxury hotel in London?

6 What does axial mean?

7 What is the name of the letter 'Z' in the Greek alphabet?

8 What is biltonc?

9 To the nearest 10, how many rivers flow into the Mediterranean Sea?

10 What is a brogue?

11 What is a teamster?

12 What in Greece is a paghoton?

13 What is a turdine?

14 What does circumvent mean?

15 What does to warped mean?

Answers **1** A thousand million **2** Concerning **3** Obstinately disobedient **4** Bluish-green **5** Savoy **6** Forming an axis **7** Zeta **8** Strips of sun dried meat **9** 70 **10** An Irish accent **11** Driver of a team of horses **12** Ice cream **13** A thrush **14** Over reach **15** Twisted

Miscellaneous — Quiz 39

1 Robert Plant was the lead singer of which rock group?

2 Which peninsular includes Spain and Portugal?

3 Shell beads formerly used as currency by native North Americans?

4 Who composed the 'Four Seasons'?

5 What is the celebrated sacred volcano of Japan?

6 Who wrote 'Men are From Mars, Women are From Venus'?

7 What was the name of the pet dog in the TV series 'Hart to Hart'?

8 What are tight riding breeches with loose-fitting hips called?

9 Which Saxon king of England from 936-46 was stabbed to death by a robber?

10 Who sacked Rome with his Visigoth army in 410?

11 Who had a hit record with 'How Do I Live' in 1997?

12 Which scientist said that "any man who likes marching has been given a brain for nothing, as just the spinal column would have done"?

13 Which period in the earth's history saw the emergence of dinosaurs?

14 Of where is Mogadishu the capital?

15 In the novel 'Rebecca' by Daphne du Maurier, what was Maxim de Winter's estate called?

Answers **1** Led Zeppelin **2** Iberian **3** Wampum **4** Vivaldi **5** Fujiyama **6** John Gray **7** Freeway **8** Jodhpurs **9** Edmund **10** Alaric **11** LeAnn Rimes **12** Albert Einstein **13** Triassic **14** Somalia **15** Mandalay

Quiz 40

Miscellaneous

		Answer starts with
1	Roman Catholic prayers said at 6 am, noon and 6 pm?	A
2	Shop selling wine, especially in Spanish-speaking country?	B
3	Group of cats?	C
4	Group of sheldrake?	D
5	Fit for food?	E
6	The study of seaweed?	P
7	The second largest lake in England?	U
8	Light steel helmet?	B
9	First portion of stomach?	D
10	Orange brown British butterfly?	F
11	Drum roll with alternative beating of sticks?	P
12	Satellite of Neptune?	N
13	A kind of Turkish tobacco?	L
14	German rifle?	J
15	A hawker?	H

Answers **1** Angelus **2** Bodega **3** Clowder **4** Dopping **5** Esculent **6** Phycology **7** Ullswater **8** Basinet **9** Duodenum **10** Fritillary **11** Paradiddle **12** Nereid **13** Latakia **14** Jaeger **15** Huckster

Miscellaneous — Quiz 41

1 Which thin crisp toast was named after an Australian soprano?

2 A leveret is the young of which creature?

3 Who is the Hindu god of love?

4 Which branch of biology deals with the study of animals?

5 Who is the patron saint of florists?

6 What is the monetary unit of Japan?

7 Who said: "I must apologise for the lack of bloodshed in tonight's programme. We shall try to do better next time"?

8 Which imperial measurement is one-eighth of a mile?

9 Which river enters the Atlantic Ocean at Lisbon?

10 Who is the Biblical founder of Israel and son of Isaac and Rebecca?

11 Popular religion of Haiti where spirits possess members in a trance?

12 By what name was John Sholto Douglas, who made an important contribution to the world of sport in the late 19th-century better known?

13 In mythology, of where was Oedipus the King?

14 Egg-shaped wind instrument whose name in Italian means 'little goose'?

15 Tree which produces pear-shaped fruit with a strong aroma?

Answers **1** Melba **2** Hare **3** Kama **4** Zoology **5** Dorothy **6** Yen **7** Alfred Hitchcock **8** Furlong **9** Tagus **10** Jacob **11** Voodoo **12** The Marquis of Queensbury (who formulated the rules of boxing) **13** Thebes **14** Ocarina **15** Quince

Quiz 42 — Miscellaneous

1 What does atrophy mean?

2 What is a porgy?

3 What does culpable mean?

4 A sweetmeat made of nuts?

5 A marsh bird of the heron family?

6 What is a sheet of water falling over a weir called?

7 A petty officer of justice?

8 What is a purple-brown colour called?

9 What is a Bishop's assistant called?

10 What word means 'having two beats to a bar'?

11 The name given to an anthem in the Roman Catholic or Luteran church?

12 What is a phalanx?

13 A wandering Hindu holy man?

14 What is a bower in seafaring terms?

15 What is the name for the upper ridge of a bird's beak?

Answers **1** Wasting away **2** A sea fish **3** Deserving blame **4** Praline **5** Bittern **6** Nappe **7** Catchpole **8** Puce **9** A coadjutor **10** Duple **11** Motet **12** A compact body of infantry **13** Sadhu **14** Either of two anchors **15** Culmen

Miscellaneous — Quiz 43

1 What is a cotillion a type of?

2 Who was the Captain whose loss of an ear was said to have caused a war between Britain and Spain in 1739?

3 Species of duck which lines its nest with soft grey down taken from its breast?

4 In Greek mythology who wandered for ten years after the fall of Troy?

5 13th-14th century fortress palace of the Moorish kings of Grenada, Spain?

6 Which fashion designer created the mini-skirt in the 1960s?

7 Species of domesticated humped cattle of Southern Asia?

8 Type of balsam used in the treatment of chronic bronchitis?

9 Cape in north west Spain, extending as a promontory into the Atlantic Ocean, whose name in Latin means 'Land's End'?

10 Who is the eponymous hero of Sir Walter Scott's famous novel in 1820?

11 What name connects an English novelist and a city in Texas?

12 Who is the former pop idol turned Eastender's Queen Vic regular who published his autobiography 'True' in 2000?

13 Where, in 1215, did King John seal the Magna Carta?

14 In the Bible which two cities were destroyed by a rain of brimstone as a punishment for the wickedness of their inhabitants?

15 Which famous poem was written by the Persian poet Omar Khayyam?

Answers **1** Dance **2** Jenkins **3** Eider **4** Odysseus **5** Alhambra **6** Mary Quant **7** Zebu **8** Friars **9** Finisterre **10** Ivanhoe **11** Austen **12** Martin Kemp **13** Runnymede **14** Sodam and Gomorrah **15** The Rubaiyat

Quiz 44 — Miscellaneous

1. What is the meaning of pendulous?
2. What does retiform mean?
3. What is binomial?
4. What does sib mean?
5. What is tautology?
6. What is bondage?
7. A golf club with an iron head and slightly lofted?
8. What is the seed of the opium poppy called?
9. What is a brahma?
10. What is the mathematical term for in the middle?
11. In India, the name for a married European lady?
12. What is a breastsummer?
13. What is to mewl?
14. What is milch?
15. What is butyric?

Answers **1** Hanging down **2** Net-like **3** Consisting of two terms **4** Related **5** Repetition of a word or phrase **6** Slavery **7** Mashie **8** Mawseed **9** A domestic fowl **10** Median **11** Memsahib **12** A beam across an opening **13** To cry feebly **14** Giving milk **15** Pertaining to butter

Miscellaneous — Quiz 45

1 What, in ancient times, was a quinquerme?

2 Which scientist said: 'To every action there is always opposed an equal reaction'?

3 What type of pen was made from the outer wing feathers of geese?

4 What is the capital and chief city of Hong Kong?

5 Who in Greek mythology is the goddess of the rainbow?

6 What is the name of the International language invented by Dr Ludwick L Zamenhof?

7 What is bread called which is made without a raising agent such as yeast?

8 What is the capital of Afghanistan?

9 The Galapagos Islands in the Pacific Ocean are a province of which country?

10 Which British physicist gave his name to a unit of energy?

11 Who was the Austrian archduke who became Emperor of Mexico in 1864?

12 With which rock group would you associate Noel Gallagher?

13 Former village, now part of the city of Sevastopol made famous in the poem 'The Charge of the Light Brigade'?

14 Who was the French composer of 'Symphonie Fantastique' (1831)?

15 Which archangel is said to have spoken to Joan of Arc?

Answers **1** An ancient Greek or Roman ship with five tiers of oars **2** Isaac Newton **3** Quill **4** Victoria **5** Iris **6** Esperanto **7** Unleavened **8** Kabul **9** Ecuador **10** Joule **11** Maximilian **12** Oasis **13** Balaklava **14** Hector Berlioz **15** Michael

Quiz 46 — Miscellaneous

		Answer starts with
1	The name for a large, imposing building?	E
2	A red wine from Bordeaux?	C
3	Made of moulded earth or clay?	F
4	The Hungarian monetary unit prior to 1946?	P
5	A figure with four angles and four sides?	T
6	Who's pendulum demonstrates the rotation of the earth?	F
7	Savoury jelly with game or eggs?	A
8	Of an uncle?	A
9	What, on a mountain, is a ben?	P
10	A fancied object of fea r?	B
11	A yellow and black Eurasian finch?	S
12	A spoilt darling?	M
13	Confine in prison?	M
14	What is obsfuscate?	D
15	The ornamental back screen of an altar?	R

Answers Edifice **2** Claret **3** Fictile **4** Pengo **5** Tetragon **6** Foucault's **7** Aspic **8** Avuncular **9** Peak **10** Bugbear **11** Siskin **12** Minion **13** Mure **14** Darken **15** Reredos

Miscellaneous — Quiz 47

1 Who said: "It is a very sad thing that nowadays there is so little useless information"?

2 What was Elvis Presley's middle name?

3 Which country was described by Mark Twain as 'mother of history, grandmother of legend and great-grandmother of tradition'?

4 Which boxer was portrayed in the 1980 movie 'The Raging Bull' by Robert de Niro?

5 Lytheon was the planet setting for which sci-fi cult 1968 movie?

6 Who were the rival families to which Romeo and Juliet belonged in Shakespeare's 'Romeo and Juliet'?

7 How many pounds does a shot put weigh?

8 Who is the wayward woman who is the central character of Somerset Maugham's novel 'Rain'?

9 Who was known as the 'First Lady of Jazz'?

10 Where in the US is the nation's gold supply stored?

11 Who was the third husband of Scarlett O'Hara in 'Gone With the Wind'?

12 Who was the oldest member of the Beatles?

13 Who ran from Marathon to Athens in September 490 BC to bring newa of the Greek victory over the Persians?

14 'Vesti la guibba' is an aria from which opera?

15 What is the name of the dish consisting of chicken, peas and carrots in a white sauce, created by Thomas Jefferson, 3rd President of the United States?

Answers **1** Oscar Wilde **2** Aaron **3** India **4** Jake La Motta **5** Barbarella **6** Montegue and Capulet **7** 16 lbs **8** Sadie Thompson **9** Ella Fitzgerald **10** At Fort Knox near Louisville, Kentucky **11** Rhett Butler **12** Ringo Starr **13** Pheidippides **14** I Pagliacci **15** Chicken-a-la-King

Quiz 48 — Miscellaneous

		Answer starts with
1	Hard cabinet wood from Ceylon?	C
2	A small cake with almonds?	M
3	French word for a lorry?	C
4	Heavy metal headed spiked club?	M
5	Tobacco nmaed from the rush basket in which it was first transported from Spanish America?	C
6	Mixed fruit or vegetables cut up small and embedded in a jelly?	M
7	The scientific name for an eye-lash?	C
8	Of the Isle of Man?	M
9	A shrill, narrow-tubed trumpet?	C
10	Of a faint sickly flavour?	M
11	French brandy?	C
12	Wicked, evil, sinful?	N
13	The French word for a hair dresser?	C
14	An era of geological time that began 600 million years ago and lasted 375 million years to the end of the Permian Period?	P
15	A mixture of materials such as mortar or plaster?	C

Answers **1** Calamander **2** Macaroon **3** Camion **4** Mace **5** Canaster **6** Macedoine **7** Cilia **8** Manx **9** Clarion **10** Mawkish **11** Cognac **12** Nefarious **13** Coiffeur **14** Palaeozoic **15** Compo

Miscellaneous — Quiz 49

1 In the Warner Brcthers cartoons what kind of creature is Foghorn J Leghorn?

2 'The Champagne Duet' (Brindisi) is from Act I of which Verdi opera?

3 Carlotte Monti was the mistress of which old time movie comedian?

4 The Astros (baseball) and Rockets (basketball) are major league teams of which US city?

5 Who were the Italian banking family who ruled Florence from the 13th-18th century?

6 Which bay is an arm of the North Atlantic Ocean between Greenland and several islands of north eastern Canada?

7 From the 13th century until 1902, which was the main prison of the city of London?

8 The ancient city of Byzantium occupied part of the site of which modern day city?

9 Who was the brother of the Bronte sisters?

10 What is situated at 11 Coronation Street?

11 Who is the patron saint of maidens who was martyred in Cologne?

12 What is a word or phrase called which reads the same backwards or forwards?

13 What is the common name for species of the genus Allium?

14 Octavius was the original name of which Roman Emperor?

15 Which bird of prey is also known as fish hawk or fish eagle?

Answers **1** A giant rooster **2** La Traviata **3** W.C. Fields **4** Houston **5** Medici **6** Baffin **7** Newgate **8** Istanbul **9** Branwell **10** The Rovers Return **11** Ursula **12** A palindrome **13** Onion **14** Augustus **15** Osprey

Quiz 50 — Miscellaneous

1 A dark Mahogany-like wood, from Africa used in plywood and as a veneer?

2 What is garget?

3 What are 'ecus'?

4 Who is the Roman Goddess of War?

5 Genocide is the killing of a nationalty or ethnic group and patricide is the killing of ones father, what is deicide?

6 Who rode a horse called Marengo?

7 What was the nationality of Karl Marx?

8 Other than a small flask, what is a flasket?

9 What is flapdoodle?

10 What is foozle?

11 The lowest yard on a foremast?

12 What is the name given to a wall-painting using watercolours on plaster?

13 What is a hurley?

14 The name given to a large stone, usually found in a prehistoric monument?

15 What is a mestizo?

Answers **1** Gaboon **2** Inflamed throat in cattle **3** European currency units **4** Bellona **5** Killing of a god **6** Napoleon I **7** German **8** Oblong shallow basket **9** Nonsense **10** A bungle **11** Foreyard **12** Fresco **13** Hockey stick **14** Megalith **15** Spanish half caste

Miscellaneous — Quiz 51

1 Which famous character first appeared in DC Comics' 'Action Comics' Series issue 1 in June 1938?

2 Which Australian city was named after the consort of King William IV of England?

3 What is a natterjack a type of?

4 Acronym used to designate the Australian and New Zealand troops engaged in the Gallipoli campaign during the first World War?

5 Former name of the islands now known as Tonga?

6 Writer whose collection of tales 'I am a Camera' set in pre-war Germany was adapted for the musical 'Cabaret'?

7 What is the capital of Sierra Leone?

8 Which group of rocks, and site of four famous lighthouses built between 1698 and 1882 in the English Channel, is the cause of many shipwrecks?

9 Who in mythology brought back the Golden Fleece?

10 Who designed Castle Howard and Blenheim Palace?

11 Member of the camel family, a close relative of the llama and native to the Andes?

12 What in the Old Testament was the name of the tent established by Moses in which the Ark of the Covenant was conveyed?

13 Who is best known for his 1828 publication 'American Dictionary of the English Language'?

14 Who created Bertie Wooster and his butler Jeeves?

15 What nationality was the ballerina Anna Pavlova?

Answers **1** Superman **2** Adelaide **3** Toad **4** ANZAC **5** The Friendly Islands **6** Christopher Isherwood **7** Freetown **8** Eddystone **9** Jason **10** Vanbrugh **11** Vicuna **12** The Tabernacle **13** Noah Webster **14** P.G. Wodehouse **15** Russian

Quiz 52 — Miscellaneous

1 What is collyrium?

2 To press pleats into a frill or decorate the gilt edge of a book with a decorative pattern?

3 A stupid person, also a US slang term for hired thugs, especially during an industrial dispute?

4 A piece of throat armour, or a band or colour on the throat of an animal, especially a bird?

5 A timber framework running out to sea, also called a spur or breakwater?

6 A thin fluid mortar used for filling gaps between tiles?

7 What was the name of the legendary founder of Troy?

8 What is imbrue?

9 What is nagor?

10 A port in West France at the head of the Loire estuary and scene of the Noyades (drownings) during the French Revolution?

11 What is a naze?

12 What is a nomad?

13 Loose fibres of rope?

14 A name given to any of various whales, especially the killer whale?

15 What is the name given to a collar on a round neck, with two rounded edges at the front?

Answers **1** A technical name for eyewash **2** Goffer **3** Goon **4** Gorget
5 Groyne **6** Grout **7** Ilus **8** Stain with blood **9** The reed buck **10** Nantes
11 A headland **12** A wanderer **13** Oakum **14** Orc **15** A Peter Pan collar

Miscellaneous — Quiz 53

1 Against what was Lady Godiva protesting when she rode naked through Coventry?

2 Who, in 'An Essay on Criticism' wrote: "To err is human, to forgive divine"?

3 Which breed of dog has ears like butterfly's wings?

4 The peregrine is a type of which bird?

5 Which condition results in difficulty in getting sufficient sleep?

6 With which rock group is Charlie Watts associated?

7 What in Britain is 'Hansard'?

8 What was the nickname of Henry Percy who was killed in 1403 at the Battle of Shrewsbury after revolting against King Henry IV

9 Lake Tiberias is another name for which sea?

10 Who is the eponymous heroine of a George du Maurier novel of 1894?

11 Which is the largest of the Canary Islands?

12 Of where is Kinshasa the capital?

13 What is the science of earthquakes called?

14 Which industrialist and philanthropist founded the museum in New York which now bears his name?

15 Which school of Buddhism stresses the personal experience of enlightenment?

Answers **1** Taxes **2** Alexander Pope **3** Papillon **4** Falcon **5** Insomnia **6** The Rolling Stones (he is their drummer) **7** The printed record of Parliamentary debates **8** Hotspur **9** Galilee **10** Trilby **11** Tenerife **12** Zaire **13** Seismology **14** Guggenheim **15** Zen

Quiz 54 — Miscellaneous

1 Pages folded 3 times into 8 leaves?

2 Last letter of the Greek alphabet?

3 What is the name of the Greek letter O?

4 A large fish-eating bird of prey, known in the US and Canada as a fish hawk?

5 What is parity?

6 What is paecker?

7 Which English King, born in 1566, was the son of Mary Stuart?

8 What does obliquely mean?

9 A unit of loudness that measures the intensity of sound by the number of decibels it is above a certain tone?

10 What type of music is pibroch?

11 What is phyletic?

12 Name the fragrant oil distilled from flowers, especially the damask rose?

13 In dressage, what is the word for 'moving in a trot'?

14 What does the word bacilliform mean?

15 What is a planch?

Answers **1** Octavo **2** Omega **3** Omicron **4** Osprey **5** Equality **6** In British slang, spirits as in 'keep one's pecker up' **7** James I **8** Slanted **9** Phon **10** Music played on a bagpipe **11** Of a line of descent **12** Attar **13** Piaffe **14** Rod-shaped **15** A slab of metal

Miscellaneous — Quiz 55

1 The movie 'Babe' is about a pig who thinks he is what kind of animal?

2 With what material did Rene Lalique work?

3 Whose members were bound by a rigid ethical code called the omerta?

4 Name applied to descendants of French-Canadians who now reside mainly in southern Louisana?

5 Which spice is produced from the outer skin of nutmeg seeds?

6 Who said: "Religion is the opium of the people"?

7 Who is Andy Capp's best friend in the famous comic strip?

8 What, in a song by Fred Fisher, was 'That Toddling Town'?

9 Rhine siren of German legend whose singing lured sailors to destruction

10 In 'Coal Miner's Daughter', the singer Loretta Lynn was played by Sissy Spacek. In the same movie, which singer was portrayed by Beverly D'Angelo?

11 Who is the patron saint of physicians?

12 Who was the sailor adventurer in the Arabian Nights?

13 Which town in Germany is associated with the Pied Piper legend?

14 In which city was Christopher Columbus born?

15 On which H.G. Wells novel is the musical 'Half a Sixpence' based?

Answers **1** Sheepdog **2** Glass **3** The Mafia **4** Cajun **5** Mace **6** Karl Marx **7** Chalkie **8** Chicago **9** Lorelei **10** Patsy Cline **11** St. Luke **12** Sinbad **13** Hamelin **14** Genoa **15** Kipps

Quiz 56 — Miscellaneous

1 What is the name of small spike for plucking strings?

2 What is the name given to the curtain at the side of an altar?

3 What is the meaning of saturnine?

4 French boxing in which blows are given by feet or hands?

5 What is a scrivener?

6 What is an axolotl?

7 A part of a barn where hay or straw is stored, or cutting the grass?

8 Branch of an Australian river that comes to a dead end?

9 The outer casing of a plane's engine?

10 What does blowsed mean?

11 Neither masculine or feminine – giving no indication of sex?

12 What is a blucher?

13 A tumour made up of nerve tissue?

14 What is a canion?

15 What does noxious mean?

Answers **1** Plectrum **2** Riddel **3** Having a gloomy, taciturn temperament **4** Savate **5** A writer **6** A Central and South American aquatic salamander **7** Mow **8** Billabong **9** Nacelle **10** Red and coarse faced **11** Neuter **12** A Prussian soldier **13** Neuroma **14** Short stuffed breeches **15** Harmful

Miscellaneous — Quiz 57

1 Which writer said "Some people say I must be a horrible person, but that's not true, I have the heart of a young boy - in a jar on my desk"?

2 What is the name of the land of tiny people in 'Gulliver's Travels'?

3 Which actor played Eliot Ness in the movie version of 'The Untouchables'?

4 Which Cape in Western Senegal is the westernmost part of Africa?

5 The adjective lupine refers to which creature?

6 The Kariba dam is on which river?

7 Which territory and river in Canada takes its name from an Indian expression meaning Great River?

8 Which German philosopher said that people should act in ways they wish everyone would act?

9 Which nymph in mythology was pursued by Apollo and changed into a laurel tree?

10 Which city was known in ancient times as Ebiana?

11 North American deer on which Eskimos in Arctic regions depend for survivial?

12 The Japanese martial art of fencing

13 Which of the Channel Islands is just 4 sq km in size?

14 Who were the French brothers who, in 1895, invented a picture camera that functioned as a projector?

15 What is the name of the computer-generated dragon in the movie 'Dragonheart'?

Answers **1** Stephen King **2** Lilliput **3** Kevin Costner **4** Cape Verde **5** The wolf **6** Zambezi **7** Yukon **8** Kant **9** Daphne **10** Dublin **11** Caribou **12** Kendo **13** Sark **14** The Lumiere brothers **15** Draco

Quiz 58 — Miscellaneous

		Answer starts with
1	A gully?	A
2	The opposite of perigee?	A
3	Fine cloth made from wool?	B
4	Of twilight?	C
5	An American card game?	E
6	Steep gully?	C
7	French island in West Indies?	G
8	Dark kind of China tea?	O
9	Sweet liqueur?	K
10	Small Spanish horse?	J
11	Tame monkey?	J
12	A poor and diseased person?	L
13	A writing desk?	E
14	A bunch of fragrant flowers?	N
15	Inland South American state?	B

Answers **1** Arroyo **2** Apogee **3** Barathea **4** Crepuscular **5** Euchre **6** Couloir **7** Guadeloupe **8** Oolong **9** Kummel **10** Jennet **11** Jackanapes **12** Lazar **13** Escritoire **14** Nosegay **15** Bolivia

Miscellaneous — Quiz 59

1 A jazz icon of the swing era and beyond, what instrument did Gene Krupa play?

2 Which actress was known as the 'Jersey Lily'?

3 Who was the British Major General who surrendered at Yorktown in the American War of Independence?

4 Which Nazi was known as the 'Angel of Death'?

5 What was the name of the hill outside Jerusalem where the crucifixion of Jesus Christ took place?

6 What do Argentines call the Falkland Islands?

7 Which flowering herb is used to make tea, perfume, medicine, hair rinse and dye?

8 Type of tail-less cat also known as rumpy?

9 Which writer created the character Philip Marlow?

10 Who directed 'Lawrence of Arabia'?

11 Which national park of central California is located in the Sierra Nevada?

12 Who was the wife of King Arthur and lover of Sir Lancelot?

13 Which prison housed Germans convicted of war crimes at Nuremberg?

14 Which strait separates Italy from Sicily?

15 What was invented in 1938 by Chester Carlson?

Answers **1** Drums **2** Lily Langtry **3** Cornwallis **4** Dr. Josef Mengele **5** Calvary **6** Malvinas **7** Chamomile **8** Manx **9** Raymond Chandler **10** David Lean **11** Yosemite **12** Guinevere **13** Spandau **14** The Strait of Messina **15** Xerography

Quiz 60 — Miscellaneous

1 What is a cirque?

2 What are the Cyclades?

3 Where is the Sistene Chapel?

4 What is nacre?

5 A Mexican beetle which when crushed is used as a red-coloured dye?

6 Pertaining to the number 8?

7 What is a coati or a coati-mundi?

8 What in English legal history was an oyer?

9 A musical composition for an orchestra and one or more soloists?

10 A wig worn by fashionable men in the 17th and 18th centuries?

11 What is to distend?

12 What is to prate?

13 The heavily fortified central tower of a medieval castle?

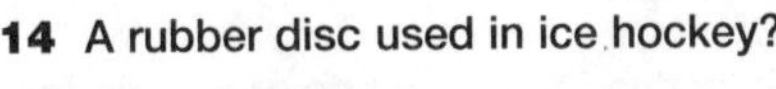

14 A rubber disc used in ice hockey?

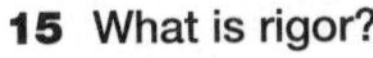

15 What is rigor?

Answers **1** A natural amphitheatre **2** A group of islands in the Aegean Sea **3** In the Vatican **4** Mother of pearl **5** Cochineal **6** Octonary **7** A civet like animal **8** A criminal trial **9** A concerto **10** A peruke **11** To swell out **12** To chatter **13** Donjon **14** Puck **15** A sudden chill

Miscellaneous — Quiz 61

1 What is the name of the midget servant played by Herve Villechaize in the TV series 'Fantasy Island'?

2 Which Asian republic constitutes most of the Malay Archipelago?

3 Which fruit are used at a certain time of the year as jack-o'-lanterns?

4 Who said, 'A single death is a tragedy, a million deaths is a statistic'?

5 Who was Secretary-General of the United Nations from 1972-81?

6 What is the name of Dr. Who's flying telephone box?

7 Who went for a 'Walk on the Wild Side' in 1973?

8 What is the sensation called when the room and nearby objects seem to be spinning around?

9 Of where is Vientiane the capital?

10 Which Bond villain was played in two movies by 7' 2" actor Richard Keil?

11 What is the name of the triangular shaped island in the South Pacific Ocean also called Rapa Hui?

12 In which vessel did Captain Cook sail to Tahiti?

13 Which word, meaning, a large lorry, is derived from the title of the Hindu deity Krishna whose idol is carried on a huge car or wagon?

14 Who in Greek mythology was the 'Goddess of the Dawn'?

15 Which Italian film director was the director of 'Amarcord' and 'La Dolce Vita'?

Answers **1** Tattoo **2** Indonesia **3** Pumpkins **4** Stalin **5** Kurt Waldheim **6** Tardis **7** Lou Reed **8** Vertigo **9** Laos **10** Jaws **11** Easter Island **12** Endeavour **13** Juggernaut **14** Eos **15** Fellini

Quiz 62

Miscellaneous

		Answer starts with
1	What is a caravel?	S
2	What were darbies?	H
3	What is an eidolon?	S
4	What is a menhir?	S–S
5	What is a fedora?	H
6	What word describes the middle line of the body	M?
7	What is the meaning of feculent?	T
8	What is a neophyte?	C
9	A word for easily crumbled	F?
10	A word which means self abuse?	O
11	A silver-grey freshwater fish?	G
12	A straw bed	P?
13	An Indian non-commissioned officer	H?
14	A piece of shoulder armour?	P
15	A long ridge of land	H?

Answers **1** Spanish ship **2** Handcuffs **3** Spectre **4** A standing stone **5** Hat **6** Mesial **7** Turbid **8** Convert **9** Friable **10** Onanism **11** Grayling **12** Pallet **13** Havildar **14** Pauldron **15** Horst

Miscellaneous — Quiz 63

1 Who wrote the epic work 'Iliad'?

2 Race of warlike women who, in Greek mythology excluded men from their society?

3 The volcano Vesuvius is on the eastern shore of which bay?

4 What is the principle male hormone or androgen?

5 Who received the head of John the Baptist as a gift for dancing?

6 Trail which was the pioneer route to the north western United States?

7 Of what was Louis Daguerre a pioneer?

8 River of southern Russia which forms part of the boundary between Europe and Asia

9 Who was the first person to cross Niagara Falls on a tightrope?

10 Of where is Windhoek the capital?

11 What is the name of the atoll in the Pacific Ocean, one of the Marshall Islands where US testing of atomic weapons began in 1946?

12 In which city was a Novocastrian born?

13 Name of fifteen popes, the last one leading the church through World War I?

14 What is the ninth month of the Muslim year called?

15 What is state capital of Alabama?

Answers **1** Homer **2** Amazons **3** Naples **4** Testosterone **5** Salome **6** Oregon **7** Photography **8** Ural **9** Blondin **10** Namibia **11** Bikini **12** Newcastle **13** Benedict **14** Ramadan **15** Montgomery

Quiz 64 — Miscellaneous

		Answer starts with
1	Inflammation of the liver?	H
2	Young salmon?	S
3	Light meal?	T
4	Rain gauge?	U
5	African gnu?	W
6	Woody tissue?	X
7	Hard, ring-shaped bread roll?	B
8	Liveried servant?	F
9	Clumsy awkward youth?	H
10	Tincture of opium?	L
11	Beyond the realms of natral knowledge?	O
12	Feeling of weariness or boredom	E
13	Capital of Bangladesh?	D
14	Author of 'Lorna Doone'?	B
15	Type of naturally occurring sugar?	G

Answers **1** Hepatitis **2** Samlet **3** Tiffin **4** Udometer **5** Wildebeest **6** Xylem **7** Bagel **8** Flunkey **9** Hobbledehoy **10** Laudanum **11** Occult **12** Ennui **13** Dacca **14** Blackmore **15** Glucose

Miscellaneous — Quiz 65

1. Who was the character in Sheridan's play 'The Rivals' who gave her name to an amusing misuse of words?
2. Which river flows through the Sea of Galilee into the Dead Sea?
3. Who is the Roman goddess of the moon and the hunt?
4. Which branch of physics deal with high-frequency sound waves?
5. The Strait of Otranto links which sea to the Adriatic?
6. To what creature does the adjective pavonine refer?
7. Which male forename means peace in Germanic?
8. What is the capital of Zimbabwe, formerly called Salisbury?
9. What is the analysis of handwriting as a guide to the character and personality of the writer called?
10. Which jazz singer was known as 'Lady Day'?
11. Which composer wrote the 'Oratorios of 'Elijah and 'St. Paul'?
12. What is the name of Tin Tin's dog?
13. In which town in Kent did Pocahontas die?
14. What is another name for calcium?
15. What type of flatfish has both eyes on its left side?

Answers **1** Mrs. Malaprop **2** The River Jordan **3** Diana **4** Ultrasonics **5** Ionian **6** The Peacock **7** Geoffrey **8** Harare **9** Graphology **10** Billie Holliday **11** Mendelssohn **12** Snowey **13** Gravesend **14** Quicklime **15** Turbot

Quiz 66 Miscellaneous

		Answer starts with
1	Archaic word for chemist?	A
2	Preserve from decay?	E
3	Locomotive crane?	J
4	Very drunk?	S
5	Irresponsible?	W
6	Vagabond?	W
7	The male of the honey bee?	D
8	French national flag?	T
9	Resembling a bear?	U
10	Schoolmaster?	P
11	Splinter of wood?	S
12	Greasy, oily?	U
13	Able to fly?	V
14	Debauchee?	R
15	Currency unit of Austria?	S

Answers **1** Apothecary **2** Embalm **3** Jenny **4** Sozzled **5** Wanton **6** Wanderer **7** Drone **8** Tricolour **9** Ursine **10** Pedagogue **11** Spillikin **12** Unctuous **13** Volant **14** Roue **15** Schilling

Miscellaneous — Quiz 67

1 Who recorded the best selling album 'Music Box'?

2 Who was the youngest of the five Marx Brothers?

3 Ossino, Olivia, Viola, Malvolio and Festa are characters in which Shakespeare play?

4 Who, in 1877, was born Lev Davidovich Bronstein?

5 What name was given to the Protestants of France from 1560 to 1629?

6 Who in the Bible was the Israelite who defeated the Midianites?

7 Which range of mountains extends between Tunisia and Morocco?

8 In which country is Mount Everest?

9 What name is given to a computer device that connects a computer with a peripheral?

10 Who is the German scholar who sold his soul to the devil and about who Gounod wrote an opera?

11 What nationality is racing driver Emerson Fittipaldi?

12 What work is performed by a farrier?

13 Who, in 1900, propounded the 'Quantum Theory'?

14 Which famous sharpshooter was born Phoebe Annie Moses?

15 What was the first name of the wife of F D Roosevelt?

Answers **1** Maria Carey **2** Zeppo **3** Twelfth Night **4** Trotsky **5** Huguenots **6** Gideon **7** The Atlas Mountains **8** Nepal **9** Interface **10** Faust **11** Brazilian **12** He shoes horses **13** Max Planck **14** Annie Oakley **15** Eleanor

Quiz 68

Miscellaneous

1 What does aseptic mean?

2 What type of footwear is a sabot?

3 What is a cyma?

4 What is fimbriate?

5 A technique of water-colour painting, using pigments bound with glue?

6 What is a horner?

7 A probationary rank held by young naval officers under training?

8 A mass of debris carried by glaciers and forming mounds when deposited?

9 What is a musquash?

10 What is a narghile?

11 The entire equipment of a warrior?

12 A body of men to suppress riots?

13 An East African soldier or policeman?

14 What is hexastyle?

15 Who was Jami?

Answers **1** Free from blood poisoning **2** A wooden clog **3** A moulding with a double curve **4** Fringed **5** Gouache **6** A maker of combs **7** A midshipman **8** Moraine **9** A musk rat **10** Oriental tobacco pipe **11** Panoply **12** Posse **13** Askari **14** A portico of six columns **15** A Persian classical poet

Miscellaneous — Quiz 69

1 What nationality was composer Franz Schubert?

2 How did Ham the chimp make the news in January 1961?

3 How was John Lydon, a performer with the Sex Pistols better known?

4 Terry Jones was a member of which comedy troupe?

5 Who, in Greek mythology was the daughter of King Agamemnon and Queen Clytemnestra?

6 Tallinn is the capital of which country?

7 What is the name of the nonsense poem written by Lewis Carroll in 'Through the Looking Glass'?

8 Russian film director whose works include 'Ten Days That Shook the World' (1928) and 'A Time in the Sun' (1939)?

9 Animal which hunts at night in small groups and utters a cry, called the pheal?

10 Which city was founded in 1653 as New Amsterdam?

11 Which instrument is similar to the xylophone but with metal bars?

12 In mythology, who was the beloved of Pyramus who killed herself on his death?

13 Who wrote 'The Picture of Dorian Gray'?

14 Which American Civil War General succeeded Sherman as Commander-in-chief of the Union Army?

15 On which island did the mutineers of the Bounty take refuge?

Answers **1** Austrian **2** The first animal sent into space by the US **3** Johnny Rotten **4** Monty Python **5** Electra **6** Estonia **7** Jabberwocky **8** Eisenstein **9** Jackal **10** New York **11** Vibraphone **12** Thisbe **13** Oscar Wilde **14** Sheridan **15** Pitcairn

Quiz 70

Miscellaneous

1 A short or tail-less Asian monkey which has cheek pouches?

2 What does rodomontade mean?

3 A domed building housing Buddhist or Jain relics?

4 An officer of David's army who was killed on David's instructions so he could marry his widow Bathsheba?

5 What is a rouleau?

6 What is a realtor?

7 What is butyric?

8 An ulcerous disease of animals?

9 What is catchup?

10 Composition made up from different authors?

11 What is a davy?

12 What is a demoiselle?

13 What is a single stroke on a drum called?

14 A light filmy substance often seen on foliage or floating in the air?

15 What is grog?

Answers **1** Macaque **2** Boastful Stupa **4** Uriah **5** A cylindrical packet of coins **6** Real estate agent **7** Related to butter **8** Canker **9** Another name for ketchup, especially in the US **10** A cento **11** A solemn oath **12** A crane with long feathers **13** A flam **14** Gossamer **15** Drink of spirits

Miscellaneous — Quiz 71

1 Who wrote 'La Boheme'?

2 What collective name is applied to the gases helium, neon, argon, krypton, xenon and radon?

3 Who said: "If you can't stand the heat, get out of the kitchen"?

4 Which romantic screen duo starred in the 1942 movie 'Woman of the Year'?

5 Ancient Germanic tribe whose name is synonymous with looting and plundering?

6 Who, in Greek mythology was the supreme god?

7 Which French mathematician and philosopher said: "Cogito, ergo, sum" (I think; therefore I am)?

8 What is the name of the salad consisting of diced walnuts, celery and apple dressed with mayonnaise?

9 In which sport do the ladies of USA and UK play for the Whiteman Cup?

10 In the ancient Greek theory of creation, what name is given to the dark silent abyss from which all things came into existence?

11 Which measurement of supersonic speed is named after an Austrian physicist and philosopher?

12 Under what name did the acclaimed 'Godfather of Punk', James Osterberg record?

13 Which Austrian composer was conductor of the New York Philharmonic from 1908-11?

14 Naxos is the largest of which group of islands?

15 Of where is Lome the capital?

Answers **1** Puccini **2** Inert **3** Harry S. Truman **4** Katherine Hepburn and Spencer Tracy **5** Vandals **6** Zeus **7** Descartes **8** Waldorf **9** Tennis **10** Chaos **11** Mach **12** Iggy Pop **13** Gustav Mahler **14** Cyclades **15** Togo

Quiz 72 — Miscellaneous

1 Line of 6 metrical feet in poetry?

2 A Low padded cushion seat or pouffe, which may have taken its name from the egg-shaped man who fell off the wall?

3 A Hindu goddess who embodies the female energy of Siva?

4 What is flabellate?

5 A poetic term for a reward or payment?

6 What does the word edible mean?

7 What is a ness?

8 The name for a long narrow flag?

9 What is pommard?

10 What is quondam?

11 What is the name for the sheath for a sword?

12 The word for a breach of unity of a church?

13 What is to scrimshank?

14 What is colloquy?

15 What is complin?

Answers **1** A hexameter **2** A humpty **3** Devi **4** Fan-shaped **5** Guerdon **6** Fit to be eaten **7** A promontory **8** Pennon **9** A red burgundy wine **10** Sometime **11** Scabbard **12** Schism **13** To shirk duty **14** Conversation **15** Last service of the day

Miscellaneous — Quiz 73

1 Who was the first Christian Emperor of Rome?

2 How many members are there on a hurling team?

3 Which US President invented the folding bed and swivel chair?

4 Who was the chief rabbit in 'Watership Down'?

5 Who was Jim Bridger?

6 Who was assassinated on 15th March?

7 Who is the villainess dognapper in the Disney movie '101 Dalmatians'?

8 John Merrick was the subject of which 1980 movie in which he was played by John Hurt?

9 Who was the Texas legislator whose name was given to unbranded cattle?

10 Who was the magician at the court of King Arthur?

11 Who was the mother of Queen Elizabeth I of England?

12 Who on TV were Sabrina Duncan, Jill Monroe and Kris Monroe?

13 Who was the first person to die of radiation poisoning?

14 Why is William P End called the 'Father of Traffic Safety' in the US?

15 Which King of England was called 'The Peacemaker'?

Answers **1** Constantine **2** 15 **3** Thomas Jefferson **4** Hazel **5** An American frontiersman and explorer (1804-1881) **6** Julius Caesar **7** Cruella De Ville **8** The Elephant Man **9** Maverick **10** Merlin **11** Anne Boleyn **12** Charlie's Angels **13** Marie Curie **14** He invented the stop sign **15** Edward VII

Quiz 74 — Miscellaneous

1 What was the name of the airship destroyed by fire in 1937?

2 A knitting stitch achieved by doing a plain stitch backwards?

3 A red dye used as a stain for biological specimens?

4 A ribbon, especially when awarded for some special achievement?

5 A sweet cordial made of raisins?

6 What is Saint Elmo's fire?

7 What does asinine pertain to?

8 What is cascara?

9 What type of sea going vessel was invented by Jacques Perio?

10 What is the capital of Sri Lanka?

11 What is the capital of New Hampshire USA?

12 What does polemic mean?

13 In Roman numerals what is the symbol for 1000?

14 The person in charge of the contents of a church, especially the sacred vessels?

15 What is a shimmy?

Answers The Hindenburg **2** Purl **3** Purpurin **4** Riband **5** Rosolio **6** A luminous area that sometimes appears round church spires **7** Asses **8** Bark of the buckthorn tree **9** The steamboat **10** Columbo **11** Concord **12** Controversial disputations **13** The letter 'M' **14** Sacristan? **15** An informal word for a chemise

Miscellaneous — Quiz 75

1 Port Natal is the harbour for which South African city?

2 Small tree native to Indonesia, whose ripe fruit resembles an olive in shape?

3 Tuscan sculptor, regarded as the founder of modern sculpture whose works include the marble statues of Saints Mark and George?

4 What is the art of Japanese flower arranging?

5 Large screen cinematograph system developed in Canada in 1968?

6 Which dam in Egypt created Lake Nasser?

7 Which variety of quartz is violet to purple in colour?

8 Who, in Norse mythology, is the god of thunder?

9 Which Germanic Christian name means 'bright clearing'?

10 Which French impressionist painter said 'I've been 40 years discovering that the queen of all colours was black'?

11 Which French writer was born Jean-Baptiste Poquello?

12 Which volcanic peak in Tanzania is the highest mountain in Africa?

13 What are the Religious Society of Friends commonly known as?

14 Which fabled pure white beast is a symbol of holiness and chastity?

15 Which is the only active volcano on the European mainland?

Answers **1** Durban **2** Clove **3** Donatello **4** Ikebana **5** Imax **6** The Aswan Dam **7** Amethyst **8** Thor **9** Shirley **10** Renoir **11** Moli're **12** Kilimanjaro **13** Quakers **14** The Unicorn **15** Vesuvius

Quiz 76 Miscellaneous

1 What is brawn?

2 What was the name of the wood carver who carved the stalls of St Paul's Cathedral?

3 What is to ululate?

4 What is trass?

5 What is a tolbooth?

6 What is a steinbock?

7 What is a siphonet?

8 The name given to a raw recruit in the army?

9 What is an eagre?

10 To reduce the size of a herd by killing a number of its members?

11 What is the name given to the husband of an unfaithful wife?

12 What is conic?

13 What is a caterwaul

14 What is brock another name for?

15 What is a flam?

Answers **1** Muscle **2** Grending Gibbons **3** To howl **4** Light coloured volcanic tufa (calcium carbonate) **5** A town hall, chiefly in Scotland **6** An alpine ibex **7** The honey tube of aphis **8** A rookie **9** A large tidal bore, especially of the Humber or Severn estuaries **10** Cull **11** Cuckold **12** Cone-shaped **13** A cat's cry **14** A badger **15** A sham story

Miscellaneous — Quiz 77

1 Which metallic element has the symbol K?

2 Who cut the Gordian knot?

3 Which legendary creature has the head of an eagle and body of a lion?

4 Who was the first man to travel in space?

5 What is the capital of Gabon?

6 Who was the Hunchback of Notre Dame?

7 What is ground in a hand-turned mill called a quern?

8 Who, in 1555, published a collection of prophecies called 'Centuries'?

9 What is the longest bone in the human body?

10 Which country was formerly called Formosa?

11 What is the valved top on an inverted bottle of spirits called?

12 Which Greek warrior was dipped in the River Styx by his mother to make him immortal?

13 What is the art of Japanese paper folding called?

14 Which is the second book of the Pentateuch in the Old Testament?

15 What, which in Nepali reads Sagarmatha, and in Chinese reads Qumolangma Feng?

Answers **1** Potassium **2** Alexander the Great **3** Griffin **4** Yuri Gagarin
5 Libreville **6** Quasimodo **7** Grain **8** Nostradamus **9** The femur **10** Taiwan
11 Optic **12** Achilles **13** Origami **14** Exodus **15** Everest

Quiz 78 — Miscellaneous

1 French province, west of the Rhine and famous for its wines?

2 What is a beneice?

3 A long cloak-like garment, made of rich fabric and worn in the east?

4 A tall narrow desk, with a slanted surface for writing and drawers at the side. In US a large sofa-bed?

5 What is an echinoid?

6 A small European falcon, also known as a pigeon hawk and often used in falconry?

7 The thick brown syrup obtained during sugar refining. In US and Canada, the word for treacle?

8 What is a noser?

9 What is osseous?

10 What is a pantile?

11 What is pawky?

12 To what facial feature does the word 'retrousse' refer?

13 A game similar to hockey which originated in Scotland?

14 An uncut loop in the pile of towelling fabric?

15 A yellow dye obtained from the 'dyer's rocket' plant?

Answers **1** Alsace **2** A church living **3** Kaftan **4** Davenport **5** A genus of sea urchins **6** Merlin **7** Molasses **8** A strong headwind **9** Having a bony skeleton **10** A curved roof tile **11** Shrewd **12** A nose turned up at the end **13** Shinty **14** Terry **15** Weld

Miscellaneous — Quiz 79

1. What did the philosopher Epicurus say was the chief good?
2. Who created the fictional island of Utopia?
3. Who sailed from Morocco to Barbados in a papyrus craft called 'Tigris' in 1970?
4. Which animal is also known as the American elk?
5. Who was the notorious female Wild West outlaw called the 'Outlaw Queen'?
6. Named after the Spanish for village, where Indians live in stone, apartment-like villages in New Mexico?
7. What is the more common name for a popular house plant 'impatiens'?
8. What is topiary?
9. Who was the Persian king defeated by the Greeks in 480 BC at the Battle of Salanus?
10. What type of entertainment evolved from family shows created by Tony Paster from 1881?
11. The 'Old Faithful' geyser is in which National Park?
12. Which artist painted a famous portrait of his mother?
13. Of which country is Caracas the capital?
14. Which actor was born William Pratt in 1887?
15. Who became President of Russia in 1991?

Answers **1** Pleasure **2** Sir Thomas More **3** Thor Heyerdahl **4** Wapati **5** Belle Starr **6** Pueblo **7** Busy-lizzy **8** The trimming of trees into ornamental designs **9** Xerxes **10** Vaudeville **11** Yellowstone **12** James Whistler **13** Venezuela **14** Boris Karloff **15** Boris Yeltsin

Quiz 80 — Miscellaneous

1. Where is the city of Differdange?
2. In which channel is the Isle of Lundy?
3. What was the name of the German Federal Republic of 1919-33?
4. What is a four-sided figure called with two parallel sides?
5. Who was the Roman slave and gladiator who led a slave uprising against Rome?
6. What animal stars with Bill Murray in the 1997 movie 'Larger than Life'?
7. Who was the sixth and last wife of Henry VIII?
8. Who recorded the album 'Songs for Swinging Lovers in the 1960s'?
9. Ailurophobia is a fear of what?
10. Who in Roman mythology was the goddess of flowers and springtime?
11. What name is given to the first Sunday in Lent?
12. The Rowan tree is another name for which tree?
13. The quagga is an extinct type of which animal?
14. What is the common name given to the pattern of stars called Big Dipper?
15. Who is the Norwegian traitor who collaborated with the Nazis in World War II?

Answers **1** Luxembourg **2** The Bristol Channel **3** The Weimar Republic **4** Trapezium **5** Spartacus **6** An elephant **7** Catherine Parr **8** Frank Sinatra **9** Cats **10** Flora **11** Quadragesima **12** Mountain Ash **13** Zebra **14** Plough **15** Quisling

Miscellaneous — Quiz 81

1 What was briefly occupied as Iraq's 19th province from August 1990 to February 1991?

2 Who wrote 'The Water Babies'?

3 In which US state is Kittyhawk where the Wright Brothers made their first flight in 1903?

4 In which vessel did the Pilgrim Fathers sail to America?

5 At which battle in 1690 did William of Orange defeat James II?

6 Which actor's real name was Taidje Khan?

7 Christine McVie is associated with which pop group?

8 Where was the 1972 Summer Olympic Games held?

9 What is the capital of Morocco?

10 In mythology, what were Acheron, Lathe and Phelgethon?

11 Which Greek philosopher was put to death by drinking hemlock?

12 With what did Nikita Khrushchev pound the desk in the UN General Assembly in 1960?

13 Which town in central Italy is famous for its garden and was a favourite summer residence of wealthy Romans from the 14th century BC?

14 The motto of which American state is 'North to the Future'?

15 Which variety of gypsum is usually snow-white in colour?

Answers **1** Kuwait **2** Charles Kingsley **3** North Carolina **4** Mayflower **5** The Battle of the Boyne **6** Yul Brynner **7** Fleetwood Mac **8** Munich **9** Rabat **10** Rivers **11** Socrates **12** His shoe **13** Tivoli **14** Alaska **15** Alabaster

Quiz 82 — Miscellaneous

1 Where were the 1986 Olympic Games held?

2 Which singer was killed when his light aircraft crashed in Monterey Bay, California in 1997?

3 Which actor, star of 'Chaplin', was sentenced to three years in prison in 1999 for violating probation for drug offences?

4 Who was the incurable optimist in Dicken's novel 'David Copperfield'?

5 Which street off Whitehall in London contains just three of its original row of terraced houses?

6 In legend, who rode a sea-horse called a hippocampus?

7 What girl's name is an anagram of a Shakespeare play?

8 What note is equal in duration to half a crotchet?

9 Which 1958 Hitchcock movie starred James Stewart and Kim Novak?

10 What is measured by an odometer?

11 Which writer died in exile in Paris, having adopted the name of Sebastian Melmoth?

12 Which is the fourth largest of North America's Great Lakes?

13 What in the 19th century was Astley's and Spangler's?

14 Who, in Greek mythology was punished by Hera so that she could only repeat another speaker's last words?

15 To what is a hedonomaniac addicted?

Answers **1** Mexico City **2** John Denver **3** Robert Downey Jr **4** Mr. Micawber **5** Downing Street **6** Neptune **7** Thelma (Hamlet) **8** Quaver **9** Vertigo **10** Distance **11** Oscar Wilde **12** Erie **13** A circus **14** Echo **15** Pleasure

Miscellaneous — Quiz 83

1 Which writer created the character Pudd'n head Wilson in his 1894 detective story?

2 What is the main ingredient of the dish angels-on-horseback?

3 The fibula, tibia and femur are all bones in which part of the human anatomy?

4 Whose third symphony is known as 'Eroica'?

5 How high above the playing surface is the basket in the game of basketball?

6 What in computer science is the name of the rate at which a modem can transmit data?

7 Which is the only mammal capable of sustained flight?

8 How many periods of play are there in a baseball game?

9 Of what material is the Statue of Liberty constructed?

10 For what was Sir Cecil Beaton famous?

11 The song 'When I Was a Lad' is from which Gilbert and Sullivan operetta?

12 What type of instrument is a 'shofar'?

13 What is the name of the connective tissue that joins the muscles of the calf to the bone of the heel?

14 What is a mudskipper a type of?

15 Which theatre at Southwark, London was constructed in 1555 by an English actor Richard Burbage in partnership with William Shakespeare?

Answers **1** Mark Twain **2** Oysters **3** Leg **4** Beethoven **5** 10 ft (3m) **6** The Baud rate **7** The bat **8** Nine **9** Copper **10** Photography **11** HMS Pinafore **12** A ram's horn **13** Achilles tendon **14** Fish **15** The Globe

Quiz 84 — Miscellaneous

1 What is the first day of Lent known as?

2 Thomas Arnold was the most famous headmaster of which English school?

3 What in computer science does the acronym COBOL stand for?

4 What is the name of the parallel of latitude 23°27' North?

5 Who, in the second half of the 19th century, designed the then world's largest steamship 'The Great Eastern'?

6 What is a gnomon?

7 Which French diplomat and engineer masterminded the Suez Canal?

8 Who was the New York City 13th Precinct police officer in the TV cartoon 'Top Cat'?

9 What are the dots on a domino called?

10 Who said: "To live a single day and hear a good teaching is better than to live a hundred years without knowing such teaching"?

11 In what season is the sun closest to the earth?

12 What is the most widely read magazine in the world?

13 Who were the mythological founders of Ancient Rome?

14 In which film did Peter Cushing play Grand Moff Tarkin?

15 Daisy Hawkins was the original title of which Lennon-McCartney composition?

Answers **1** Ash Wednesday **2** Rugby **3** Common Business-Orientated Language **4** The Tropic of Cancer **5** Isambard Kingdom Brunel **6** The shadown producing central device on a sun-dial **7** Ferdinand de Lesseps **8** Officer Dibble **9** Pips **10** Buddha **11** Winter **12** Readers Digest **13** Romulus and Remus **14** Star Wars **15** Eleanor Rigby

Miscellaneous — Quiz 85

1 How many ounces does an official baseball weigh?

2 Which millionaire was a virtual recluse in his penthouse apartment at the Desert Inn, Las Vegas from 1966-1976?

3 Which astronomer was almost burned at the stake for maintaining that the earth revolved round the sun?

4 Which flower did singer Billie Holliday always wear in the right side of her hair?

5 What was the name of Audrey Hepburn's character in 'Breakfast at Tiffany's'?

6 What is a male adult pig called?

7 What in computer science does MIPS stand for?

8 Who was beheaded for siding with the Catholic Church in its opposition to the divorce of Henry VIII from Catherine of Aragon?

9 Which planet has the shortest day of just 10 hours?

10 In the country of Panama, over which oceans does the sun set and rise?

11 Who was shot and killed by Jack McCall on Aug 2, 1876 while playing cards?

12 The city of Budapest is divided by which river?

13 How many cards are there in a Tarot deck?

14 What are the colours on the flag of Israel?

15 Which Greek physician was called the Father of Medicine?

Answers **1** Five ounces **2** Howard Hughes **3** Galileo **4** A gardenia **5** Holly Golightly **6** A boar **7** Million instructions per second **8** Sir Thomas More **9** Jupiter **10** It rises over the Pacific and sets over the Atlantic **11** 'Wild Bill' Hickok **12** The Danube **13** 66 **14** Blue and white **15** Hippocrates

Quiz 86

Miscellaneous

1 What type of clock was invented by Christian Huygens in 1659?

2 Who said: "We are not amused"?

3 The Golden Poppy is the state flower of which American state?

4 In which movie did Macualay Caulkin star as the richest boy in the world?

5 Where in the world is Queen Maud Land?

6 Lightweight, half-lightweight and extra-lightweight are classes of which sport?

7 Which Greek god is portrayed as half man, half goat?

8 At the end of the opera 'Madame Butterfly', what is the child seen to be waving?

9 Who was the fugitive played by David Janssen in the famous TV series?

10 Which record company was formed by the Beatles?

11 Who married Hillary Rodham in 1975?

12 Who was the woman cured of evil spirits by Jesus?

13 Who wrote 'Treasure Island?

14 Who was the Archduke assassinated at Sarajevo on June 28, 1914?

15 Which was the first American-bred and trained horse to win the Grand National at Aintree?

Answers **1** The Pendulum Clock **2** Queen Victoria **3** California **4** Richie Rich **5** Antarctica **6** Judo **7** Pan **8** The American flag **9** Dr. Richard Kimble **10** Apple **11** Bill Clinton **12** Mary Magdalene **13** Robert Louis Stevenson **14** Franz Ferdinand **15** J. Trump

Miscellaneous — Quiz 87

1 What gift is said to be acquired by kissing the Blarney stone?

2 Who in the French Revolution were 'tricoteuses'?

3 What is a saltarello?

4 For what did Hans Brinker receive immortal fame in Holland?

5 Killed in action in 1918, by how was Baron Manfred von Richtofen better known?

6 What is the world's most spoken language?

7 What is the official language of the Dominican Republic?

8 In which country is Respect for the Aged day a national holiday on 15 September?

9 The Winter signs of the Zodiac are Capricorn, Aquarius and which other sign?

10 Which National Anthem was composed in 1792 by Captain Claude Joseph Rouget de Lisle?

11 The St Lawrence seaway links which bodies of water?

12 With which sporting team would you link Meadowlark Lemon?

13 What nationality was Charles Richter who devised the earthquake - measuring scale that bears his name?

14 Who was the leader of France's Vichy government in World War II?

15 Of where is Maseru the capital?

Answers **1** The gift of eloquence **2** Parisian women who sat knitting white watching guillotinings **3** A type of dance **4** He was the Dutch boy who held his finger in the dyke **5** The Red Baron **6** Chinese **7** Spanish **8** Japan **9** Pisces **10** The French Anthem "La Marseillaise' **11** The Atlantic Ocean and the Great Lakes **12** The Harlem Globetrotters **13** American **14** Marshal Henri Petain **15** Lesotho

Quiz 88 — Miscellaneous

1 Which is the brightest star in the sky which appears as an orange star in the constellation Bootes?

2 What is measured by a barometer?

3 In computer science what is the name of the process of moving through a document in a window to permit viewing of any desired portion?

4 According to the book of Genesis, how old was Methuselah when he died?

5 What is the capital of New Zealand?

6 Which ancient city, whose name means 'gate of god' is today a broad area of ruins east of the Euphrates River south of Baghdad, Iraq?

7 Which jazz icon wrote and performed 'Mood Indigo' and 'Sophisticated Lady'?

8 Which three world leaders took part in the 1945 Yalta conference?

9 Which mountain contains the carved heads of four US Presidents?

10 By what name is the northernmost part of Finland which lies above the Arctic Circle also known as?

11 What is the name of the fodder plant also known as lucerne?

12 Montego Bay is in which country?

13 How many years are celebrated by a Coral wedding anniversary?

14 What is meant by the musical expression legato?

15 What is a tsunami?

Answers **1** Arcturus **2** Atmospheric pressure **3** Scrolling **4** 969 years **5** Wellington **6** Babylon **7** Duke Ellington **8** Franklin Roosevelt, Winston Churchill and Joseph Stalin **9** Rushmore **10** Lapland **11** Alfalfa **12** Jamaica **13** 35 **14** Smoothly **15** A tidal wave

Miscellaneous — Quiz 89

1 Which US jazz saxophonist was nicknamed 'Bird' or 'Yardbird'?

2 In which country is Lake Ladoga, the largest lake in Europe?

3 In which country are the Angel Falls, the world's highest waterfall?

4 Who wrote the 'Call of the Wild'?

5 Which acid takes its name from milk?

6 What device is also known as a polygraph?

7 What is a painted lady?

8 Whose first big hit was 'Born to Run' in 1976?

9 What is chiromancy better known as?

10 What name connects a small ostrich, the fifth natural satellite of Saturn and a Titan in Greek mythology?

11 Which actress was famous for her roles in sophisticated plays written by her friend Noel Coward?

12 On which islands are the world's largest tortoises to be found?

13 Which was the oldest of the Seven Wonders of the Ancient World?

14 Which animal was George Stubbs most famous for painting?

15 What is etymology the study of?

Answers **1** Charlie Parker **2** Russia **3** Venezuela **4** Jack London **5** Lactic acid **6** Lie detector **7** A butterfly **8** Bruce Springsteen **9** Palmistry **10** Rhea **11** Gertrude Lawrence **12** The Galapagos Islands **13** The Egyptian Pyramids **14** Horses **15** Words

Quiz 90 — Miscellaneous

1 What nationality was the Protestant reformer Martin Luther?

2 What relative was Prince Albert to Queen Victoria before their marriage?

3 Which opera was composed by Verdi to commemorate the opening of the Suez Canal?

4 Which novel was written in 1924 by Percival Christopher Wren, an ex-member of the French Foreign Legion?

5 Who in the world of pop music are Maurice, Barry and Robin?

6 Which home-made bomb is named after a Russian statesman?

7 Which sportswoman in 1971 became the first woman to win $100,000 in a single year?

8 What instrument was originally known as a sackbut?

9 What in World War II was 'Operation Barbarossa'?

10 Zelda was the wife of which American novelist?

11 Who is the conniving rabbit in Joel Chandler Harris's 'Tales of Uncle Remus'?

12 What nationality was skater and movie actress Sonja Henie?

13 What kind of creature is a kelpie?

14 Who was the illegitimate grandson of Harry Houdini who in 1977 became the first person to be executed in the United States in ten years?

15 In the Alex Haley book 'Roots', who was the son of Omoro and Binta?

Answers **1** German **2** First cousin **3** Aida **4** Beau Geste **5** The Bee Gees **6** The Molotov Cocktail **7** Billie Jean King **8** The trombone **9** The codename for the German invasion of Russia **10** F.Scott Fitzgerald **11** Brer Rabbit **12** Norwegian **13** A dog, bred for herding sheep in Australia **14** Gary Gilmore **15** Kunte Kinte

SECTION 6

Categories

Categories

Sporting Icons

1 Which cricketer was known as 'The Don'?

2 Which aquatic first was achieved by US Olympic Triple medalist Gertrude Ederle in 1925?

3 Which boxer retired in 1955 with the perfect record of 49 fights, 49 wins, 42 by knockout?

4 Who was the Ethiopian who became the first black African to achieve Olympic victory when he won the 1960 marathon in Rome?

5 Which US jockey is now confined to a wheelchair after a car crash in 1991?

6 In the 1950s an Associated Press poll voted which movie star the greatest swimmer of the century?

7 Which athletics event did Ed Moses dominate for more than a decade in the 70s and 80s?

8 What is the name of the ten times British and six times World Squash Championship titles, which means 'Conqueror of the World'?

9 Which American runner tripped over Zola Budd in the 1984 Olympic 3000m final?

10 Which racehorse dominated steeple chasing in England in the 1980s and was nicknamed 'Dessie'?

11 After seeing Jack Nicklaus win the 1965 Masters by nine strokes, which other golfing icon said "Jack is playing an entirely different game – a game I'm not ever familiar with"?

12 Which East German figure skater was known as 'the beautiful face of Communism'?

13 Which cricketer scored 364 against Australia in 1938?

14 Dubbed the greatest athlete of all time, which sprinter and long-jumper won a total of eight Olympic gold medals?

15 At which event did Al Oerter win the Gold Medal at four consecutive Olympics?

Answers **1** Sir Donald Bradman **2** First woman to swim the English Channel **3** Rocky Marciano **4** Abebe Bikila **5** Bill Shoemaker **6** Johnny Weissmuller **7** 400m hurdles **8** Jahangir Khan **9** Mary Decker **10** Desert Orchid **11** Bobby Jones **12** Katarina Witt **13** Sir Len Hutton **14** Carl Lewis **15** The discus

Mythology 1 | Categories

1 Lada was the mortal loved by Zeus when taking the form of what creature?

2 What were Hamadryads?

3 What saved Arion when thrown overboard by pirates?

4 Who slew the serpent Python which was born from slime left by Deluge?

5 Who was the muse of choral dance and song?

6 Which part of Achilles was vulnerable?

7 Who was the Titan who held the world on his shoulders as punishment for warring against Zeus?

8 Who was the prophetess and daughter of Priam who was never believed?

9 Which king was given the gift of turning all he touched to gold?

10 What was the name of the three-headed dog which guarded the entrance to Hades?

11 As one of his labours what did Hercules have to do to the Augean stables?

12 Who was the Monster of Thebes who killed those who could not answer her riddle?

13 Who was the Babylonian youth who made love to Thisbe through a hole in a wall?

14 What was the only thing that did not escape from Pandora's box?

15 Who was the Roman god of woods and fields?

Answers **1** A swan **2** Tree nymphs **3** A dolphin **4** Apollo **5** Terpsichore **6** His heel **7** Atlas **8** Cassandra **9** Midas **10** Cerberus **11** Clean them **12** The Sphinx **13** Pyramus **14** Hope **15** Silvanus

Categories — Computers

1 Which term, in common use by Internet users, was coined by science fiction writer William Gibson in his first book 'Neuromancer'?

2 What do the initials LAN stand for?

3 Invented in 1980 by Dan Bricklin and Bob Frankston, of what was 'Viscalc' the first one of?

4 What term was coined in 1965 by a computer scientist John McCarthy?

5 What general term refers to a computer devices or series of devices that store information?

6 What does CPU stand for?

7 What term in computer science is short for picture element; sometimes called a pel?

8 What is the name of the small hand-held device for controlling the cursor movement on a screen?

9 What was the name of the virus, originating in the Philippines that caused worldwide disruption to computer systems in May 2000?

10 Who was the British mathematician who worked on the Enigma code in World War II and was a pioneer in the work of computer logic?

11 What measurement is equal to 1,024 bytes?

12 What resource on a computer stores a copy of the last information that was 'copied' or 'cut'?

13 Which company introduced Bubble Jet technology in 1981?

14 What does the 'E' stand for in E-mail?

15 What general name is given to the list of files stored on a computer?

Answers **1** Cyberspace **2** Local Area Network **3** Spreadsheet **4** Artificial Intelligence **5** Memory **6** Central Processing Unit **7** Pixel **8** Mouse **9** The Love Bug **10** Alan Turing **11** Kilobyte **12** A clipboard **13** Canon **14** Electronic **15** Directory

Rivers

Categories

1 The Lahn, Lippe, Main, Mosel, Necker and Ruhr are tributaries of which river?

2 Which river rises in the Black Forest region of Germany and flows into the Black Sea?

3 The Susquehanna is a river in which country?

4 Which river flows along the Texas-Mexico border into the Gulf of Mexico?

5 The city of Marseille is linked by canal to which river?

6 The Arkansas river in the Western US is a major tributary of which river?

7 The Karun is the only navigable river of which country?

8 The Stanley Falls are on which river, which is the second longest river in Africa?

9 Which river unites with the Euphrates River at Al-Qurnah to form the Shatt al-Arab?

10 In which country do the White and Blue Niles converge to form the Nile proper?

11 The river Amazon is chiefly in which country?

12 Which river enters the Atlantic Ocean at Lisbon?

13 Which river, forming the border between the Cape of Good Hope and Namibia empties into the Atlantic Ocean at Alexander Bay?

14 On which river was Custer's last stand?

15 Which river is regarded by Hindus as the most sacred river in the world?

Answers **1** Rhine **2** Danube **3** USA **4** Rio Grande **5** Rhone **6** Mississippi **7** Iran **8** Congo **9** Tigris **10** Sudan (at Khartoum) **11** Brazil **12** Tagus **13** Orange **14** The Little Bighorn **15** Ganges

Categories **Dinosaurs**

1 The Hadrosaurus, which ate marsh grass and other vegetation had a bill which resembled what familiar creature?

2 The Heterodontosaurus, which stood only one meter tall had what valuable assest that saved it from its many predators?

3 The Ptersoaurs were the first non-insect animals to develop what?

4 What was distinctive about the Triceratops that served as defensive weapons against predators?

5 In which Central Asian desert did an expedition led by an American naturalist Roy Chapman discover dinosaur eggs between 1921-30?

6 What was the predominant diet of the four-legged sauropode group of dinosaurs which included the Apatosaurus and Diplodocus?

7 The 1993 movies Jurassic Park, was based on a novel by which writer, who has been described as 'The Father of the Techno Thriller'?

8 What was the largest variety of flesh-eating dinosaur?

9 Compsognathus was a genus of tiny carnivorous dinosaurs that lived during the late Jurassic period, growing to about 60cm (2 ft) long and weighing little more than 3 kg (6.5lb). What familiar creatures did they most closely resemble in appearance?

10 The Nobel Prize winning American scientist, Luis Walter Alvarez published what controversial theory about the extinction of dinosaurs?

11 In which classic 1948 musical starring Frank Sinatra and Gene Kelly does the skeleton of a dinosaur get accidentally knocked over and reduced to a pile of bones during the singing of the number "Pre-Historic Man'?

12 What is the meaning of the Greek word 'bronte' in the name of the huge dinosaur, brontosaur, which implies the animal shook the ground when it walked?

13 Dinosaurs dominated life on land for 140 million years from the late Triassic period until their extinction during which period some 64 million years ago?

14 In which country is Dinosaur Provincial Park, where, in the early 20th century, fossil remains of 60 different species of dinosaur were discovered?

15 What is the meaning of the word 'sauros' as contained in the names of dinosaurs such as Apatosaurus?

Answers **1** Duck **2** It was the fastest of all dinosaurs **3** The power of flight **4** It had horns **5** The Gobi Desert **6** Plants (they were vegetarian) **7** Michael Crichton **8** Tyrannosaurus **9** Birds **10** That a giant meteorite had struck the earth **11** On the Town **12** Thunder **13** The Cretaceous period **14** Canada (in Alberta) **15** Lizard

Phobias

Categories

1. Keraunophobia, brontophobia and toinitrophobia are all fear of which phenomenon?
2. What is the fear of open spaces, or going out in public?
3. What is toxiphobia the fear of?
4. What is claustrophobia?
5. What does a ereuthrophobiac fear doing?
6. Scotophobia, myctophobia, achiuophobia and lygophobia are frightened of something that occurs every day. What is it?
7. What is ichthyophobia fear of?
8. What is zoophobia the fear of?
9. What is an hodophobiac very reluctant to do?
10. What is onerirophobia?
11. What is fear of spiders?
12. What creatures terrify an ophidiophobiac?
13. What does a pyrophobiac fear?
14. Why do thermophobiacs like to remain cool?
15. What is chrometophobia?

Answers **1** Thunder **2** Agoraphobia **3** Poisons **4** Fear of confined spaces **5** Blushing **6** The dark **7** Fish **8** Animals **9** Travel, it is fear of travel **10** Fear of dreams **11** Arachnaphobia **12** Snakes **13** Fire **14** They fear heat **15** Fear of money

Categories — Chemistry

1 What instrument is used to measure the specific gravity or density of a liquid?

2 Which colourless pungent gas, highly soluble in water, is an important by-product of the manufacture of fuel gases, and during the Middle Ages, when it was obtained by heating the horns and hoofs of oxen, was known as hartshorn?

3 Which acid, widely used in the chemical industry, and in dyeing and tanning, occurs in the poisons of stinging nettles and ants?

4 Marie Curie won the Nobel prize for Chemistry in 1911 for discovering radium and which other element?

5 The Rh factor in blood derives its name from which creature?

6 What is the chief source of cresols, a group of chemicals used in antiseptics, creosote oil, paint removers and plastics?

7 Which gas is also known as laughing gas?

8 Which British chemist first described colour blindness?

9 Born in 1776 and knighted in 1812, who was the British Chemist of whom Samuel Taylor Coleridge said, if he "had not been the first chemist, he would have been the first poet of his age"?

10 Which ancient art, practised during the middle ages, devoted chiefly to discovering a substance that would transmute common metals into gold, is said to be the predecessor of chemistry?

11 What colourless and highly flammable liquid, whose molecule consists of a closed ring of six carbon atoms, was discovered in 1825 by Michael Faraday?

12 What term is applied to materials, the solutions of which aid in the removal of dirt from surfaces?

13 Which gas, later given its modern name by Antoine Lavoisier, was named inflammable air by Joseph Priestly in 1781?

14 What name was given to the assumption propounded in the 17th century, that when anything burned, its combustible part was given off to the air?

15 Which alkaloid constitutes the principal active chemical constituent of tobacco?

Answers **1** Hydrometer **2** Ammonia **3** Formic **4** Polonium **5** The Rhesus Monkey **6** Coal Tar **7** Nitrous oxide **8** John Dalton **9** Sir Humphrey Davy **10** Alchemy **11** Benzene **12** Detergents **13** Hydrogen **14** Phlogiston **15** Nicotine

Countries

Categories

1 The name of which country, bounded on the north by the Barents Sea, means 'Northern Way'?

2 Thimphu is the capital of which Himalyan country?

3 In which country is Cape Horn, the southernmost part of the continent of South America?

4 Which country borders on more countries than any other nation?

5 Which country comprises the eastern two-thirds of the island of Hispaniola?

6 Vilnius is the capital of which country?

7 Which country is bounded on the southeast by Burma, on the south by the Bay of Bengal and to the West by India?

8 Kathmandu is the capital of which country?

9 The Atlas Mountains extend across which hereditary monarchy of North Africa?

10 The Markka is a unit of currency in which country?

11 Which country was formerly a British colony known as the Gold Coast?

12 Rub al-Khali, known in English as the Great Sandy Desert extends over much of the south east of which Southwest Asian monarchy?

13 In which ocean are the Solomon Islands?

14 What is the capital of the African republic of Guinea?

15 Asmara is the capital of which independent nation of northeastern Africa on the Red Sea opposite Yemen?

Answers **1** Norway **2** Bhutan **3** Chile **4** Russia **5** Dominican Republic **6** Lithuania **7** Bangladesh **8** Nepal **9** Morocco **10** Finland **11** Ghana **12** Saudi Arabia **13** Pacific **14** Conakry **15** Eritrea

Categories **Plants**

1 What pigment gives plants their green colour?

2 What is the common name for the plant 'Dionaea muscipula' that feeds on insects and other small animals?

3 Commonly found in arid regions, which is the largest family of succulent plants, which have fleshy stems and leaves swollen with water-storage tissues?

4 What name is given to the cultivation of ornamental flowering plants for aesthetic purposes?

5 What is the common name of the late-flowering perennial garden plant which has long-pointed, lance-shaped leaves and numerous tiny, deep yellow-shaded flower heads in a pyramid-shaped pinnacle?

6 Hybrid tea, floribunda, miniature and climbing are all species of which garden plant?

7 What word describes the study of plants, including their classification, structure, physiology and ecology?

8 In 'The Winter's Tale', which plant did Shakespeare describe as 'the fairest flowers o' the season'?

9 Which fruit has its seeds on the outside?

10 Oil extracted from the seeds of which plant are used in cooking, as salad oil, and in making margarine?

11 What type of plants are sorrel, angelica, burnet and hyssop?

12 Which parasitic plant, widely used as a Christmas decoration, was venerated by the Druids, who cut it ceremonially from their sacred oak with a golden knife?

13 'Gros Vert de Laon', 'green globe' and 'Jerusalem' are all varieties of which vegetable?

14 On its mutinous voyage, the 'Bounty' had spent five months in Tahiti where it had been sent to gather what type of plants for the West Indies?

15 Calluna, erica and daboecia are three genera of which small, bushy evergreen shrub?

Answers **1** Chlorophyll **2** Venus flytrap **3** Cactus **4** Floriculture **5** Golden rod
6 Rose **7** Botany **8** Carnation **9** Strawberry **10** Sesame **11** Herbs
12 Mistletoe **13** Artichoke **14** Breadfruit **15** Heather

The name's the same

Categories

1 What name connects a US family of film comedians and the author of 'Das Kapital?

2 What name connects an English conspirator and purjurer and an English hero of Scott's ill-fated 1912 expedition to the South Pole?

3 What name connects a Rock 'n' Roll singer of the 1950s with the first woman to break the speed of sound?

4 What name connects the inventor of the shoelace with the 35th President of the US?

5 What name connects a kidnapper and bootlegger with the nickname 'Machine Gun' and an Australian outlaw who wore an iron mask?

6 What name connects a convicted murderer who actress Sue Lyon married in 1973 while he was still in prison, and the married couple who raised Elsa the lioness?

7 What name links an Irish novelist and an English saint and martyr?

8 What name connects the American inventor of Jell-O desserts in 1845 with a British boxer who floored Cassius Clay at Wembley in 1963?

9 What name connects the 31st President of the US with a Director of the FBI?

10 What name connects a famous bandleader and a former husband of Marilyn Monroe?

11 What name connects a film actor born Emmanuel Goldenberg and a British artist who drew absurd and complicated designs?

12 What name connects half of an English team of composers with the actor who starred with Greta Garbo in the movie 'Queen Christina'?

13 What name connects the actor who was General Montgomery's double in World War II with a pair of outlaw brothers?

14 What name connects the English inventor of the vacuum cleaner and Shakespearean actor who assassinated Abraham Lincoln?

15 What name connects an economist who wrote 'An Enquiry into the Nature and Causes of the Wealth of Nations', and a former Prime Minister of Rhodesia?

Answers **1** Marx **2** Oates **3** Cochran **4** Kennedy **5** Kelly **6** Adamson
7 Becket **8** Cooper **9** Hoover **10** Miller **11** Robinson **12** Gilbert
13 James **14** Booth **15** Smith

Categories

Inventors and Inventions

1 Who invented the telephone?

2 In which country was paper invented in AD 105?

3 What type of rays were first generated by means of the Crooks tube, an invention of a British physicist Sir William Crookes?

4 Who invented the power loom in 1785?

5 Which French inventor and chemist (1822-1895) is known for his pioneer work with vaccines against anthrax and rabies as well as a process of sterilization?

6 Who invented the vacuum bottle which sometimes bears his name?

7 Which Scottish inventor patented the waterproof fabric in 1823 which now bears his name?

8 The invention of which weapon is generally credited to a German monk, Berthold Schwarz in the early 14th century?

9 Who invented telegraph signals, and built the first telegraph line between Baltimore and Washington?

10 Which double-reed instrument with wood body was invented in the 17th century by two French musicians Jean Holterre and Michel Philidor

11 Which hunting knife bears the name of the American frontiersman who invented it?

12 Which Greek mathematician is credited with inventing the compound pulley and hydraulic screw?

13 What did Evangelista Torricelli invent in 1643?

14 Who designed a locomotive known as the Rocket in 1829?

15 Which opera impresario made a fortune from a cigar making machine?

Answers **1** Alexander Graham Bell **2** China **3** Cathode rays **4** Edmund Cartwright **5** Louis Pasteur **6** Sir James Dewar **7** Charles Macintosh **8** The cannon **9** Samuel Morse **10** The oboe **11** The Bowie knife **12** Archimedes **13** The barometer **14** George Stephenson **15** Oscar Hammerstein

Art and Culture

Categories

1 Apart from painting, in which other field was Man Ray a leading exponent?

2 Which Jerome Kern musical was based on an Edna Ferber novel?

3 Which artist painted the ceiling of the Sistine Chapel?

4 What is the better known name of Dvorak's Symphony No. 9?

5 Andres Segovia was a virtuoso on what instrument?

6 Whose paintings include 'Moses Smashing the Commandments', 'The Jewish Bride', 'Bathsheba' and 'The Noble Slav'?

7 Who wrote the 'Minute Waltz'?

8 Who sculptured 'The Thinker'?

9 Whose last words were, "I shall hear in heaven"?

10 What is the occupation of Jose, who kills Carmen in Bizet's opera?

11 Who painted the 'Last Supper'?

12 In which city is the Prado art gallery?

13 What was discovered on the Greek island of Melos in 1820?

14 Which French artist painted cabaret stars, prostitutes, barmaids and actors of the Montmartre district of Paris and was portrayed in the 1952 movie 'Moulin Rogue' by Jose Ferrer?

15 In which city did Beethoven write his fifth symphony while it was being invaded by the forces of Napoleon?

Answers **1** Photography **2** Showboat **3** Michelangelo **4** New World **5** Guitar **6** Rembrandt **7** Chopin **8** Rodin **9** Ludwig van Beethoven **10** Soldier **11** Leonardo da Vinci **12** Madrid **13** The Venus de Milo **14** Toulouse Lautrec **15** Bonn

Categories — Sport

1 What nationality is former world motor racing champion Sir Jack Brabham?

2 Which ice-skater fell from grace when her associates engaged in knee-whacking her rival?

3 Who won his first Derby in 1953 on Pinza shortly after being knighted by Queen Elizabeth II?

4 Who was the trainer of three times Grand National winner Red Rum?

5 Which Welsh boxer was known as "the ghost with the hammer on his hands"?

6 Which US tennis player who turned professional at 21 in 1949, when professional tennis was virtually unknown, once took part in Wimbledon's longest ever match when he defeated Charlie Pasarell 22-24, 1-6, 16-14, 6-3, 11-9 in 5 hours 12 minutes?

7 Which athlete raised a black-gloved clenched fist on the victory podium at the 1968 Mexico Olympics after winning the 200m sprint?

8 Who did Arthur Ashe defeat to win Wimbledon in 1975?

9 Which sportsman described Marilyn Monroe as his "warm, big-hearted girl that everybody took advantage of"?

10 What was the sport in which Greg Louganis is regarded as the greatest ever?

11 Who, with Nicklaus and Palmer was a member of golf's Big Three in the 1960s?

12 Who was the first boxer to regain the World Heavyweight boxing championship?

13 Apart from establishing a world long jump record, fishing, hunting and representing England at soccer, at which sport was C.B. Fry a record breaker around the turn of the 19-20th century?

14 Who in 1986 inspired Argentina's World Cup victory and scored his infamous 'Hand of God' goal against England?

15 Which US swimmer won five gold, one silver and one bronze medal at the 1988 Seoul Olympics?

Answers **1** Australian **2** Tonya Harding **3** Sir Gordon Richards **4** Ginger McCain **5** Jimmy Wilde **6** Pancho Gonzales **7** Tommie Smith **8** Jimmy Connors **9** Joe Di Maggio **10** Diving **11** Gary Player **12** Floyd Patterson **13** Cricket **14** Diego Maradona **15** Mat Biondi

Literature

Categories

1 About what event “on the eighteenth of April, in Seventy-five” did Henry Wadsworth Longfellow write”?

2 Which of Aesop’s fables ends with the line, “Little fellows may prove great friends”?

3 Which 1968 Rock Hudson – Ernest Borgnine movie was based on an Alistair MacLean novel of the same name?

4 Which book begins “Mr. Phileas Fogg lived, in 1872, at No. 7, Saville Row, Burlington Gardens ...”?

5 Who wrote ‘Lady Chatterley’s Lover’?

6 Apart from his Tarzan novels, Edgar Rice Burroughs wrote a number of successful science fiction works, based mainly on which planet?

7 ‘Lolita’ by Vladimir Nabokov, and ‘Breakfast at Tiffany’s’ by Truman Capote were both published in which decade?

8 Who wrote ‘The Ugly Duckling’ and ‘The Emperor’s New Clothes’?

9 Who is the eponymous hero of Miguel de Cervantes most famous novel?

10 The Cole Porter musical ‘Kiss Me Kate’ was based on which Shakespeare play?

11 Which classic novel starts “Mrs Rachel Lynde lived just where the Avonlea main road dipped down into a little hollow...”?

12 Sidney Carton is the hero of which Dickens’ novel?

13 Which novel by Robert James Waller was made into a film starring Clint Eastwood and Meryl Streep?

14 Which of Edgar Allan Poe’s works begins, “Once upon a midnight dreary, while I pondered weak and weary...”?

15 Pudd’nhead Wilson was the creation of which author?

Answers **1** Paul Reveres Ride **2** The Lion and the Mouse **3** Ice Station Zebra **4** Around the World in 80 Days **5** D.H. Lawrence **6** Mars **7** 1950s **8** Hans Christian Andersen **9** Don Quixote **10** The Taming of the Shrew **11** Anne of Green Gables **12** A Tale of Two Cities **13** The Bridges of Madison County **14** The Raven **15** Mark Twain

Categories | **Medicine**

1 Lobotomy is concerned with which part of the human body?

2 Who was the South African surgeon who performed the first successful human heart transplant in December 1967, at Grout Schuur hospital on his patient Louis Washkansky?

3 Which salt is used in medicine in hypertonic baths to reduce swelling?

4 What first was achieved in the United States in 1849 by Elizabeth Blackwell?

5 The fibula, tibia and femur are all bones in which part of the human body?

6 What is the system of treatment which, by the use of massage and manipulation and the stretching of various joints, concentrates on the treatment of backache and pain in the legs, neck and head?

7 Which highly infectious disease was eradicated in 1979 as a result of a World Health Organisation programme including vaccination?

8 The pineal body, the parietal lobe and the frontal lobe are in what part of the human body?

9 What type of medicine is used in the detection of crime?

10 What is the name of the curved bone, also called the collar bone, which lies between the sternum (breastbone) and scapula (shoulder bone)?

11 What word, to describe the technique for limiting addictive behaviour and relieving anxiety, first used by Mesmer in France, was coined by the British surgeon James Braid?

12 What is treated by the medicine calamine?

13 Which ancient Chinese medical procedure involved inserting needles into the human body?

14 Which disease is treated by insulin?

15 Which lifesaving device was developed as a result of research combining engineering with medical electronics carried out by an electrical engineer Winston Greatbatch (born 1919)?

Answers **1** The brain **2** Dr. Christian Bernard **3** Epsom salts **4** The first woman medical doctor in the US **5** Leg **6** Osteopathy **7** Smallpox **8** The brain **9** Forensic **10** Clavicle **11** Hypnosis **12** Skin inflammation **13** Acupuncture **14** Diabetes **15** The cardiac pacemaker

Women in history

Categories

1 Who was the American religious leader who founded the Christian Science movement?

2 Mary Todd was the wife of which US President?

3 Who said: "If the people have no bread, let them eat cake"?

4 In which spacecraft did the first woman astronaut, Valentina Terishkova, make her historic space journey?

5 Whose mistress was Emma, Lady Hamilton?

6 Benazir Bhutto became Prime Minister of which country in 1993?

7 Who wrote "Uncle Tom's Cabin"?

8 Who was the scheming wife of the Roman Emperor Claudius?

9 Which woman bore Julius Caesar a son named Caesarion?

10 Who said "Europe will never be like America. Europe is a product of history. America is a product of philosophy"?

11 What was the nickname of Catherine II of Russia?

12 In which field did Maria Montessori gain eminence?

13 Who, in 1907, was the first woman to receive the Order of Merit?

14 Where was Joan of Arc burnt at the stake?

15 Who was the lover, then wife of the French philosopher Peter Abeland?

Answers **1** Mary Morse Eddy **2** Abraham Lincoln **3** Marie Antoinette **4** Vostok **5** Lord Nelson **6** Pakistan **7** Harriet Beecher Stowe **8** Messalina **9** Cleopatra **10** Margaret Thatcher **11** The Great **12** Education **13** Florence Nightingale **14** Rouen **15** Heloise

Categories — One liners

1 Who said: "horse sense is the thing a horse has which keeps it from betting on people"?

2 What did Sigmund Freud describe as "a mistake, a giant mistake"?

3 Who said: "I took a speed reading course and read 'War and Peace' in twenty minutes. It involves Russia"?

4 What did Fred Allen describe as a "fine place to live – if you happen to be an orange"?

5 Who said: "How can you govern a country which has 246 varieties of cheese?"?

6 Who said: "People can have the Model T in any colour...so long as it's black"?

7 What did Elbert Hubbard say was "just one damned thing after another"?

8 Who said: "I never forget a face, but in your case I'll be glad to make an exception"?

9 Who said: "Man is the only animal that blushes – or needs to"?

10 Who said: "A hospital is no place to be sick"?

11 Who, on his deathbed as he sipped champagne said: "Alas, I am dying beyond my means"?

12 Who said: "Facts are stupid things"?

13 Who said: "I love Mickey Mouse more than any woman I've ever known"?

14 Who said: "If we don't succeed, we run the risk of failure"?

15 Who said: "There are three kind of lies: lies, damned lies, and statistics"?

Answers **1** W.C. Fields **2** America **3** Woody Allen **4** California **5** Charles De Gaulle **6** Henry Ford **7** Life **8** Groucho Marx **9** Mark Twain **10** Sam Goldwyn **11** Oscar Wilde **12** Ronald Reagan **13** Walt Disney **14** Dan Quayle **15** Benjamin Disraeli

The Old Testament

Categories

1 Who was the mighty hunter and son of Cush?

2 Zipporah was the wife of which prophet?

3 Who was the mistress and betrayer of Samson?

4 Who was the Patriarch and forefather of the Jews and was also the father of Isaac and Ishmael?

5 Who was the father of Ham, Japath and Sham?

6 Who was the son of Haran who escaped the destruction of Sodom?

7 Who was the son of Isaac who sold his birthright to his brother Jacob?

8 Who was the Philistine slain by David?

9 Which King of Babylon destroyed Jerusalem?

10 What relation was Noah to Methusalah?

11 Of what disease was the Syrian captain Naaman cured by Elisha?

12 Which Patriarch underwent many afflictions and was comforted by Bildad, Elihu, Eliphaz and Zophar?

13 Who was the father of David?

14 Which prophet went to heaven in a chariot of fire?

15 Who was the father of Cain and Abel?

Answers **1** Nimrod **2** Moses **3** Delilah **4** Abraham **5** Noah **6** Lot **7** Esau **8** Goliath **9** Nebuchadnezzar **10** Grandson **11** Leprosy **12** Job **13** Jesse **14** Elijah **15** Adam

Categories

Spies or Lies

Are the following 'spytalk' definitions **TRUE** and **FALSE**?

1 'Boxed' is to be examined by a polygraph lie detector?

2 A 'shoe' is a false passport?

3 A 'swallow' is to take a cyanide pill when apprehended?

4 "Mongoose' is legally gathered information from published sources?

5 'Naked' is operating without back-up or cover?

6 A 'wet job' is an operation on board a ship?

7 'Rice Bowl' is an attempt to infiltrate Chinese Triad gangs?

8 'Spook' is American slang for spy?

9 'Terminated with extreme prejudice' means mission aborted?

10 A 'cobbler' is a spy who inserts a micro-radio transmitters into shoe heels?

11 An 'asset' is an agent or sympathiser positioned in a target country?

12 A 'raven' is a male seducer to lure women into honey trap?

13 A 'musician' is a radio operator?

14 A 'flaps and seals' man is an undercover circus performer?

15 'Legend' is the most experienced spy available?

Answers **1** True **2** True **3** False – it is a female seducer to lure man into honey trap **4** False – it was the code name for the continuing attempts by the Kennedy brothers to get rid of Casto following the Bay of Pigs disaster **5** True **6** False – it is an operation where blood is shed, Russian 'Mokrie dela' **7** False – it was the code name for the doomed attempt by the United States to rescue its fifty-three diplomats held hostage in the siezed US Embassy by the Iranians **8** True **9** False – it means murdered **10** False – it is a forger **11** True **12** True **13** True **14** False – it is an expert at undetected opening and closing of mails **15** False – it is an invented name and biography to hide the name of a spy

Astrology

Categories

1. There are four elements, air and fire are two of them, what are the other two?
2. What sign of the Zodiac is represented by the scales of justice?
3. What is the ruling planet of Sagittarius?
4. What name is given to the angles found between any two planets?
5. Which sign of the Zodiac is said to be ruled by the Sun?
6. What would be your sign of the Zodiac is you were born on 5th November?
7. What animal is represented by the sign of Taurus?
8. Name the planet associated with the process of regeneration?
9. There are four cardinal signs; Aries, Libra and Cancer are three of them, what is the fourth?
10. Which part of the body is said to be ruled by Pisces?
11. Which planet represents the principle of communication?
12. What name is given to the part of the Zodiac crossing the eastern horizon at the time of birth?
13. Name the traditional symbol of Aquarius?
14. Which sign of the Zodiac is ruled by the moon?
15. Which planet is said to govern the Zodiac signs of Taurus and Libra?

Answers **1** Earth and water **2** Libra **3** Jupiter **4** Aspects **5** Leo **6** Scorpio **7** Bull **8** Pluto **9** Capricorn **10** The feet **11** Mercury **12** Ascendant **13** Water-carrier **14** Cancer **15** Venus

Categories — Latin terms

1 What phrase means "to the point of disgust"?

2 What is meant by the phrase "vox populi"?

3 What phrase and initials mean "which was to be demonstrated"?

4 What phrase means 'by itself"?

5 What is meant by the phrase "in toto"?

6 To what does the phrase "alma mater" refer"?

7 What phrase means unscripted or improvised?

8 What is something if it is described as "bona fide"?

9 Which phrase means "among other things"?

10 Which phrase means "at first sight; on the face of it"?

11 What is meant by the phrase "quid pro quo"?

12 What is something if it is described as being "sui generis"?

13 What is "modus vivendi"?

14 Which phrase means literally "my fault" and is acknowledgement of one's guilt?

15 Which phrase literally means "course of life"?

Answers **1** Ad nauseam **2** The voice of the people **3** QED (quod erat demonstrandum) **4** Per se **5** Completely, as a whole **6** One's old school (literally 'nourishing mother') **7** Ad lib **8** In good faith **9** Inter alia **10** Prima facie **11** Something in return for something else e.g. a favour returned **12** Unique **13** Way of living **14** Mea culpa **15** Curriculum vitae

Dances

Categories

1 Which national dance of Spain is also connected with ice-dance partnership of Torvill and Dean?

2 Which dance is a ritual performed by the Hopi Indians of North America as a petition to the nature gods to bring rain?

3 Which traditional English dance is performed by a team of men with jingles strapped to their legs?

4 The Galliard is a 16th century court dance originating from which country?

5 What, in Scotland, is the Gillie Callum dance a type of?

6 What dance is named from a German word meaning 'to revolve'?

7 In which country did the Tango originate?

8 The varsovienne was an offshoot of which dance that originated in Poland in the 1500s?

9 Bill 'Bojangles' Robinson became America's most famous exponent of what type of dance?

10 Named from a French word meaning 'small' what dance became popular during the 17th century at the court of Louis XIV of France?

11 Which dance, which became popular in the music halls of Paris about 1840, has a name derived from a French word meaning 'scandal'?

12 A type of what dance is featured in the opera 'The Bartered Bride' by the Czech composer Smetana?

13 Which ballroom dance stems from Afro-Cuban folk origins?

14 Which dance, performed to big-band swing music in the 1930s and 40s was spread worldwide by US armed forces during World War II?

15 Which Spanish dance in triple time is usually accompanied by guitars and castanets?

Answers **1** Bolero **2** Snake dance **3** Morris dance **4** Italy **5** Sword dance **6** Waltz **7** Argentina **8** Mazurka **9** Tap dance **10** Minuet **11** Cancan **12** Polka **13** Rumba **14** Jitterbug **15** Fandango

Categories **Food and Drink**

1 What country does gorgonzola cheese come from?

2 What type of lettuce is named after the Greek island where it originated?

3 From what country does 'petit suisse' cheese come?

4 What type of food is coulibiac?

5 If food is served lyonnaise, with what is it garnished or cooked?

6 The potent spirit 'aqua vitae' is the national drink of which country?

7 What spirit is named after the German word for cherry?

8 What is the name of the Indian curried meat soup?

9 In Japan what name is given to small snacks of raw fish and cold rice?

10 What is grissini?

11 What are the main ingredients of 'cock-a-leekie' soup?

12 In France it is called 'potiron' and is a large round fruit with thick orange rind and pulpy flesh. What is its English name?

13 If a dish is described as Veronique, with what is it garnished?

14 Guacamole dips originate from which country?

15 What is the main ingredient of sauerkraut?

Answers **1** Italy **2** Cos **3** France **4** Traditional Russian fish pie **5** Onions **6** Denmark **7** Kirsch **8** Mulligatawny **9** Sushi **10** Long, thin Italian breadsticks **11** Chicken and leek **12** Pumpkin **13** White grapes **14** Mexico **15** Cabbage

The beautiful game

Categories

1 Which two football league teams have their stadiums at opposite ends of Stanley Park?

2 In the Stanley Matthews Cup Final of 1953, who scored the winning goal for Blackpool to complete his hat-trick?

3 Which Northern Ireland international captained Tottenham Hotspur to the League and Cup double in 1961?

4 Who captained Manchester United when they won the treble of FA Cup, Premiership and European Championship in 1999?

5 For which country was Sandor Kocsis an international during the 1950s?

6 Who is the Mozambique-born player of Portugal and Benfica whose nine goals made him the leading scorer in the 1966 World Cup?

7 Which team play at Filbert Street?

8 Which manager took Liverpool to three European Cup titles, in 1977, 78 and 81?

9 Who was capped 105 times for England, a record, and played in three World Cups, 1950, 1954 and 1958?

10 What is the name of the trophy which is competed for in the World Cup?

11 Who were the first ever winners of the FA Cup when it was competed for at the Kennington Oval in 1872?

12 Which player known as 'Der Kaiser' skippered West Germany to victory in the 1974 World Cup Final against Holland?

13 Who in the 1927-28 season scored a still-unrivalled 60 League goals in 39 games as Everton's centre forward?

14 Which former Holland international was for a period manager of Newcastle United in the late 1990s?

15 Who in 1966 became the first man to score a hat-trick in a World Cup Final?

Answers **1** Liverpool and Everton **2** Stan Mortenson **3** Danny Blanchflower **4** Roy Keane **5** Hungary **6** Eusebio **7** Leicester City **8** Bob Paisley **9** Billy Wright **10** The Jules Rimet Trophy **11** The Wanderers **12** Franz Beckenbauer **13** Dixie Dean **14** Ruud Gullit **15** Geoff Hurst

Categories — Assassinations

1 Which black Muslim leader was assassinated while addressing a rally in New York City in 1965?

2 Ross McWhirter, assassinated by the IRA in London in November 1975, was associated with which famous publication?

3 Who was the five times Prime Minister of Italy assassinated in 1978 after being kidnapped in Rome by terrorists?

4 Who was the US Senator assassinated by Dr. Carl A. Weiss in Baton Rouge in September 1935?

5 Who is the only British Prime Minister to have been assassinated?

6 In which city was the archduke of Austria, Franz Ferdinand and his wife assassinated in 1914?

7 Which Egyptian President was assassinated on 6 October 1981 by Islamic fundamentalists within his own army?

8 Who, in 1793, assassinated the French revolutionist Jean Paul Marat by stabbing him in his bath?

9 The Rye House Plot was a conspiracy to assassinated which British King?

10 Humbert I, assassinated in 1900, was the King of which country?

11 Who assassinated President Abraham Lincoln?

12 On what date in 44 BC was Julius Caesar assassinated?

13 Who was the Irish patriot who was assassinated on 22 August 1922 after signing the peace treaty with Great Britain that brought the Irish Free State into existence?

14 Who was assassinated in Russia in 1916 by a group of aristocrats during a midnight tea party to which they invited him?

15 Who was assassinated in New Delhi on 20 January 1948 by Natheram Jodre, a Hindu fanatic?

Answers **1** Malcolm X **2** The Guinness Book of Records **3** Aldo Moro **4** Huey Long **5** Spencer Perceval **6** Sarajevo **7** Anwar al-Sadat **8** Charlotte Corday **9** Charles II **10** Italy **11** John Wilkes Booth **12** 15 March (the ides of March) **13** Michael Collins **14** Rasputin **15** Mohandas Gandhi

Rock music

Categories

1 Which rock star made a cameo appearance in the movie 'Young Guns II' and wrote the movie soundtrack including its main theme 'Blaze of Glory'?

2 'The Rose', starring Bet Midler was supposedly based on the life of which rock star?

3 Whose maiden album was 'Hot Cool and Vicious' in 1981?

4 Whose most successful album was 'Hotel California'?

5 In the 1960s who billed themselves as 'the greatest rock and roll band in the world'?

6 Who had a hit with Bob Dylan's 'Mr. Tambourine Man' in 1965?

7 Which vintage rock and roller is known as 'The Killer'?

8 Who is famous as leader of the British pop group 'Pulp'?

9 Whose 1984 album 'Private Dancer' sold 10 million copies?

10 Whose 1976 best selling single was 'Bohemian Rhapsody'?

11 Who was a 'Dead Ringer for Love' with Cher in 1981?

12 'Remain in Light' was a 1980 album hit for which group fronted by songwriter and vocalist David Burn?

13 Which pop duo made a reunion at London's Albert Hall on 23 September 1983 after 10 years of estrangement?

14 Who shot to stardom after the release of their first single 'Supersonic' in April 1994?

15 Whch group took their name in 1984 from a 1960 Robert Wagner/Natalie Wood movie?

Answers **1** Jon Bon Jovi **2** Janis Joplin **3** Salt 'n' Pepper **4** The Eagles **5** The Rolling Stones **6** The Byrds **7** Jerry Lee Lewis **8** Jarvis Cocker **9** Tina Turner **10** Queen **11** Meat Loaf **12** Talking Heads **13** The Everly Brothers **14** Oasis **15** Fine Young Cannibals

Categories

Movie partnership

1 Who became known as 'America's Sweethearts' who teamed up for such musicals as 'Naughty Marietta' and 'Rose Maries'?

2 In 'To Have and Have Not' who said to Humphrey Bogart "You know how to whistle, don't you, Steve? You just put your lips together and blow"?

3 Born Joseph Levitch and Dino Paul Crocetti they made 16 films together, the first in 1946. By what names were they better known?

4 Which romantic film duo starred in 'Pillow Talk' in 1959?

5 Who played married attorneys Amanda Bonner and Adam Bonner in the 1949 comedy 'Adam's Rib'?

6 Which couples who have been romantically attached in several movies met on the observation deck of the Empire State Building in 'Sleepless in Seattle'?

7 In which movie did Fred Astaire and Ginger Rogers first appear together?

8 And which was their last movie in 1949?

9 Which comedy team "Meet Frankenstein' in 1948?

10 Which actor, born Joe Yule Jr, starred with Judy Garland in a number of breezy musicals in which they coined the phrase 'Let's put on a show'?

11 Said to be their best feature film, which duo starred in 'Sons of the Desert' in 1933?

12 Who were 'Grumpy Old Men' Max Goldman and John Gustafson in 1993?

13 In which movie did Woody Allen and Diane Keaton first team up together?

14 Which then husband and wife team starred in 'Much Ado About Nothing' in 1993?

15 For which 1966 movie in which she played opposite Richard Burton did Elizabeth Taylor win Best Actress Oscar?

Answers **1** Jeanette MacDonald and Nelson Eddy **2** Lauren Bacall **3** Dean Martin and Jerry Lewis **4** Doris Day and Rock Hudson **5** Katherine Hepburn and Spencer Tracy **6** Meg Ryan and Tom Hanks **7** Flying Down to Rio **8** The Barkleys of Broadway **9** Bud Abbot and Lou Costello **10** Mickey Rooney **11** Stan Laurel and Oliver Hardy **12** Walter Matthau and Jack Lemmon **13** Annie Hall **14** Emma Thompson and Kenneth Branagh **15** Who's Afraid of Virginia Woolf?

William Shakespeare

Categories

1 Helsingor Castle in Denmark is the locale of which Shakespeare play?

2 Who was Shakespeare's mother?

3 Petruchio, Katharina and Sly are characters in which Shakespeare Comedy?

4 "The prince of darkness is a gentleman" is a quote from which Shakespeare Tragedy?

5 Who did Shakespeare marry in 1582?

6 What did Shakespeare address to a 'fair young man' and a 'dark lady'?

7 Where is Shakespeare buried?

8 "Double, double, toil and trouble; Fire burn and cauldren bubble" is from which Shakespeare tragedy?

9 Prospero, Miranda, Ferdinand, Ariel and Caliban are characters from which late Comedy?

10 Which play, written in 1592, depends for its appeal on the mistakes in identity between two sets of twins involved in romance and war?

11 Who is the fat knight who appears in several Shakespeare plays including Henry IV?

12 In which play do the characters of King Oberon and Queen Titania appear?

13 "If music be the food of love play on" is a line from which Middle Comedy?

14 Which play features a userer named Shylock?

15 Whose wife is Desdemona?

Answers **1** Hamlet **2** Mary Arden **3** The Taming of the Shrew **4** King Lear **5** Anne Hathaway **6** His sonnets **7** At Stratford-on-Avon **8** Macbeth **9** The Tempest **10** A Comedy of Errors **11** Falstaff **12** A Midsummer Night's Dream **13** Twelfth Night **14** The Merchant of Venice **15** Othello

Categories — Jazz

1 What instrument was played by Thelonius Monk?

2 Whch jazz violinist was a member of the Hot Club of France together with jazz guitarist Django Rheinhardt?

3 Which jazz clarinetist was known as the King of Swing?

4 What was the nickname of New Orleans cornetist Joe Oliver?

5 Which jazz musician appeared in the movies 'Cabin in the Sky' (1943), 'High Society' (1956) and 'The Five Pennies' (1959)?

6 Which jazz musician was known as "Bird" or "Yardbird"?

7 Which jazz pianist made several recordings with singer Mel Torme?

8 Until his early death in 1931 at the age of 28 Bix Beiderbecke was a featured cornet player with which band?

9 What instrument was played by Jack Teagarden?

10 Who wrote 'Mood Indigo', 'Sophisticated Lady' and 'Solitude'?

11 Born Eleanora Fagan, who co-wrote and recorded 'God Bless the Child' in 1939?

12 'Kind of Blue' was a 1958 album by which trumpeter who pioneered 'cool', or 'understated', jazz?

13 What was the MJQ formed in 1952 by John Lewis, Milt Jackson, Percy Heath and Kenny Clark?

14 What instrument was played by Sidney Bechet, Lester Young and Coleman Hawkins?

15 What was the real first name of Count Basie?

Answers **1** Piano **2** Stephane Grappelli **3** Benny Goodman **4** King Oliver **5** Louis Armstrong **6** Charlie Parker **7** George Shearing **8** The Paul Whiteman Band **9** Trombone **10** Duke Ellington **11** Billie Holiday **12** Miles Davis **13** The Modern Jazz Quartet **14** Saxophone **15** William

Sport

Categories

1 What nationality is tennis player Ilie Nastase?

2 Which legendary Canadian racehorse won 14 of 18 starts on both sides of the Atlantic including setting a record time in the Kentucky Derby in the mid-1960s?

3 Who, in 1985, became the first Frenchman to win the World Motor Racing Championship?

4 Which boxer's story was told in the film 'Somebody up There Likes Me' which gave Paul Newman his first starring role?

5 Which athlete was the first to break the 4 minute mile?

6 Who is the Belgian cyclist who won the Tour de France five times in the 1960s and 1970s?

7 What was the sport of Yves Saint-Martin?

8 Who, after holing four pitch shots to defeat Tony Jacklin in the 1972 British Open said, "God is a Mexican"?

9 Which Cuban sprinter, who won the 400m and 800m gold medals at the 1976 Montreal Olympics was known as the 'White Lightning'?

10 Who was Franz Klammer?

11 Who took 19 wickets in a Test Match against Australia in 1956?

12 Who recovered from a horrendous crash at the Nurburgring circuit in the 1976 Grand Prix after receiving the Last Rites?

13 How was soccer player Edson Arantes de Nascimento better known to the sporting world?

14 Who was the Australian tennis player who never won Wimbledon, and lost in his fourth final at the age of 39, losing to Jimmy Connors?

15 What dramatic incident occurred in a sporting event in Hamburg on 30 April 1993?

Answers **1** Rumanian **2** Northern Dancer **3** Alain Prost **4** Rocky Graziano **5** Roger Bannister **6** Eddy Merckx **7** He was a French jockey **8** Lee Travino **9** Alberto Juantorena **10** An Austrian Alpine skier **11** Jim Laker **12** Niki Lauder **13** Pele **14** Ken Rosewall **15** Monica Seles was stabbed in the back by a fan of Steffi Graf

Categories — Clothes

1 Who might wear a maniple and tunicle?

2 To what does the term 'haute couture' refer?

3 What is the skirt-like Malay garment called, formed by a long bright cloth?

4 What is a Dolly Varden?

5 What is the name of the veil worn by Muslim women in public?

6 What type of clothing is a cagoule?

7 Who in the 1800s would be seen waring a Shako?

8 What is the name of the leather shorts with braces worn by Austrian men?

9 What was the loose gown called which had its name derived fron a north Italian city and which was worn in the 17th century?

10 Consisting of a horsehair support with an overskirt bunched up what was the name of the distinctive feature of women's fashion in the Victorian era?

11 What is a peignoir?

12 What is the name of the broad sash that is worn round a kimono?

13 What is a dicky?

14 What is another, more common, name for a tarboosh?

15 What type of footwear is a sabot?

Answers **1** A cleric **2** Clothing of high fashion **3** Sarong **4** A ladies decorative hat **5** Yashmak **6** A light hooded raincoat **7** It is a tall decorative cap for Army officers **8** Lederhosen **9** Mantua **10** The Bustle **11** A negligee **12** Obi **13** A bib-like detachable shirt front **14** Fez **15** A wooden clog

Kings and Queens

Categories

1 Which king was nicknamed the 'Lionheart'?

2 In mythology, Paris was the son of which King of Troy?

3 Which English king, whose struggle for power helped to begin the War of the Roses, died a prisoner in the Tower of London?

4 Queen Marie of Romania who wrote 'The Story of My Life' (1934) was the granddaughter of which monarch?

5 Which king was portrayed by Graham Chapman in the 1975 movie 'Monty Python and the Holy Grail'?

6 Who was called the Virgin Queen?

7 Which king abdicated on 11 December 1936?

8 Boudicca was the queen of which British tribe?

9 Which queen married her cousin Lord Darnley in 1565?

10 Frederick VIII was king of which country from 1906-12?

11 Henrietta Maria was the wife of which English king?

12 Which king was twice portrayed in movies by Peter O'Toole; in 'Becket' (1964) and in 'The Lion in Winter' (1968)?

13 Which king died in battle at Bosworth Field during the Wars of the Roses?

14 Which game was outlawed by King Edward IV of England, it not being made legal again until 1748?

15 Who was the third wife of Henry VIII who died 12 days after giving birth to the future King Edward VI of England?

Answers **1** Richard I of England **2** King Priam **3** Henry VI **4** Queen Victoria **5** King Arthur **6** Queen Elizabeth I **7** Edward VIII **8** Iceni **9** Mary Queen of Scots **10** Denmark **11** Charles I **12** King Henry II of England **13** Richard III **14** Cricket **15** Jane Seymour

Categories

Coins and Currency 1

1 Which unit of currency was originally a gold coin minted in 1360 with the inscription: "Johannes Del Gracia Francorum Rex"?

2 The 'groat' was a coin of which country?

3 The cruzado is a unit of currency in which country?

4 What was the popular name for the paper currency issued by the Federal government during the American Civil War?

5 Which unit of currency is worth 100 groszy in Poland?

6 Which US motto became obligatory to appear on all US currency in 1955?

7 What name is given to the study of coins?

8 In which country is the Dong the unit of currency?

9 Prior to 1949 which unit of currency was divided into 100 sen and 1000 rin?

10 Prior to 1990 the ostmark was the currency of which country?

11 The guilder or florin is the currency of which country?

12 What is the unit of currency in Russia?

13 In which East European country is the Lev equal to 100 stotinki?

14 What is the unit of currency in Thailand?

15 Which unit of currency is equal to 100 pfennigs?

Answers **1** The Franc **2** It was an English coin worth fourpence **3** Brazil **4** Greenback **5** Zloty **6** In God We Trust **7** Numismatics **8** Vietnam **9** Yen **10** East Germany **11** The Netherlands **12** Ruble **13** Bulgaria **14** Baht **15** Mark

Composers

Categories

1 Which American composer wrote the ballet 'Appalachian Spring'?

2 What nationality was Antonin Dvorak?

3 Which composer had an intimate relationship with the French writer George Sand?

4 Which Hungarian composer performed as a pianist and was the founder of the solo piano recital?

5 Which Australian-born pianist and composer whose compositions were based on folk music was a friend of the Norwegian composer Edvard Grieg?

6 Who wrote the opera 'Prince Igor?

7 Which composer was born at Bonn in Germany on 16 December 1770?

8 Which Austrian composer conducted the New York Philharmonic from 1910-11?

9 Who wrote 'Cosi Fan Tutte'?

10 Besides his prolific output of music, how many children did Johann Sebastian Bach find time to father?

11 Whose work includes the oratorios 'St. Paul' and 'Elijah' and the concert overture 'The Hebrides'?

12 Which family of composers were known as the 'waltz kings'?

13 Which composer fell in love with composer Robert Schumann's wife Clara?

14 Which French composer wrote 'La Mer'?

15 Which is the most famous work of the Italian composer Pietro Mascagni?

Answers **1** Aaron Copland **2** Czech **3** Frederic Chopin **4** Franz Liszt **5** Percy Granger **6** Borodin **7** Ludwig van Beethoven **8** Gustav Mahler **9** Mozart **10** 20 **11** Mendelssohn **12** Johann Strauss the elder and Strauss the younger **13** Johannes Brahms **14** Debussy **15** Cavalleria Rusticana

Categories — Crimes and Criminals

1 In the Wild West, what nickname was given to Harry Longabaugh?

2 Who was the 'brides in the bath' murderer who drowned three of his bigamous brides in the bath between 1912 and 1914?

3 Who was the last woman to be hanged in Britain?

4 Which famous landmark was sold by 'Count' Victor Lustig – twice?

5 Who was the tenant of 10 Rillington Place hanged for crimes committed by his landlord John Christie in 1953?

6 Who did John W. Hinckley shoot on 30 March 1981?

7 Who was said to become the first murderer when he killed his brother Abel?

8 Who was the art historian who admitted to spying for the Soviet Union with Donald McClean and Guy Burgess?

9 Who shot Billy the Kid?

10 What poison was used to murder Belgian broadcaster Georgie Markov in London 1978, by stabbing him with the tip of an umbrella?

11 Who was the famous Scotland Yard detective whose exploits led to a television series in the 1950s?

12 Who was the doctor convicted of killing fifteen of his patients in the UK in 1999?

13 In which city was highwayman Dick Turpin hanged?

14 Organised by 'Lucky' Luciano in the 1930s what was the name given to the pool of killers who committed murders only when the gang bosses decided someone was stepping out of line?

15 Which US gangster was known as "Public Enemy Number One"?

Answers **1** The Sundance Kid **2** George Joseph Smithn **3** Ruth Ellis **4** The Eiffel Tower **5** Timothy Evans **6** President Ronald Reagan **7** Cain **8** Anthony Blunt **9** Sherrif Pat Garrett **10** Recin **11** Fabian of the Yard **12** Dr. Harold Shipman **13** York **14** Murder Incorporated **15** John Dillinger

American States

Categories

1 Bismarck is the capital of which state?

2 The name of which state is derived from an Indian tribe meaning 'people of the mountains'?

3 What is the collective name given to the six states of the northeastern United States?

4 What is the 'Green Mountain State'?

5 Of where is Little Rock the state capital?

6 Called the North Star State, which state's name is a Sioux Indian phrase meaning 'cloudy water'?

7 Which state is nicknamed Prairi State, or Land of Lincoln?

8 Which state's capital is noted as a centre of country and western music?

9 Which is known as the First State because on 7 December 1787 it became the first of the original 13 states to ratify the US constitution?

10 The cities of Arlington, Corpus Christi and Garland are in which state?

11 Annapolis is the capital of which state?

12 Which state, one of the Mountain states, is called the Equality State and has its name derived from a Delaware Indian term meaning 'place of the big plain'?

13 In which state did the Piligrim fathers found Plymouth Colony in 1620?

14 Which state is named for an English king and is known as the Empire State of the South?

15 Which state, whose name is derived from two Choctow Indian words meaning 'red people' was admitted to the Union on 16 November 1907 as the 46th state?

Answers **1** North Dakota **2** Utah **3** New England **4** Vermont **5** Arkansas **6** Minnesota **7** Illinois **8** Nashville, Tennessee **9** Delaware **10** Texas **11** Maryland **12** Wyoming **13** Massachusetts **14** Georgia **15** Oklahoma

Categories The life and films of John Wayne

1 What was John Wayne's birth name?

2 In which 1939 movie which propelled Wayne to stardom did he play the Ringo Kid?

3 Which 1960 film, in which Wayne starred and directed, was nominated for Best Picture Oscar?

4 In which 1949 film directed by John Ford does Wayne play Nathan Brittles a cavalry officer on his last mission before retirement?

5 In the 1962 Western, who played Liberty Valance who was shot by Wayne?

6 In which 1975 movie does Wayne reprise his character from the 1969 movie 'True Grit'?

7 By what nickname was John Wayne affectionately known?

8 What was Wayne's last film in which he plays a dying gunman?

9 For which movie did Wayne win his only Oscar?

10 Which actress played opposite Wayne in the 1952 movie 'The Quiet Man'?

11 In which 1970 movie, also starring Forrest Tucker, does Wayne play a cattle-baron pitted against corrupt officials threatening to disrupt peaceful territory?

12 In which 1965 movie do Wayne, Earl Holliman, Michael Anderson Jr and Dean Martin play the sons of a frontier woman who set out to avenge her death?

13 In which film does John Wayne make a cameo appearance as a Roman centurion supervising Christ's crucifixion?

14 Which 1963 movie in which Wayne plays opposite Maureen O'Hara was a Western version of 'The Taming of the Shrew'?

15 Which Wayne film, the title of which means 'danger' in Swahili, is about wild-animal trappers in Africa, and was filmed in Tanganyika?

Answers **1** Marion Michael Morrison **2** Stagecoach **3** The Alamo **4** She Wore a Yellow Ribbon **5** Lee Marvin **6** Rooster Cogburn **7** Duke **8** The Shootist **9** True Grit **10** Maureen O'Hara **11** Chisum **12** The Sons of Katie Elder **13** The Greatest Story Ever Told **14** McLintock! **15** Hatari!

Reptiles

Categories

1 The majority of reptiles are oviparous. What is the meaning of this term?

2 What is a cayman a type of?

3 On which islands are the world's largest species of tortoise found?

4 What type of reptile is a gecko?

5 What is characterised by the body of reptiles of the order Chelonia?

6 What is the common name for any reptile belonging to the sub-order Serpentes?

7 The name of which reptile is derived from a Spanish phrase meaning 'the lizard'?

8 What is the monitor a species of?

9 Tuetaras, which are the sole descendants of an order of ancient reptiles that lived more than 200 million years ago, are now only found on a few islands off the coast of which country?

10 Which reptiles that first evolved in the period are the closest living relatives of dinosaurs?

11 From the French "lance head" what is the Fer-de-Lance a type of?

12 What is the Leatherback a type of?

13 What is the common name for the water snake, the most common snake found in Europe?

14 What is the common name for either of two Asian crocodiles, distinguished by an extremely long slender snout?

15 The diamondback is a variety of which species of edible North American turtle?

Answers **1** Egg-laying **2** Crocodile **3** The Galapagos Islands **4** Lizard **5** It is encased in a shell (as the turtle) **6** Snake **7** Alligator (el largato) **8** Lizard **9** New Zealand **10** Crocodiles **11** Snake **12** Turtle **13** Grass snake **14** Gavial **15** Terrapin

Categories — La Bella France

1 Which mountain range forms a barrier between France and Spain?

2 Which islet is connected to the French mainland by a causeway and is crowned by a Benedictine monastery?

3 What type of brandy is named after a town in the wine-producing department of Charente?

4 Which ancient province of northern France is bounded on the West by the English Channel and on the South by Normandy?

5 What are the three principal rivers of France?

6 Which vast inlet of the Atlantic Ocean is bounded on the North and East by France and on the South by Spain?

7 The town of Grasse in France has for many years been the centre of which industry?

8 What is the capital of the Flemish coast and the third largest port in France?

9 What is the name of the road, originally built by Napoleon between Nice and Genoa, which is cut into precipitous cliffs of the Maritime Alps overhanging the Mediterranean?

10 What, in France, are 'Allos', 'Galibier', 'Tourmalet' and 'Petit St. Bernard'?

11 What structure stands at the centre of the Etoile at the top of the Champs Elysees in Paris?

12 What are the citizens of Cannes called?

13 What is the name of the wind that blows towards France from the South?

14 Which city and resort on the French Riviera is capital of the Alpes Maritimes department?

15 For what is Carnac, a village in Brittany, famous?

Answers **1** The Pyrenees **2** Mont St. Michel **3** Cognac **4** Picardy **5** Seine, Loire, Rhone **6** The Bay of Biscay **7** The production of perfume **8** Dunkirk **9** The Corniche **10** Mountain passes **11** Arc de Triomphe **12** Cannois **13** Mistral **14** Nice **15** A remarkable group of megalithic monuments

Religion

Categories

1. What is the square cap worn by clergy?
2. A name for consecrated or holy oil unction?
3. What is the usual name for a Godhead divinity?
4. What is the name of the official who calls Muslims to prayer?
5. Gold or rich embroidery on ecclesiastical clothing?
6. A Syrian translation of the Bible?
7. The share of the revenues of a cathedral?
8. The name given to the book of psalms, especially when printed separately from the rest of the Bible?
9. Evening services?
10. A church living?
11. A hood worn by a monk?
12. The leader of the singing in a church?
13. The middle or main body of a basilica?
14. A part of a church at right angles to the nave?
15. A hat worn by bishops?

Answers **1** Biretta **2** Chrism **3** Deity **4** Muezzin **5** Orphrey **6** Peshito **7** Prebend **8** Psalter **9** Vespers **10** Benefic **11** Capuche **12** Cantor **13** Nave **14** Transept **15** Mitre

Categories

Printing and Publishing

1 What is the name given to an incription at the end of a book?

2 Name the method of printing in which an image is cut into the surface of a plate?

3 What is the process of making a printing plate called?

4 What is printing from stone called?

5 What is the name given to the part ruled off the bottom of a page?

6 What do you call someone who steals writing from another and publishes it as his own?

7 A photographic quality, black and white printer's proof?

8 In one colour?

9 The name of a decorative foot at the end of a stroke on a printed character?

10 To mark each page with a successive number?

11 Small decorative image without a border?

12 A compositor who distributes copy?

13 The bed on which anything rests?

14 An old type 8-point?

15 A printer's proof to check positioning of pictures and text?

Answers **1** Colophon **2** Intaglio **3** Gravure **4** Lithography **5** Feuilleton **6** Plagiarist **7** Bromide **8** Monochrome **9** Serif **10** Paginate **11** Vignette **12** Clicker **13** Matrix **14** Brevier **15** Ozalid

Legal terms

Categories

1 What is the meaning of mandatory?

2 A person who sees that a will is carried out?

3 What is the name given to a formal, written accusation?

4 A financial agent authorised to act for another?

5 The offence of trying to influence a juror?

6 An illegal bargain where one person agrees to help another in a legal suit?

7 A written law?

8 What does 'caveat emptor' mean?

9 What does 'viva voce' mean?

10 What does 'stipendiary' mean?

11 What does 'causa causans' mean?

12 What does 'subpoena' mean?

13 What is an advocate?

14 What is the name given to a person who vexatiously stirs up lawsuits

15 What is a feeoff?

Answers **1** To command to follow out instructions **2** Executor **3** Indictment **4** Procurator? **5** Embracery **6** Champerty **7** Statute **8** Let the buyer beware **9** By oral testimony **10** Receiving a salary **11** The immediate cause **12** A writ to attend court **13** A prosecutor of crimes **14** Barrator **15** To grant possession of land

Categories Grammar and the written word

1 Any of the mystic letters of the ancient German alphabet?

2 The word given to three related stories from Welsh literature?

3 A word or phrase added to a sentence?

4 The name given to a foot of two short (unstressed) syllables followed by a long (stressed) syllable?

5 What is amoebaean?

6 What is the name of the symbol used to signify the word 'and'?

7 An understatement by negation of the contrary?

8 What is an antithesis

9 What is versal?

10 The name for a jingle in two couplets of some notable person?

11 A summary of a book for example?

12 A sign for a word?

13 What is a trochee?

14 Used in three cases only?

15 What is hyperbole?

Answers **1** Runes **2** Triad **3** Adjunct **4** Anapest **5** Answering alternately, responsive as in pastoral poetry **6** Ampersand **7** Litotes **8** A figure in which words are balanced in contrast **9** The whole single individual **10** Clerihew **11** Synopsis **12** Logogram **13** A foot of two syllables (a stressed followed by an unstressed syllable) **14** Triptote **15** Poetical exaggeration

Tools

Categories

1 What is a plummet?

2 What is a mandril?

3 What is another name for a crow-bar?

4 What is a woolder?

5 What is a sheerleg?

6 What is a hummelver?

7 What is a strickle?

8 What is a ploughshare?

9 What is a capstan?

10 What is a governor?

11 What is a bandsaw?

12 What is a grapnel?

13 What is a scalpel?

14 What is a thimble?

15 What is a throstle?

Answers **1** A lead weight on a plumb line **2** A bar of iron fitted to a turning lathe **3** A gavelock **4** A stick used in winding a rope on a mast **5** One of the spars for hoisting heavy weights **6** A machine for removing barley awns **7** An instrument for levelling the top of a measure of grain **8** A machine for turning the sod **9** A machine for turning bars **10** It is an instrument placed on motors to restrict the speed **11** A long strip of toothed metal formed into a circle for cutting timber **12** A lifting device with claws **13** A surgeon's cutting tool **14** A metal ring with a grooved edge to prevent chafing **15** A machine for twisting and winding

Categories

Common abbreviations

1. What does NASA stand for?
2. What does LCD stand for?
3. What does KKK stand for?
4. What does ROM stand for in computers?
5. What does PLA stand for?
6. What does VIP stand for?
7. What does RPI mean?
8. What does PAYE mean?
9. What does RSPB mean?
10. What does RNA mean?
11. What does TNT mean?
12. What does OB stand for?
13. What does SSR stand for?
14. What does DC/dc mean?
15. What does GATT stand for?

Answers **1** National Aeronautical and Space Administration **2** Liquid Crystal Display **3** Klu Klux Klan **4** Read Only Memory **5** Peoples Liberation Army **6** Very Important Person **7** Retail Price Index **8** Pay As You Earn **9** Royal Society for the Protection of Birds **10** Ribonucleic Acid **11** Trinitrotolvene **12** Order of the Bath **13** Soviet Socialist Republic **14** Direct Current **15** General Agreement on Tariffs and Trade

Theatre

Categories

1 A form of court entertainment, popular in 16th and 17th centuries?

2 A device to create an effect of slow motion?

3 A clown or buffoon?

4 A sad white-faced clown?

5 What are dundrearies?

6 Who is the enigmatic heroine of 'All's well that ends well'?

7 A hard working anonymous member of the chorus line in musicals?

8 A part of the stage that projects beyond the proscenium?

9 What was the 'Alhambra'?

10 A modern version of the Japanese Kabuki drama?

11 A contemptuous name for an actor?

12 To dismantle a stage set?

13 The buffoon in Old English plays?

14 American slang for a travelling tent show?

15 A traditional name for a ladies maid?

Answers **1** A masque **2** A lobsterscope **3** A pickelhering **4** A pierrot **5** Long side whiskers **6** Helena **7** A gypsy **8** The apron **9** A musical hall in London's Leicester Square **10** A shimpa **11** A mummer **12** Strike **13** Vice **14** A rag opery **15** 'Abigail'

Categories

Medical terms

1 Where is the cochlea?

2 What is another name for the gullet?

3 What is a lymphocite?

4 What does sphygmic mean?

5 What is theine?

6 What does progeria mean?

7 What does temporal mean?

8 What is herpes?

9 Where is the ileum?

10 What is insulin?

11 What was jail fever?

12 What does jugular mean?

13 What is a lesion?

14 What is a ligament?

15 To what does 'lingual' pertain?

Answers **1** The inner ear **2** The oesophagus **3** A white blood cell **4** Relating to the pulse **5** The alkaloid found in tea **6** Premature senility **7** Pertaining to the side of the head **8** An inflammatory skin disease **9** The last part of the smaller intestine **10** The endocrine secretion of the pancreas **11** The old name for typhus **12** Pertaining to the neck **13** An injury or a change in an organ **14** A band of fibrous tissue connecting bones forming a joint **15** The tongue

Music

Categories

1 What does “de capo” mean?

2 What is the general name given to any kind of keyboard instrument?

3 A male’s very high voice?

4 What is another name for a hautboy?

5 What is the unit of frequency?

6 Popular melody dating from the 17th century?

7 What does “lusingando” mean?

8 What is a melodeon?

9 What does “mosso” mean?

10 What is an ocarina?

11 A continuous musical phrase?

12 A double reeded woodwind instrument?

13 A secondary role in an opera played by a maid?

14 The bridge of a stringed instrument?

15 A vigorous cossack dance?

Answers **1** From the beginning **2** Clavier **3** Falsetto **4** An oboe **5** Hertz **6** Lilliburlero **7** Enticing **8** A type of accordion **9** Moving fast **10** A whistle flute **11** A riff **12** A shawm **13** A soubrette **14** A steg **15** A trepak

Categories — Mythology 2

1 What is another name for the god Jupiter?

2 Who was Kronos?

3 Who was the daughter of Zeus and Hera?

4 Who was Glumdalclitch?

5 Who was the muse of erotic poetry?

6 Who was the nymph in love with Narcissus?

7 What was the white wand called carried by Roman heralds?

8 What is the 1st sign of the Zodiac?

9 What was the name of the physician to the gods?

10 Who was Morgan le Fay?

11 Who was Midas?

12 What was the little finger called in legend?

13 Who was the god of this world?

14 Who were the "Maenads"?

15 What is the cult name of the Hindu goddess of death?

Answers **1** Jove **2** One of the Titans of Greek mythology **3** Hebe **4** A nine year old girl in Gulliver's Travels **5** Erato, one of the nine muses **6** Echo **7** Caduceus **8** Aries, the ram **9** Paean **10** The fairy sister of King Arthur **11** The legendary King of Phrygia **12** Mercurial finger **13** Mammon **14** Female attendant of Bacchus **15** Kali

Flowers

Categories

1 What is a North American genus of primrose called?

2 An evergreen shrub of Eastern Asia with a beautiful flower?

3 What is another name for 'digitalis'?

4 A plant of the marigold genus formerly used for healing wounds?

5 A shrub with jasmine-like flowers?

6 What plant sprang from the blood of a youth accidentally killed by Apollo?

7 An evergreen shrub with red or white flowers, the rose bay or bay laurel?

8 A Mexican and South American genus with yellow and orange flowers?

9 Wild verena long believed to have medicinal powers?

10 What is wisteria?

11 What is another name for the cornflower?

12 What does dasyphyllous mean?

13 What is another name for the amarylis?

14 A plant with pink, red and white flowers. often cultivated under the name 'geranium'?

15 A hardy perennial akin to the pinks, but like chickweed in aspect?

Answers **1** Clarkia **2** Camellia **3** Foxglove **4** Calendula **5** Forsythia **6** Hyacinth **7** Oleander **8** Tagetes **9** Vervain **10** An ornamental climber **11** The bluebottle **12** Having crowded, thick, or woolly leaves **13** The belladonna lily **14** Pelargonium **15** Gypsophilia

Categories — Trees

1 What are trees from the genus Moringa better known as?

2 Deodar is the hard sweet-smelling wood from which type of tree in the Himalayas?

3 What is camphor?

4 A tropical tree whose sweet, acidic pulp is used to make drinks and medicines?

5 A gigantic tropical tree with hollow stems?

6 What is shittim?

7 What is the national tree of Lebanon?

8 What kind of fig tree is also known as the great maple?

9 The American spice-bush?

10 A member of the European birch tree family, which produces edible nuts of the same name?

11 Where can the Yacca tree be found?

12 Another name for the Canary or American whitewood tree?

13 Which tree bears a small, bright red fruit, having a large hard stone?

14 An edible nut encased in a prickly shell, is the product of which tree?

15 A tree of the genus 'acer' from whose timber sugar and syrup can be made?

Answers **1** Horse-radish tree **2** Cedar tree **3** A solid essential oil obtained from the camphor tree having an aromatic smell **4** Tamarind tree **5** Bamboo **6** The wood of the shittah tree, which is similar to acacia **7** Cedar **8** Sycamore **9** Benjamin tree **10** Hazel tree **11** the West Indies **12** Tulip tree **13** Cherry tree **14** Chestnut tree **15** Maple

Jewels and Jewellery **Categories**

1 What colour is sapphire?

2 What is the more usual name given to a bluish-violet quartz?

3 What colour is cornelian?

4 The name given to intricate latticework of gold and silver?

5 Jacinth and jargoon are varieties of which mineral?

6 What is a diadem?

7 What is coral?

8 What are the hardest of all minerals?

9 What is a bezel?

10 What is the colour of jade?

11 What is the commonest rock-forming mineral?

12 Name for beads made from shells used as money by native Americans?

13 A dark red semi-precious stone?

14 A milky white stone, with fine play of colour?

15 A variegated chalcedony?

Answers **1** Blue **2** Amethyst **3** Red **4** Filigree **5** Zircon **6** A jewelled headband **7** A living, calcareous sea animal, once used to make jewellery **8** Diamonds **9** Part of the setting in jewellery **10** Various shades of green and sometimes almost white **11** Quartz **12** Wampum **13** Garnet **14** Opal **15** Agate

Categories — Military

1 What is a projecting watch tower called?

2 What is the word for, 'to equip a warrior'?

3 What does decimate mean in military terms?

4 What is a portcullis?

5 What is a flat-topped defensive mound called?

6 A military force, originally of Circassian slaves?

7 What is a shabrack?

8 What is a pike?

9 What is the outwork in the main ditch called?

10 What is the decorative shoulder piece of a military or naval uniform called?

11 What do you call a body of men in file?

12 What is an attack with cannon called?

13 What is a small fortress called?

14 What is the name of the statue on whom the safety of Troy depended?

15 What is the name given to a litter of military mules?

Answers **1** Barbican **2** Accoutre **3** To kill every tenth man **4** A grate to close a gateway **5** Rampart **6** Mamelukе **7** A trooper's saddle cloth **8** A weapon with a long shaft **9** A tenaille **10** Epaulette **11** Enfilade **12** Cannonade **13** A fortalice **14** Palladium **15** Cacoley

Food

Categories

1 A Scottish cake of oatmeal and barley?

2 Which part of an animal is brisket?

3 A thick stew of fish and vegetables, especially common in North America?

4 Curds mixed with cream, then sweetened and flavoured?

5 A fruit or vegetable candied, or in syrup?

6 A mixture of cheese and eggs baked in a dish or a small round, straight-sided baking dish?

7 A fillet of herring rolled up and doused in vinegar?

8 What is a gigot?

9 A Chinese -style dish of shredded meat and vegetables served with fried noodles?

10 What is a sherbet water ice called?

11 A stew of green Indian corn with beans and pork?

12 A hard wheat semolina, common in North Africa?

13 The name given to a shell of pastry or small round mould?

14 A sea dish, comprising of a stew or hash with vegetables or biscuit?

15 What is bratwurt?

Answers **1** Bannock **2** The breast, next to the ribs **3** Chowder **4** Junket **5** Succade **6** Succade **7** Rollmop **8** A leg of lamb **9** Chow-mein **10** Sorbet **11** Succotash **12** Couscous **13** Dariole **14** Lobscouse **15** A German sausage

Categories **Drinks**

1 A liqueur containing eggs and rum and lemon juice?

2 What is the name of the liqueur prepared from anise seed?

3 What is the flavouring in Curacao?

4 A brand of aromatic bitters, which originated in a town in Venezuala

5 A maize whisky from the USA?

6 Welsh fermented liquor made from honey?

7 Wine made from grape or pears?

8 A dry plum brandy?

9 An aromatic port like wine from Catalonia?

10 A sherry-like white wine produce in Spain

11 A red or white wine of Tuscany?

12 What is an aniseed-flavoured liqueur containing extract of wormwood called?

13 A liqueur distilled from a cherry from Dalmatia?

14 What is usquebaugh?

15 A West Indian drink of diluted and sweetened wine?

Answers **1** Advocaat **2** Anisette **3** Bitter orange peel **4** Angostura **5** Bourbon **6** Metheglin **7** Muscadin **8** Slivovitz **9** Tarragona **10** Montilla **11** Chianti **12** Absinthe **13** Maraschino? **14** Whisky **15** Sangaree

Coins and Currency 2

Categories

1 What is a Toman?

2 What is the currency of Guatemala?

3 What is the name of a Roman coin which was worth 4 asses?

4 What is the monetary unit of Venezuela?

5 The currency of North African countries?

6 Any of numerous old gold coin of varying values?

7 What is the name of a Russian coin one hundredth of a rouble?

8 An old Venetian silver coin?

9 What is a hundredth part of a Zambian kwatcha?

10 What is a scudo?

11 An English gold coin worth originally 21 shillings?

12 A twenty-franc French gold coin?

13 An old American coin of 5 cents?

14 A 2 "real" piece, old Spanish coin, was currency in USA?

15 An obsolete British gold coin, worth about one-third of a pound sterling?

Answers **1** A Persian gold coin worth 10,000 dinas **2** Quetzale **3** Sesterce **4** Boliva **5** Piastre **6** Pistole **7** Kopeck **8** Ducatoon **9** Ngwee **10** It is an old Italian silver coin **11** Guinea **12** Napoleon **13** Picayune **14** Pistaroon **15** Noble

Categories — Fruit

1 A small golden orange from China?

2 A Greek grape that makes strong sweet wine?

3 A kind of orange, whose aromatic rind yields an oil used in perfumery?

4 A coarse green-skinned banana, used as a staple food in tropical countries such as India?

5 A date-plum from a tree of the African or American genus Diospyros ?

6 A gourd, or its shell may be used as a vessel, such as a tobacco pipe?

7 A hybrid between a raspberry and a blackberry?

8 Muscatel made from grape or pear?

9 The pod of the shrub filled with sweet reddish black pulp?

10 The fruit of the egg plant?

11 A small ribbed musk-melon in USA?

12 A type of orange, either a type of tangerine or a cross between a tangerine and an Orange?

13 Any fleshy fruit with a stone?

14 A damson or damson plum, a native of Damascus?

15 A grape from North Carolina which makes a sweet wine?

Answers **1** Kumquat **2** Malmsey **3** Bergamot **4** Plantain **5** Persimmon **6** Calabash **7** Loganberry **8** Muscadine **9** Tamarind **10** Augbergine **11** Cantaloupe **12** Clementine **13** Drupe **14** Damascene **15** Scuppernong

Women through history

Categories

1. In which country was Joan Sutherland born?
2. Who was the 3rd sister of Anne and Charlotte Bronte?
3. Who wrote 'Frankenstein'?
4. How many children did Queen Victoria have?
5. Where was Jean Harlow born in 1911?
6. How was Grace Kelly killed?
7. In which city was Florence Nightingale born?
8. Who was the Olympic-winning skating star born in Norway?
9. In which country was Bob Hope born?
10. Where in England was Margaret Thatcher born?
11. What silvery-white metal did Marie Curie discover?
12. Who played the wife in "The Glen Miller Story"?
13. What was Marilyn Monroe's real name?
14. Joan of Arc was born in France, near which region?
15. In which European city was champion tennis player Martina Navratilova born?

Answers **1** Australia **2** Emily **3** Mary Shelly **4** Nine **5** Missouri **6** Car accident **7** Florence **8** Sonja Hene **9** England **10** Grantham **11** Radium **12** June Allyson **13** Norma Jean **14** Champagne **15** Prague

Categories — Films

1 Who said in 1937:"Either he is dead, or my watch has stopped"?

2 Who said in 1933: "Beulah, peel me a grape"?

3 Who is Shirley McLain's movie-star brother?

4 Which Hollywood actress did Harry James the trumpet player marry?

5 Maurice Micklewhite is the name of which famous film star?

6 Who wrote the score of 'West Side Story'?

7 Where did 'The Yellow Brick Road' lead to?

8 Which former wife of Frank Sinatra was once married to Andre Previn?

9 What nationality was Ingrid Bergman?

10 What is the name of the cartoon cat who chases 'Tweetie Pie'?

11 What did Glenn Close's devil character, Cruella de Ville, own in the film version of '101 Dalmatians'?

12 What Walt Disney film features a Cheshire cat?

13 What kind of birds are featured in the film 'Fly Away Home'?

14 What was the name of the time-travelling police box in 'Dr Who'?

15 Who was the director of the Biblical epic, 'The Ten Commandments'?

Answers **1** Groucho Marx **2** Mae West **3** Warren Beatty **4** Betty Grable **5** Michael Caine **6** Leonard Bernstein **7** Emerald City **8** Mia Farrow **9** Swedish **10** Sylvester **11** A fashion house **12** Alice in Wonderland **13** Geese **14** Tardis **15** Cecil B. De Mille

Vehicles

Categories

1 A two wheeled hooded carriage, drawn by a man or men?

2 A convertible motor car in which a portion can be covered or uncovered?

3 An open 4-wheeled carriage drawn by one or two horses?

4 A name sometimes given to a removal van?

5 A light open one-seater carriage?

6 A luxury railway sleeping car?

7 An early form of bicycle, whose name signifies 'speed'?

8 What is a laplander boat shaped sledge called?

9 A light open carriage for one or more persons?

10 What is a box borne on poles on men's shoulders for travelling?

11 A Russian covered wagon or sledge?

12 A two wheeled military cart used for conveying victims to the guillotine during the French Revolution ?

13 A hackney-coach or a cob, which takes its name from a hotel in Paris where it was first used?

14 The rear part of an open topped motor car, where the passengers sit?

15 A 4-wheeled carriage for 2 or more persons, named after William IV?

Answers **1** Jinrichshaw **2** Landaulette **3** Phaeton **4** Pantechnicon **5** Stanhope **6** Pullman car **7** Velocipede **8** Pulkha **9** Chaise **10** Palanquin **11** Kibitka **12** Tumbril **13** Fiacre **14** Tonneau **15** Clarence

Categories — Architecture

1 What is an acropolis?

2 What is the covered arcade, used by monks, called?

3 A Welsh word for a prehistoric stone circle?

4 What was the temple Athene called?

5 What is a campanile?

6 A temporary tomb-like structure, used in funeral ceremonies?

7 What is the level space between a citadel and the houses called?

8 An upper storey with a row of windows, especially in a church?

9 What is a Soffit?

10 What is the name given to a gallery, storey or arcade over an aisle?

11 A back door or gate?

12 What is a mansard roof?

13 What is an abattoir?

14 A Babylonian, pyramid-shaped temple tower?

15 What is a vaulted roof?

Answers **1** A citadel, especially of Athens **2** Cloisters **3** Cromlech **4** Athenaeum **5** A bell tower **6** Catafalque **7** Esplanade **8** Clerestory **9** A ceiling or underside of a staircase **10** Triforium **11** Postern **12** A roof having the lower part steeper than the upper **13** A slaughter house **14** Ziggurat **15** Arched, concave overhead

Inventions

Categories

1 Which German invented the motor cycle in 1885?

2 Who invented the newspaper in 59 BC?

3 Who invented the cash register in 1892?

4 Which Englishman invented the generator in 1831?

5 Which country invented the suspension bridge in 25 BC?

6 Who invented the aeroplane in 1903?

7 Which American president invented bifocal lens in 1780?

8 Who invented the airship in 1900?

9 Which Frenchman invented the adding machine in 1642?

10 Which Swiss company invented instant coffee in 1937?

11 Which American invented the credit card in 1950?

12 Which Englishman invented table tennis in 1890?

13 Which Frenchman invented pasteurization in 1863?

14 Which Englishman invented the ship with a metal hull?

15 Who invented the telegraph code in 1837?

Answers **1** Gottlieb Daimler **2** Julius Caesar **3** William Burroughs **4** Michael Faraday **5** China **6** Orville and Wilbur Wright **7** Benjamin Franklin **8** Graf Ferdinand Von Zeppelin **9** Blaise Pascal **10** Nestle **11** Ralf Scheider **12** James Gibb **13** Louis Pasteur **14** Isambard Kingdom Brunel **15** Samuel Morse

Categories

Collective nouns

1 What is the name given to a group of kittens?

2 What is the name given to a group of ravens?

3 What is the name given to a group of choughs?

4 What is the name given to a group of crows?

5 What is the name given to a group of hermits?

6 What is the name given to a group of ducks?

7 What is the name given to a group of starling?

8 What is the name given to a group of elephants?

9 What is the name given to a group of owls?

10 What is the name given to a group of whales?

11 What is the name given to a group of cats?

12 What is the name given to a group of horses?

13 What is the name given to a group of leopards?

14 What is the name given to a group of lions?

15 What is the name given to a group of larks?

Answers **1** Kindle **2** Unkindness **3** Chattering **4** Murder **5** Observation **6** Paddling **7** Murmuration **8** Herd **9** Parliament **10** Pod **11** Clowder **12** Harass **13** Lepe **14** Pride **15** Exultation

Bones in the body

Categories

1 What is the knee bone called?

2 Where is the mandible?

3 What is the name given to the fingers and toes?

4 Where is the sternum?

5 What is the name given to the collar bone?

6 What is a fracture of the lower part of the leg bones called?

7 Where is the ulna?

8 What is the bone in the thigh called?

9 Where is the tibia?

10 What is the large bone in the lower arm called?

11 What are the bones next to the fingers called?

12 What is the name of the collar bone?

13 What are the bones at the wrist called?

14 What are the bones at the ankle called?

15 What is the large bone at the lower back called?

Answers **1** Patella **2** The jaw bone **3** Phalanges **4** Breast bone **5** Clavicle **6** Pott's fracture **7** In the lower arm **8** Femur **9** In the lower leg **10** Radius **11** Meta carpal **12** Clavicle **13** Carpal **14** Tarsal **15** Pelvis

Categories — Fish

Answer begins with

1 P – A European sea fish, common off Cornwall. Like the herring, but smaller, thicker and rounder. Caught for food and is often canned?

2 H – A large, elongated flat fish which lives on the sea bed of the Atlantic. A food fish traditionally eaten on Holy days?

3 P – Brown with orange spots, this European flat fish lives on shallow sea beds and is a food fish?

4 R – A member of the carp family, this silvery-coloured sport fish is found in European freshwater lakes and rivers?

5 S – An elliptical flat fish. One variety takes its name from a sea-side town in Kent?

6 S – Also known as white bait, it will take one of these to catch a mackeral?

7 S – Large fish of northern temperate waters whose eggs are prized as caviar?

8 S – A large tropical fish whose top jaw has been prolonged as a stabbing weapon?

9 T – A freshwater fish of the salmon family, known as brown or sea?

10 D – What is a coryphene?

11 S – A tropical sea bed-dweller with a formidable barbed spine on its tail?

12 W – Brightly-coloured fish that live on reefs and rocky coasts of Europe and North Africa. One species, has the same name as an Emperor of France.

13 T – A large marine fish, important as food. The catching of this fish was implicated in the death of many dolphins who were caught in the nets?

14 S – Freshwater fish related to the salmon, with a cucumber-like smell?

15 S – The male of this small, spiny-backed river fish, builds the nest?

Answers **1** Pilchard **2** Halibut **3** Plaice **4** Roach **5** Sole **6** Sprat **7** Sturgeon **8** Swordfish **9** Trout **10** Dolphin **11** Stingray **12** Wrasse **13** Tuna **14** Smelt **15** Stickleback

States of the USA

Categories

1 Which state's nickname is the "Gem state"?

2 What is the capital of New Jersey?

3 Which state's tree is the sugar maple?

4 Which state's bird is chickadee?

5 What is the capital of Louisiana?

6 Which is the magnolia state?

7 What is the nickname of Utah?

8 What is the national tree of Ohio?

9 What do Americans call New York state?

10 What is the capital of Nebraska?

11 What is the flower of the state of California?

12 What is the fish of Michigan?

13 What is the capital of Connecticut?

14 What is the flower of Hawaii?

15 What is the capital of Vermont?

Answers **1** Idaho **2** Trenton **3** Vermont **4** Maine **5** Baton Rouge
6 Mississippi **7** Mormon state **8** Buckeye **9** Empire state **10** Lincoln
11 Golden poppy **12** Trout **13** Hartford **14** Hibiscus **15** Montpelier

Categories — Birds

1 Which bird from S. America has the largest wing span up to 3m?

2 Which bird walks up to 20/30 km per day?

3 The fastest bird on two legs?

4 Which bird is known as the South American ostrich?

5 What is the name of a British black bird that is intelligent with a complex social system?

6 Which bird has a bright plumage and a huge bill?

7 Which bird has a colourful plumage and dives to catch its prey?

8 Which bird has a excrescence on its bill?

9 A bird of the albatross and fulmar family which resembles the auk?

10 A sea bird that lives in cliff dwellings and lays shaped eggs so that they do not run off cliff edges?

11 Lives in burrows in very large colonies on cliffs?

12 A general name for a bird of the family that lapwings and dotterels belong?

13 A small nocturnal bird that is the national bird of New Zealand?

14 Hunting bird with remarkable powers of flight and sight?

15 A bird which hunts by flying low in search patterns?

Answers **1** Condor **2** Secretary bird **3** Ostrich **4** Rhea **5** Crow **6** Toucan **7** Kingfisher **8** Hornbill **9** Petrel **10** Guillemot **11** Puffin **12** Plover **13** Kiwi **14** Falcon **15** Harrier

Gods

Categories

1 Ares is the Greek god of war, who is the Roman god of war?

2 Maia is the Roman goddess of fertility. Who is the Greek goddess of fertility?

3 Who is the Greek god of love?

4 Who is the Greek god of the sea?

5 Who is the Greek messenger god?

6 Who is Jupiter?

7 Who is the Roman god of death?

8 Who was father of Zeus?

9 Who is the Roman god of honesty?

10 Who is the greek god of the north wind?

11 Who is the Greek goddess of the moon?

12 Who is the Greek goddess of youth?

13 Who is the Greek goddess of the hearth?

14 Who is the Roman goddess of funeral rites?

15 Who is the Greek god of rain?

Answers **1** Mars **2** Artemis **3** Cupid **4** Poseidon **5** Hermes **6** The Roman god of the sky **7** Orcus **8** Cronus **9** Fides **10** Boreas **11** Hecate **12** Hebe **13** Hestia **14** Libitina **15** Ganymede

Categories **Mathematics**

1 What does this sign mean œ ?

2 What does this sign mean ∪ ?

3 What does this sign mean < ?

4 This sign means > ?

5 What sign means parallel?

6 What does this sign mean Ci?

7 What does this sign mean √ ?

8 What does this sign mean « ?

9 What is the sign of percentage?

10 What is the sign for approximately equal to?

11 This sign means ∑ ?

12 What does this sign mean Δ ?

13 What sign means degree?

14 What does this sign mean *ƒ* ?

15 What sign does this mean (   ) ?

Answers **1** Infinity **2** Union **3** Less than **4** Greater than **5** ll **6** Curie **7** Square root **8** Much less than **9** % **10** ≈ **11** Summation **12** Increment **13** ° **14** Integral **15** Brackets

Mythology 3

Categories

1 In Greek myth, what is the name of an avenging demon?

2 The Greek goddess of fortune and chance?

3 Who was the King of Troy, at the time of the Trojan war?

4 Ancient Latin goddess presiding over fruit trees?

5 Who flew over the Aegean sea and flew too close to the sun?

6 In ancient Persian myth, who are the female spirits?

7 A fire breathing legendary monster part lion, part goat, and part dragon?

8 The fabulous winged horse?

9 Who was the Greek god of the South Wind?

10 Who is the Japanese god of fertility?

11 What was the name of the dog who guarded the entrance to Hades?

12 In Polynesian myth, who is the sun god and culture hero?

13 Who is the Japanese god of learning?

14 A nymph, daughter of Poseidon?

15 A group of mischievous dwarfs in Norse myth?

Answers 1 Alastor **2** Tyche **3** Priam **4** Pomona **5** Icarus **6** Peris
7 Chimaera **8** Pegasus **9** Notus **10** Daikoku **11** Cerberus **12** Maui
13 Tenjin **14** Lotis **15** Alfa

Categories **Animals**

1 What is a Chamois?

2 What is a Vicuna?

3 Describe a kinkaju?

4 What is a madrill?

5 The name for the scaly anteater?

6 What is a Cachalot?

7 What is the name given to any old cat?

8 What is another name for a puma?

9 What is a Quagga?

10 What in America is a Chickadee?

11 What animal is allied to the civet?

12 What is the Brazilian tapeti?

13 What animal has virtually no thumbs?

14 What is a dromedary?

15 What is a South African baboon called?

Answers **1** Goat-like antelope in the mountains of Europe **2** A wild species of the llama **3** South American animal similar to the racoon **4** West African baboon **5** Pangolin **6** Sperm whale **7** Grimalkin **8** Cougar **9** An extinct South African wild ass **10** Titmouse **11** Genette **12** Rabbit **13** Colobus **14** A one-humped Arabian camel **15** Chacma

Dogs

Categories

		Answer starts with
1	A keen scented hunting dog used for chasing hares?	H
2	A short-legged, long-eared dog of German origin used for Badger hunting?	D
3	A dog which is like a coarse-haired terrier?	G
4	Thick set powerful variety of dog, used as a watchdog?	M
5	A breed of dog, a terrier, large with a smooth coat and long forelegs?	D
6	A toy spaniel, named after a butterfly?	P
7	A white coated dog from Siberia?	S
8	A Welsh royal dog?	C
9	A very old German breed of terrier?	S
10	A fast sporting dog, used for gambling?	G
11	A mixed breed of dog?	M
12	A dog with a sharp pointed face, sometimes called a spitz?	P
13	A short-legged Scottish terrier?	D/D
14	A long-bodied, slightly-built terrier, swiftest of its kind?	B
15	An Australian wild dog?	D

Answers **1** Harrier **2** Dachshound **3** Griffon **4** Mastiff **5** Doberman Pincher **6** Papillon **7** Samoyed **8** Corgi **9** Schnauzer **10** Greyhound **11** Mongrel **12** Pomeranium **13** Dandy Dinmont **14** Bodlington **15** Dingo

Categories Nautical

1 A box in which the compass is kept?

2 What is an area near the Equator where clam breezes prevail?

3 What is a picaroon?

4 A sailor's stew with vegetables and ship's biscuits?

5 A place where ships are cleaned?

6 What is the name given to Pig iron in a ship's hold for ballast?

7 What is another name for a stevedore?

8 What is the lowest deck on a ship called?

9 Where is the mizzen mast?

10 What are bilboes?

11 What is the meaning of 'Jettisoned'?

12 What is grapnel?

13 What is a 'Corvette'?

14 What is a Lanyard?

15 What is the term for changing the course of a ship by moving the sails?

Answers **1** A binnacle **2** The doldrums **3** A pirate **4** Lobscourse **5** Careenage **6** Kentledge **7** A longshoreman **8** An orlop deck? **9** The hindmost of the fore and aft masts **10** Bars with sliding shackles **11** Goods thrown overboard and washed up on shore **12** An anchor with hooks **13** An escort vessel **14** A short rope for fastening **15** Tacking

Geographical terms

Categories

1 What is the name of a tract of level land, covered with low vegetation, treeless, or dotted with trees?

2 What is the name given to a narrow neck of land connecting two larger portions?

3 What is the name given to a group of islands originally those in the Aegean sea?

4 What is the name given to a projection of land into the sea?

5 Of the West?

6 A piece of land that is almost an island?

7 The territorial division of a country?

8 A tract of soft wet ground?

9 What is the name of a treeless plain in Russia?

10 What is the name of an Arctic plain with frozen subsoil?

11 What is the name of a little brook?

12 Pertaining to Australasia?

13 Division of a country especially in Switzerland?

14 Of the North wind' or 'of the North'?

15 The public registry of the land?

Answers **1** Savanna **2** Isthmus **3** Archipeligo **4** Promontory **5** Occidental **6** Peninsular **7** Wapentake **8** Morass **9** Steppe **10** Tundra **11** Runnel **12** Austral **13** Canton **14** Boreal **15** Cadastral

Categories

Scientific terms

1 What are lipids?

2 What is a word for native, not imported?

3 What is the name given to a grass eating animal?

4 What is the term for a full set of chromosomes?

5 What is the scientific term for the distance from the earth to the sun?

6 What is the term for one of the units of DNA?

7 What is the name given to a flesh eating mammal?

8 What is a cyclone?

9 What temperature is absolute zero?

10 What is an annulus?

11 What is the Richter scale?

12 What is 'El Nino'?

13 What is dry ice made from?

14 What is a nerve cell called?

15 What measurement is a parsec?

Answers **1** General terms for oils, fat, in living tissue **2** Indigenous **3** A herbivore **4** A genone **5** An astronomial unit **6** A gene **7** A carnivore **8** A region of low pressure **9** -273.15 C **10** A plane surface bounded by two concentric circles, like a washer **11** A rating for earthquakes from **1** to **10** **12** A warm tropical ocean current **13** Solid carbon dioxide **14** A neuron **15** 3.26 light years

Heraldry

Categories

1 On the right hand side?

2 What is another name for a swastika?

3 What is a ring or belt called?

4 What is a bezant?

5 What is a trefoil?

6 What is white fur, like a stoat?

7 What is an etoile?

8 What does rampant mean?

9 What is the shape of a St Andrew's cross called?

10 What is a couche?

11 What is walking to the right?

12 What is a metal tag, anything dangling?

13 What is to adorn with figures?

14 What is the meaning of naissant?

15 What is a river nymph called?

Answers **1** Dexter **2** Flyfot **3** An annulet **4** A gold coin, a small yellow circle **5** A three lobed form **6** Ermine **7** A star-shaped object **8** Standing in profile **9** A saltire **10** An evening reception **11** Passant **12** Aiglet **13** Emblazon **14** Rising or coming forth **15** A naiad

Categories — Dances

1 What is the name of an American shivering dance of the 1920's?

2 What is the name of a slow solemn old Spanish dance in triple time?

3 What is a Pavan?

4 A French West Indian dance in bolero rhythm?

5 What is a Polonaise?

6 An Argentinian dance in 4-4 time?

7 A lively Neopolitan dance in triplets?

8 A provencal dance performed in long string?

9 A quick dance, a sideways gallop is called a ?

10 A slow graceful dance in triple measure?

11 What is a square dance for four couples in five movements?

12 A stage dance of French origin?

13 A lively Polish dance in triple time?

14 What is the name of a Spanish national dance, which is the same word as a jacket or waistcoat that doesn't reach the waist or meet at the front?

15 What is the name of a 'new' Brazilian dance as well as a popular genre of music?

Answers **1** The Shimmy **2** A Passacaglia **3** A Spanish dance, slow and in 4-4 time **4** The Beguine **5** A Polish national dance called, in 3-4 time **6** The Tango **7** A Tarantella **8** A Farandole **9** A Gallopade **10** A Minuet **11** A Quadrille **12** A Cancan **13** A Mazurka **14** A Bolero **15** The Bossa Nova

Biology

Categories

1 What does epigael mean?

2 What is an oocyte?

3 An extract from the pancreas for treating diabetes?

4 A mixture of carbohydrates found in fruits?

5 What is a tooth socket called?

6 The main division in the animal kingdom?

7 What is dicephalous?

8 The spongy tissue in the skull?

9 What is the thallus?

10 What is abscisin?

11 What does isogeny mean?

12 What is keratin?

13 What does lacteal mean?

14 What is a leaf stalk called?

15 What is an imago?

Answers **1** Growing or lying close to the ground **2** An ovum before it divides **3** Insulin **4** Pectin **5** Alveolus **6** Phylum **7** Two-headed **8** Diploe **9** The whole of the plant body **10** Plant hormones **11** Likeness of origin **12** The ingredient of horny tissue **13** Of milk **14** A petiole **15** The perfect state of an insect

Categories

Clothes

1 What is a leather made of shark's skin called?

2 A plaited border or flounce used as a decorative ornament?

3 A leather half-boot or high shoe named after a Prussian General at Waterloo?

4 What is a silken material with a raised design called?

5 A man's felt hat with a narrow brim and crown?

6 A long robe worn by clergy?

7 A thick velvety cord made of silk or wool?

8 What is white fur such as 'ermine' called?

9 A silk yarn of two or more threads?

10 What is a woollen fabric with a distinctive pattern called?

11 The word for a silk fabric with a short pile?

12 A fabric made from goat's hair?

13 What is honeycombing on a yoke or cuffs called?

14 The name for a double veil worn by Muslim women?

15 A Turkish robe with slight sleeves?

Answers **1** Shagreen **2** Furbelow **3** Blucher **4** Brocade **5** Homburg **6** Cassock **7** Chenille **8** Miniver **9** Organzine **10** Paisley **11** Velvet **12** Cashmere **13** Smocking **14** Yashmak **15** Dolman